ARMING the FLEET

ARMING THE FLEET

U.S. Navy Ordnance in the Muzzle-Loading Era

SPENCER TUCKER

Naval Institute Press, Annapolis, Maryland

Library of Congress Cataloging in Publication Data

Tucker, Spencer, 1937–
Arming the fleet : U.S. Navy ordnance in the muzzle-loading era / Spencer Tucker.
p. cm.
Bibliography: p.
Includes index.
ISBN 0-87021-007-6
1. United States. Navy—Ordnance and ordnance stores. I. Title.
VF23.T83 1988
359.8'2'0973—dc19 88-1391
CIP

Designed by Moira Megargee

Printed in the United States of America

This book is dedicated to the memory of my father,
Colonel Cary S. Tucker, and to my mother,
Elizabeth B. Tucker

Contents

Illustrations

Tables

Preface

THIS IS THE FIRST book devoted to the development of U.S. Navy ordnance through the Civil War. It was inspired by my father, Colonel Cary S. Tucker. An expert on early ordnance, he had intended to write a multivolume world history of muzzleloaders. Toward that end he assembled copious notes and illustrations. After his death in 1962 my mother, Elizabeth B. Tucker, and I discussed publication possibilities with Mendel Peterson of the Smithsonian Institution. Because the work was not complete, he suggested I apply for a grant as a visiting research associate at the Smithsonian to finish it. This I did, and I am most grateful to the Smithsonian for enabling me to spend a year in Washington working through source materials, including those in the National Archives and the Library of Congress.

It soon became clear to me that the scope of the book had to be greatly narrowed. I decided to limit it to U.S. Navy guns—only a small portion of the original work—and to expand its scope to include a discussion of the founding of cannon, the working of guns, and charges in ship batteries.

The earliest information we have on U.S. ordnance is contained in books of ordnance instruction. Most of these publications are of English origin. One of the earliest and certainly the most important is John Muller's *Treatise of Artillery,* first published in 1757. Born in Germany, Muller was employed in the Tower of London by 1736. Later he was professor of fortifications and artillery at Woolwich. Muller's *Treatise* was a vehicle for his views concerning the most efficient ordnance design. Ironically, his ideas had much more influence in the United States than in England. A pirated edition of his work was published in Philadelphia in 1779, probably the only ordnance manual readily available in this country during the American Revolution. As a result, although the British did not follow his advice on centerline trunnion placement, Americans did. Muller's formula for the construction of ship carriages also seems to have been adopted by Americans.

Another work, this one giving gun dimensions, is Captain George Smith's *Universal Military Dictionary,* published in London in 1779. These two books give a reasonably complete picture of English artillery at the time of the American Revolution. And, since most U.S. ordnance was simply copied from British designs modified by some of Muller's ideas, the books also give a reasonably clear picture of the earliest American ordnance.

However, during the Revolutionary war and well after it there was great flux in U.S. designs. This was made clear by Louis de Tousard, a French officer who had come to this country to fight for the American cause and who wrote, at George Washington's suggestion, the first U.S. ordnance manual. In 1809 Tousard published his two-volume *American Artillerist's Companion.* He relied heavily on French practice and design, noting that there was no American artillery as such but only a collection of ordnance from different countries.

Contemporary with Tousard's work was William Duane's *Military Dictionary* (Philadelphia, 1810). Unfortunately, neither he nor Tousard provide much in the way of detailed information about the appearance of U.S. Navy guns.

The U.S. Navy of this period simply adopted the best of Royal Navy gun design, and descriptions of the pieces are few. In 1822 George Marshall published his *Practical Marine Gunnery,* but while it is useful on the subject of ordnance stores, it provides little information on guns themselves. Fortunately, the National Archives houses a number of drawings of U.S. Navy guns, beginning with those of the 1820s. Better yet, some of the GI guns themselves (named for the Gradual Increase Act under which they were authorized) survive.

Inventories of ordnance are only partially helpful. The most complete, of guns in navy yards, was made in 1833 by Captain Thomas Ap Catesby Jones. The result of his efforts was the "Inspection Report of the Ordnance of the Navy of the United States, 1833." It contains no drawings but includes gun dimensions and some discussion of gun origins.

In the 1820s Colonel Henri Paixhans of France developed a new system of ordnance. His ideas drew a response from the greatest American naval ordnance expert of the time, John Dahlgren. Dahlgren wrote a number of books, the most important being *Shells and Shell Guns,* published in Philadelphia in 1856. He did not provide detailed information or drawings. His intention, rather, was to replace the existing system of many shot guns with a system of fewer but larger shell guns.

About this time, in 1852, the first official ordnance manual for the U.S. Navy was published. A subsequent edition appeared in 1860. These two editions contain many of the drawings as well as nomenclature utilized here.

By the 1850s other writers were also publishing books exclusively on naval ordnance. These include General Sir Howard Douglas's *Treatise on Naval Gunnery* (1819 or 1820), William Jeffers's *Concise Treatise on the Theory and Practice of Naval Gunnery* (1850), Commander James Ward's *Elementary Instruction in Naval Ordnance and Gunnery* (revised edition, 1861), and a text for the Naval Academy, Edward Simpson's *Treatise on Ordnance and Naval Gunnery* (1862). All have been helpful in writing this study.

In discussing the ordnance of the period, I have begun with a brief history of the use of guns at sea up to the time of the War of the American Revolution. Chapter 2 treats, in a general way, gunnery practice of the eighteenth and nineteenth centuries; chapter 3 deals with the practice of cannon founding and discusses the principal founders for the U.S. Navy; and chapters 4 through 7 discuss the chronological development of ordnance and ship design as well as the armament of U.S. Navy vessels. Appendices contain information on the nomenclature of guns, terms and definitions, and U.S. Navy cannon contracts.

I deeply appreciate the assistance and permissions provided by the Department of the Navy, the National Archives, Dr. Harold Langley of the Smithsonian, *National Geographic,* the Metropolitan Museum of Art, the National Park Service, the editors of the *Mémorial d'artillerie française,* James Gooding of the Museum Restoration Service, the American Foundrymen's Society, *The American Neptune,* and Charles McDonald of the *Nautical Research Journal.*

The illustrations are an important part of this book. A number were drawn by my father. Those not credited are from the hand of William J. Clipson, retired chair of the Art Department at the Naval Academy. I was indeed fortunate in securing his services to redraw some fifty figures. He worked quickly, with marvelous results.

I am indebted to a number of other people who have generously given of their time. The late Harold Peterson and Ed Rich lent me encouragement, as did E. Ray Lewis and Malcolm Muir, Jr. Jamie Gleason, history department secretary at Texas Christian University, waded through charts and tables and retyped with the utmost skill. My colleague Professor Donald Worcester graciously read the manuscript several times, making useful suggestions based on his many years of editorial experience. Edwin Olmstead has been particularly helpful. One of a handful of experts on early American ordnance, he pointed out discrepancies and made a number of suggestions for which I am most grateful. I am also appreciative of the careful, judicious, and always sympathetic work of my editor, Connie Buchanan. Any errors or omissions are my own.

Texas Christian University was also generous in granting me a semester's leave to finish writing the manuscript.

ARMING the FLEET

CHAPTER I

From the Introduction of Cannon at Sea to the American Revolution

FOR TWO THOUSAND years, until the invention of cannon, naval warfare resembled war on land. The principal weapon at sea consisted of a ram built into the bow of a ship; the fighting vessel was essentially a floating fortress. An enemy ship could be destroyed by ramming, burning with an incendiary known as Greek fire, sinking with *catapultae* and *ballistae*, or boarding and overpowering the crew in hand-to-hand battle.

By the Middle Ages—when the principal fortification on land was the castle, and the most effective method of attacking it was to build something higher—ships incorporated structures resembling castles on the bow and the stern. (The fore part of the spar deck came to be known as the forecastle, while the aft part became the quarterdeck.) The height advantage thus gained allowed attackers to overcome an opposing vessel's bulwarks and strike at the enemy crew on the decks. The higher a ship's castle, the more difficult it was to take that ship; even if boarders fought their way to the vessel's waist, the defenders could retreat to the castles and continue fighting. These structures, for battle only, were temporarily erected on merchant vessels outfitted as fighting ships.

As the medieval ship moved into combat, it attempted to ram an enemy vessel. If this was not feasible, it would close with the vessel so the crew could board it. During his battle against the Spanish in 1350, King Edward III reportedly ordered his helmsman, "Lay me against the Spaniard who is coming, for I wish to joust with him."[1] In a typical engagement the ship maneuvered alongside the enemy vessel, whose deck was showered with *triboli* (brutal, three-pronged pieces of iron that would disable anyone who stepped or fell on them), incendiaries, and sometimes a soapy solution that made it difficult for seamen to keep their footing. Once the ships had been securely lashed together, the attackers leaped onto the enemy's deck, while men in the fighting tops picked off enemy crewmen with arrows or spears and dropped large stones or iron bars onto their ship to sink it.[2] These tactics, with some variations, were used until the fourteenth-century revolution in naval warfare brought cannon and gunpowder into ships' armaments.

The word *cannon,* derived from the Latin *canna,* meaning "reed" or "tube," dates back to the thirteenth century. Originally it did not refer to mortars or howitzers, but it has come to mean all firearms larger than small arms, specifically muzzle-loading smoothbore guns. The date that cannon were first employed on land or sea can probably never be known with certainty. In an oft-quoted statement, Sir Harris Nicolas asserted that three of Edward III's ships were armed with them in 1338, but this date has been challenged.[3] A French fleet may have employed a few guns in 1356, a Spanish ship in 1359. The Genoese and Venetians were said to have used them at sea in the War of Chioggia (1378–81). Froissart made reference to their naval use by Spaniards in 1372. One of the first known casualties of the new weapon was Squire Christoffer Atterdag, hit by a cannonball during an engagement between the Danes and a fleet from Lübeck in 1362.[4]

Ships were certainly carrying cannon by the second half of the fourteenth century. Early types were small, averaging 20 to 40 pounds in weight, and were only part of an arsenal that also included swords, pikes, crossbows, spears, javelins, and poleaxes. Guns such as the harquebus, which was hand-held, destroyed men, not ships. The first cannon were probably fired over the bulwarks (the gunwale, as it is known even today). In all likelihood they resembled the "bombards" used ashore—short weapons with bell mouths. Later guns were longer. The advent of heavy cannon made it possible to destroy another vessel without closing with it, and in 1513 gunfire actually sank a ship. In time, cannon became the raison d'être of the warship and exerted a tremendous influence on the development of ship types.

Because of the difficulty of heating iron sufficiently to pour it into a mold, medieval gun founders did not cast their cannon. In the fifteenth century cannon were made of longitudinal strips of wrought iron welded together on a mandrel, the interstices filled with melted lead. Over this iron hoops or rings were driven for further strength. Most early cannon were crude predecessors of the breechloader developed in the nineteenth century with the advantage of more sophisticated technology. A separate chamber held the powder and was attached to the breech. Bar guns of this type may be seen today at Woolwich and in the Tower of London.

Fifteenth-century cannon were cumbersome, slow, and dangerous to fire; seamen regarded them as more perilous to use than to face. While an English naval inventory of 1410 listed several ships that carried cannon, none was equipped with more than three.[5] These early guns had two sections: the barrel

Fig. 1. A Late Medieval Warship. (After Valturius, 1470–1500, in *Quellen zur Geschichte der Feuerwaffen* [Leipzig, 1872]. Redrawn by C. S. Tucker in "Introduction of Cannon at Sea," *Nautical Research Journal* 22, no. 2 [June 1976].)

that held the shot and the chamber that contained the powder charge. Purchase bars inserted in a capstan-type head clamped the sections together. There were often loops or lugs for loose rings so that ropes could be rigged to handle, control, and maneuver the piece. The smaller cannon were usually provided with more than one chamber to facilitate reloading.

The first cannon may not have had the benefit of carriages to hold them. Guns could recoil along the deck if they were not attached to a fixed mount. Later guns might have lain in a groove, and still later, in a grooved log. Finally wheels, or trucks, as they came to be known, were added to carriages. These changes all made handling easier and increased rate of fire.

Fig. 2. A Bombard on a Deck Mount. The bombard is late fourteenth- or early fifteenth-century Burgundian and was found in the Meuse River. The mount is modern. (The Metropolitan Museum of Art, Bashford Dean Collection.)

Another type of cannon had a removable, wedged-in breech and a wheeled carriage. This improved design consisted of a core of short tubes of wrought iron. The end of each had a lip, and the tubes were held together by iron bars beaten around the barrel where the lips met. A cannon salvaged from the English warship *Mary Rose,* which sank in 1545, belongs to this type. The L-shaped carriage was generally made from a single piece of timber, which gave added strength to absorb recoil, and it may have been reinforced by side bracing. The breech was provided with a neck or taper to fit into the barrel and usually had a bore smaller than the gun itself. At the end of the sixteenth century, the chamber of a cannon was generally two-thirds the bore in diameter and four times the diameter in length.

The ability to handle artillery on land or sea was seen as something of a magic art, and gunners were regarded as guildsmen. They appear to have kept their trade secrets well, judging from the lack of concrete information that has come down to us. Apparently they had no control over elevation, and not much over aim, so the effects of firing on the enemy were largely unpredictable. After firing, in a cloud of smoke from the breech, the gunner had to dodge the heavy, lunging cannon; he could only hope that the breech was still wedged in position and the cannon did not explode.

Around the end of the fifteenth century, an important change took place in the way guns were mounted on ships. Up to that time, a man-of-war carried relatively heavy cannon in the waist (to be fired over or through the bulwarks) and lighter pieces in the castles at each end. But castles, built too high and weighted down with ordnance, had made ships like the *Henry Grâce à Dieu* (*Great Harry*) unwieldy and top-heavy. Now heavier guns were installed in ships; their weightier shot could penetrate the sides of an enemy vessel at greater range, thus rendering castles obsolete. These heavier guns were carried between decks and fired out of holes cut in the ships' sides known as gun ports. According to tradition, gun ports were invented in 1501 by a shipbuilder from Brest named Descharges. This event, whenever it occurred, cleared the way for the use of heavier cannon at sea. The English enthusiastically adopted the innovation; the *Henry Grâce à Dieu* was rebuilt in 1540 as a vessel of 1,000 tons with a double tier of gun ports.

As cannon grew heavier and less numerous and came to be located principally on gun decks, ship lines changed. High castles and towers shrank, resulting in the relatively clean lines generally associated with the age of fighting sail. This alteration was well under way by 1637, when the first three-decker on record was built, the *Sovereign of the Seas*. Her castles were greatly reduced. She carried 102 bronze guns, the heavier ones on the lower decks.

Proper gun port placement was learned by trial and error. The *Mary Rose* was pursuing French vessels off Spithead in 1545 when in a sudden turn she heeled and water entered her open gun ports, which were only 18 inches above the waterline. She capsized and sank, a victim of too many guns topside and gun ports too close to the waterline. Three centuries later, in 1836, a diving bell salvaged a wrought-iron breechloader, fragments of two others, and some bronze cannon from the wreck of the *Mary Rose*. The breechloader is 9 feet 8 inches long and has a bore diameter of about 8 inches. One of the fragmented breechloaders still has a stone shot lodged in its bore. The bronze guns range in length from 8 feet 6 inches to 11 feet and have bores from 4.56 to 8.54 inches. Other cannon have recently been retrieved which, along with the remains of the *Mary Rose,* can be seen in the museum at Portsmouth.

Additional early cannon include those from the remains of a Spanish treasure fleet wrecked off Padre Island, Texas, in 1553, as well as the "Anholt finds," eleven guns recovered in 1840–47 and 1937 from shipwrecks off the

Danish island of Anholt and dated between 1500 and 1575. They were each mounted in a stock formed of a single piece of oak. Though varying in length, their bores are all between 3 and 4.5 inches in diameter. The Anholt guns are now in the Royal Danish Arsenal Museum.

Soon after the advent of gun ports, guns began to change. From the mid-sixteenth century the blast furnace improved iron smelting and made possible the casting of guns. The heavy wrought-iron breechloader was gradually replaced by the safer, stronger muzzleloader cast in a mold and then bored. Later the muzzleloader was cast around a core slightly smaller than the intended bore and then bored to the true caliber. The exact date of the switch to muzzle-loading guns is not known; bronze muzzleloaders appeared about 1500, the cheaper iron ones around 1550.

During the first two hundred years guns were used at sea, most were produced in Italy and the Low Countries. In England light bronze guns had been cast by 1470, but the gun-making industry did not actually appear until fifty or sixty years later, during the reign of Henry VIII. It was the custom in England to employ foreigners as founders before Henry VIII encouraged the development of a national munitions industry. He was also responsible for introducing heavy guns on the larger English ships. In 1543, the first large English iron gun was cast on Henry's orders at Buxted in Sussex, beginning a new period in the history of artillery. By 1600, annual production of iron cannon in Sussex had reached 800 to 1,000 tons, and English ordnance—whether because of iron quality or technology—was recognized as the best in the world.[6] Sweden was another leading producer.

Founders continued to have difficulty producing castings, which may have delayed the advent of the muzzleloaders, but in the decade after 1550 the old breechloader began to be superseded. By the reign of Elizabeth I (1558–1603), the large wrought-iron guns of the Plantagenets had almost disappeared and smaller wrought-iron pieces were regarded only as secondary armament. An inventory of 1559 listed 264 bronze and 48 iron guns on board ships and 48 bronze and 8 iron guns in store. In addition, there were approximately 1,000 small pieces—slings, fowlers, port pieces, bases, and harquebuses.[7] The proportion of secondary to battery pieces was thus quite high. In the early seventeenth century, the English navy was equipped largely with cast-bronze guns. Light breech-loading man-killers were an exception.

The breechloader had certain advantages that prolonged its use in some countries and under certain conditions. It could be worked by fewer men—it did not have to be hauled back into battery after firing—and it could be reloaded quickly, especially the smaller breechloader. It was said that a harquebus could endure three hundred firings a day. The breechloader was also relatively light for the weight of its shot, particularly when stone was used. These factors appealed to the captains and owners of merchantmen, and had there been the additional advantage of lathes to make tighter fittings between chamber and breech, it is possible that the breechloader would have

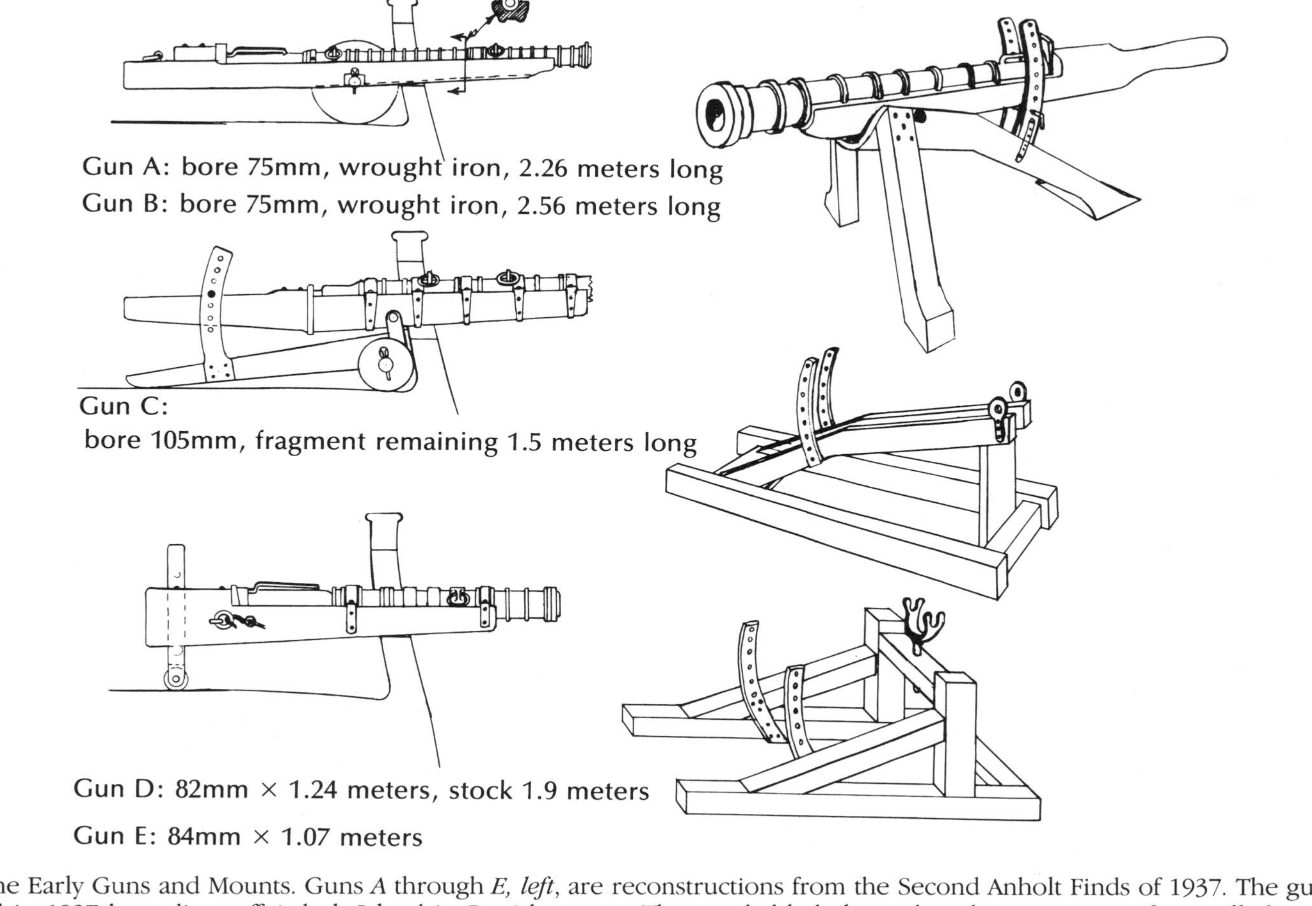

Fig. 3. Some Early Guns and Mounts. Guns *A* through *E, left*, are reconstructions from the Second Anholt Finds of 1937. The guns were discovered in 1937 by a diver off Anholt Island in Danish waters. They probably belonged to the armament of a small ship carrying ordnance and iron from England to Denmark between 1560 and 1575. The illustration, *top right*, is of a gun mount that might date as early as the fifteenth century. The same type appears in a mounting in the Metropolitan Museum of Art; it is identified as a Robinet of 1580–1628. It was probably made from a tree trunk hollowed out to provide a trough for the gun to lie in. A pin was put through the stock and mount, another through the uprights and beneath the stock, and then the piece was ready for loading. Mounts such as this or the two below it were probably used for most smaller guns of the period. (Drawing after V. Nielson by C. S. Tucker in "Introduction of Cannon at Sea.")

continued even longer in use. The breech-loading principle was retained in smaller pieces, especially swivel guns. The bronze swivel of a 4-pounder with a removable breech was found off Australia where a Dutch ship had wrecked in 1727. Light breech-loading swivels were also used during the American Revolution.

Another factor hastening the change to muzzleloaders was the improvement of gunpowder. The original "mealed" or "serpentine" powder was slow burning and impure, and the guns into which it was loaded were structurally weak. Powder improved when it was made into grains, or corned, but it burned so rapidly that gas often leaked from the gun. To solve this, and the problem of wrought iron corroding rapidly at sea, especially from repeated swabbings, increased efforts were made to cast large guns from both iron and bronze.

Bronze (ninety parts copper and ten tin) continued for some time to be the favorite metal for cannon, because it stood the shock of discharge better than iron and was easier to cast. (Increasing the proportion of tin hardened bronze but also made it more brittle; decreasing the amount of tin made the metal too soft for cannon and also less elastic.) European craftsmen were well

Key to fig. 4.

Gun no. 1: A bronze sakar of Henry VIII. Made by the Owen brothers in 1538. It has a hinged vent cover. Length of gun overall is 7′ 9⅞″, caliber is 3.75″.

Gun no. 2: A bronze sakar of Henry VIII. Marked with the name Franciscus Arcanus and dated 1529. Length of gun is 7′ 4″ overall, caliber is 3.65″.

Gun no. 3: A bronze culverin bastard of Henry VIII. It is one of the guns recovered from the *Mary Rose*. There are hinge fittings on the gun for a vent cover. The gun is twelve-sided. Length is 9′ 4″ overall, caliber 4.56″.

Gun no. 4: A bronze demi-cannon of Henry VIII, also recovered from the *Mary Rose*. The dolphins represent lions' heads. Overall length is 12′ 2″, caliber 6.4″.

Gun no. 5: A bronze cannon royal of Henry VIII, recovered from the *Mary Rose*. There are roses and fleurs-de-lis as ornaments on the chase. The dolphins are lions' heads (the loop or handle is made by the open mouths with the front teeth touching). It has a hinged vent cover. On the reinforce is an inscription with the name John Owen and the words Cannon Royal. Length is 9′ 9″, caliber 8.54″.

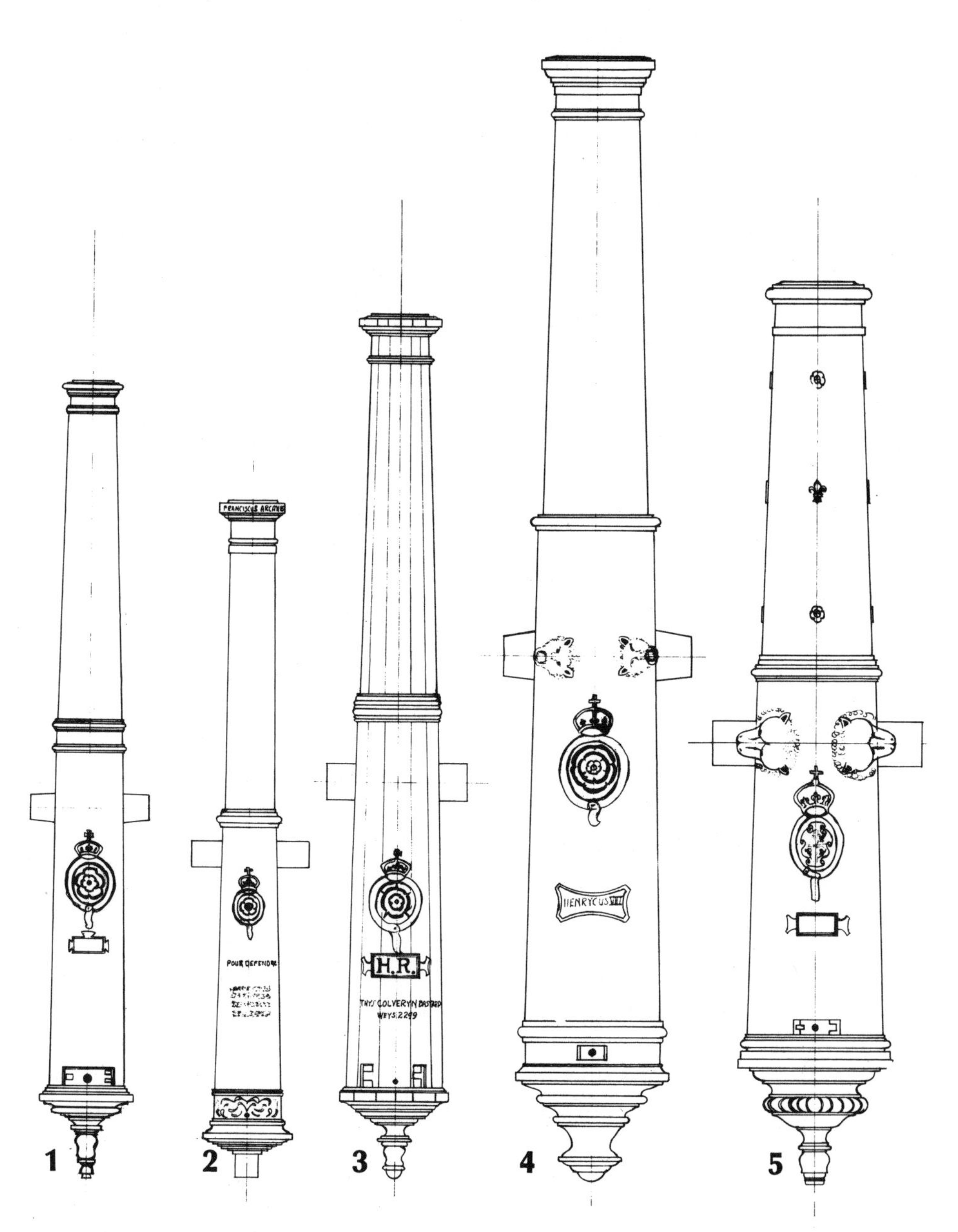

Fig. 4. English Naval Guns of the Sixteenth Century. (Drawing by C. S. Tucker.)

acquainted with bronze casting techniques from the demand for church bells. When a defective bronze gun broke, it was more likely to crack open or bulge than explode, as iron might, and thus was less dangerous for the gunners. Bronze guns were also easily recast when worn. Since they could be made slimmer, these guns often weighed less than iron ones even though the metal itself was 20 percent heavier. (Cannon of the same size and metal could vary by as much as two to three hundred-weight [one hundred-weight, or cwt, was 112 pounds].) Bronze guns could also be embellished with elaborate decoration, unlike those of coarse iron. Bronze cannon were considerably more expensive, costing three to four times as much as comparable iron guns. With this notable exception, their advantages outweighed those of iron guns, and they were preferred by gunners. As late as 1621, the Dutch government requested that new bronze guns be cast each year to replace those of iron, which were considered too dangerous for ships and crews.[8]

By the late fifteenth century, cannon were being cast with pivots set on the axis of the bore. These pivots, or trunnions, as they came to be called, supported the gun on its carriage and helped elevate it. There was controversy in succeeding centuries over the most effective position for trunnions. Placing them low reduced recoil and made sighting along the side of the gun easier, but it also put greater strain on the carriage. The new trunnioned gun was mounted on a carriage with four trucks and held in position by tackle and breeching. It was elevated by means of one or more wedges or quoins under the breech. Gun crews wielded hand spikes to traverse the gun and its carriage. Lighter guns sat on swivel forks mounted on wooden tripods or in the rail of a ship—hence the later term swivels for smaller pieces.

There were quite a few types of shot available for use in early cannon. The first manufactured projectiles were stone, cut as precisely to size as possible by masons in order to reduce windage—the difference between the diameter of the projectile and that of the gun bore—and hence gas loss. Iron shot, first forged and later cast, had been used since the late fourteenth century, but stone shot continued in use throughout the seventeenth century, at least in forts and other fixed locations. It only weighed a third as much as iron shot of the same diameter. Some of the smaller guns also used lead shot, which weighed half again as much as iron shot of the same diameter, but although denser than iron, it was too soft and too costly. In England, lead shot seems to have been limited to use in the serpentine and robinet.

The larger muzzleloaders were not rapid-fire weapons. William Eldred, writing in the mid-seventeenth century, put the average at eight shots an hour and warned against the dangers of exceeding this rate: "One may well make 10 shots an hour if the peeces be well fortifyed and strong; but if they be ordinary peeces, then 8 is enough, always provided that after 40 shots you refresh and coole the peece, and let her rest an hour, for fear lest 80 shots shall break the peece, being not able to endure the heat."[9]

Muzzle-loading cannon came into general use gradually. Those of the late

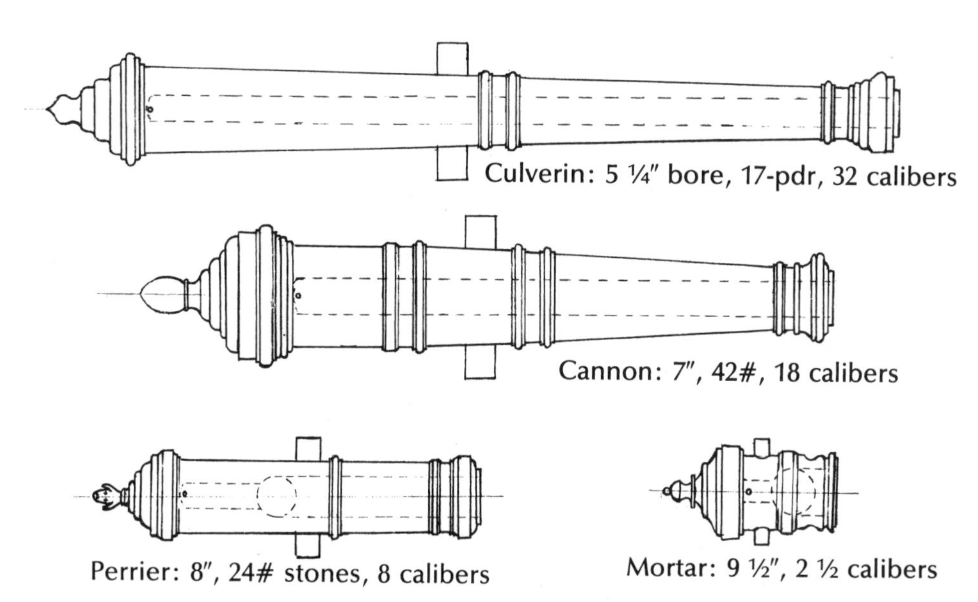

Fig. 5. Classification of Guns in 1588. In 1537 an Italian, Nicholas Tartaglia, published a book on gunnery and ballistics. This was translated and published by Cyprian Luccar in England in 1588. The drawings Luccar included of guns were redrawn to conform correctly to his stated proportions by Michael Lewis and included by him in a series of articles in the *Mariner's Mirror*. They were subsequently published in book form as *Armada Guns* (London, 1961). The drawings are after those of Lewis, redrawn by C. S. Tucker. They first appeared in "Introduction of Cannon at Sea."

sixteenth century were divided into three classes: culverins, cannon, and perriers. These classes were based on rough measures of bore-to-length ratio, culverins being the longest and perriers the shortest. The culverin family included all pieces that were around 30 bore-diameters (calibers) long, including the culverin, demi-culverin, saker, falcon, and falconet. The culverins had relatively thicker walls for long-range firing. Cannon were about 15 to 20 calibers in length, usually 10-pounders or heavier. This family included the cannon-royal, cannon, demi-cannon, and in Spain, thirds-of-cannon (*tercias*) and quarter-cannon. These names indicated the bore diameter of the piece as well as its length. The perrier (*petrero, pedrero,* or *cannon pedro*) or stone thrower was 16 to 8 or less calibers in length; it had a large bore for its length and fired stone shot at low velocity. The perrier family included petards, mortars, and trabuccos or howitzers. Perriers came to be referred to by the diameter of the bore in inches or by the older names for small breechloaders. The word *perrier,* incidentally, continued to be used by the French navy to describe a gun of 3-pound shot or less that was mounted in the tops of men-of-war.

It is quite difficult to categorize early ordnance, particularly since terminology was not at all precise. Cyprian Lucar identified something like forty different kinds of guns in 1588, and his was not an exhaustive list.[10] Culverin length was classified as ordinary (30–33 calibers), extraordinary (long, up to 42 calibers), or bastard (short, 26–28 calibers). Metal thickness was characterized in the first half of the seventeenth century as ordinary or fortified, extraordinary or double fortified, and bastard or less fortified. These terms were repeated in the names of the guns themselves.

Classification by name was imprecise and unsatisfactory and dropped early in most countries so that guns could be identified by the weight of the shot they fired. But in England the old system of classification remained until the beginning of the eighteenth century, and the British did not approve proportions for classifying guns until 1863.

From the earliest days, certain muzzleloaders were given a powder chamber smaller in diameter than the bore of the gun. This eliminated air space between the shot and the powder, which was believed to increase the chance of a gun bursting. The powder chamber was most common in the early perriers, as the density of the stone ball was relatively low and the powder occupied only a short length of the bore. The chamber also secured a good thickness of metal around the powder without increasing the gun's diameter. Later weapons of low velocity, such as howitzers and carronades, were made with chambers.

Naval guns developed from the culverin type rather than the cannon because of length ratio and metal thickness. The perrier was the ancestor of the howitzer. There was no uniformity of ordnance, and since each country used different weights and measures, the shot for a gun bored to a particular measure for one country was not the same as the shot made for a gun of the same nominal size in another country.

The location of cannon on shipboard came to be an important aspect of naval gunnery. Until the introduction of gun ports and the mounting of a complete tier of guns on the lower deck, the amount of armament a ship could carry was sharply limited, though all naval guns were relatively light. In the early sixteenth century shipbuilders maintained a ratio of 1 ton of guns to 15 of ship. English capital ships in the early sixteenth century carried a nominal armament of one hundred guns or more, but the majority of these were fairly light man-killers. Henry VII's *Sovereign,* launched before the introduction of gun ports, had 141 guns, but 110 of these were iron serpentines, most mounted in the castles.

Henry VIII wanted his ships to carry much heavier guns, and this forced the construction of bigger vessels. The 1,000-ton *Henry Grâce à Dieu* has sometimes been called the first British battleship. Built in 1514, she originally carried 184 guns; after a major rebuilding in 1536–39 she was armed with 251 guns—21 of bronze and 230 of iron, 100 of the latter being handguns. But most of these guns were still relatively small, firing 1- to 3-pound shot. Even allowing a generous interpretation of gun size, the *Henry* carried only nineteen heavy guns. The big innovation was that heavy guns made use of gun ports and were carried on what had earlier been the cargo deck.

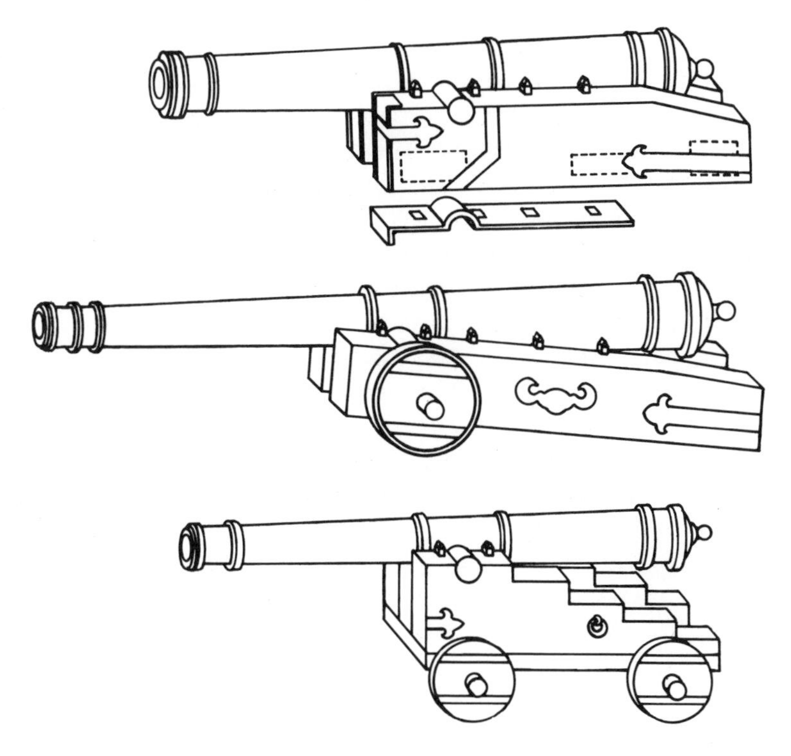

Fig. 6. Seventeenth-Century Cannon for Mediterranean Galleys. *Top:* Corsica-type mount, pointed by turning the helm, little elevation possible. *Middle:* Two trucks, capable of pointing independently of the helm. *Bottom:* Four trucks, capable of pointing and elevation. (After Pietro Sardi, *L'Artiglieria*, 1689.)

The same arrangement, a few heavy guns and many small ones, held for galleys. A Mediterranean galley of the sixteenth century carried three to five heavy guns facing forward, with lighter pieces to port, to starboard, and aft for defensive purposes. The entire vessel had to be turned to aim the heavier pieces. These consisted of one 2- to 3-ton cannon mounted along the keel line and firing a 30- to 50-pound shot, and two to four cannon on either side of the main gun (10- to 12-pounders and 3- to 6-pounders). All were fixed for elevation, and the big guns recoiled between parallel timber guides. The smaller guns on either side were placed on pivot mounts. These forward-firing guns were in essence an extension of the ram.

The cannon required for a Florentine galley in 1574 included one 50-pounder *cannone,* two 10-pounder *sagri* (sakers), two 4-pounder *mezzi sagri* (minions) or two 12-pounder *petriere* (perriers), and eight 4-pounder breech-loading *smerigli,* probably mounted on the sides.[11]

The galleass, which appeared at the Battle of Lepanto in 1571 and disappeared in the seventeenth century, had a considerable broadside battery in place of the few smaller pieces that the galley carried in the same position. But the heavy cannon made the vessel sluggish under the limited power supplied by oars, and this ship type was not successful. It was not the big gun but rather the harquebus that decided the Battle of Lepanto. It and other small pieces were used to reduce enemy crews before boarding.

The big gun did not come into its own until the defeat of the Spanish Armada in 1588. In that battle the English vessels were smaller, more maneuverable, better manned, and probably better armed. From the first the English planned to make it a long gun fight, while the Spanish counted on close-in, ship-to-ship fighting where heavier guns and small arms would be the chief weapons. The main power of Spanish ordnance resided in cannon and demi-cannon, short-barreled guns that threw shot of between 30 and 60 pounds in weight. The English ships were inferior to the Spanish in total weight of broadside, but their culverins and demi-culverins were long guns that far outranged those of their opponents. Neither the artillery of the British nor that of the Spanish proved decisive, but the running engagement demonstrated conclusively that cannon could be an effective means of sinking an enemy vessel. Thereafter the great gun was the ship's principal weapon. Eventually this arrangement fostered the broadside and line of battle tactics that turned ships into little more than platforms for increasingly heavy guns.

It will be noted from table 1 that the perrier weighed only 60 to 80 times as much as its stone shot, the cannon weighed 100 to 129 times its projectile, and the culverin weighed 250 to 280 times its shot.[12] The heaviest guns, those with 200 or more pounds of shot, came to be known as double fortified.

Until around 1650 land and sea ordnance differed only in size. Ships of the line, being relatively small, could not mount or effectively use the largest land guns for reasons of dimension and weight (land pieces in the early days of artillery were made with the largest possible dimensions, in part for prestige). Later on, when warships had become floating gun platforms, naval guns were larger than those on land save for the very largest coastal defense pieces. This change did not take place, however, until the first half of the eighteenth century. Quite possibly, experiments were made with guns as much as 20 feet long, but these pieces could not be used even by the largest ships except as forward-firing chase guns. The heaviest ball fired by guns used as standard armament (until the "shell guns" of the 1840s) was the 48-pounder, which the French employed in the 1690s. Meanwhile, except for the large-caliber, low-velocity perrier, the largest common ship gun to fire iron shot was the 30- to 36-pounder demi-cannon.

There was also a variety of smaller ship guns such as fowlers and port pieces, mostly cast in bronze. A contemporary described them as "such Peeces as onley shoote stone, or else Murthering shot, both which and Fire-balls may be likewise shot out of the aformentioned Ordnance."[13] "Bases," "slyngs," and "murtherers" were usually made of wrought iron.

During the seventeenth century, weapon sizes and types grew more uniform. In the earlier era of naval ordnance, bore diameters could measure every half inch from 1 to 8.5 inches. Now founders concentrated on producing

TABLE 1

ENGLISH SIXTEENTH- AND EARLY SEVENTEENTH-CENTURY GUNS

							Range of Paces	
Name of Ordnance	*Later Designation*	*Length (ft-in)*	*Caliber (in)*	*Weight of Cannon*	*Weight of Shot (lbs, iron)*	*Weight of Powder (lbs)*	*Point-blank*	*Random*
Cannon royal	—	12-0	8.5	8,000	66.0	30.0	800	1,930
Cannon	—	9 or 10	8.0	6,000	60.0	27.0	770	2,000
Cannon serpentine	42-pdr	—	7.0	5,500	53.5	25.0	200	2,000
Bastard cannon	42-pdr	9-6	7.0	4,500	41.0	20.0	180	1,800
Demi-cannon	32-pdr	11-0	6.75	4,000	30.5	18.0	170	1,700
Cannon petro	—	—	6.0	3,000	24.5	14.0	160	1,600
Culverin	18-pdr	10-11	5.5	4,500	17.5	12.0	200	2,500
Basilisk	12-pdr	—	5.0	4,000	15.0	10.0	230	3,000
Demi-culverin	9-pdr	9-0	4.0	3,400	9.5	8.0	200	2,500
Bastard culverin	—	8-6	4.0	3,000	5.0	5.75	170	1,700
Sacar	6-pdr	6-11	3.5	1,400	5.5	5.5	170	1,700
Minion	—	6-6	3.5	1,000	4.0	4.0	150	1,500
Falcon	—	6-0	2.5	660	2.0	3.55	150	1,500
Falconet	—	3-9	2.0	500	1.5	3.0	150	1,500
Serpentine	—	—	1.5	400	0.75	1.5	140	1,400
Rabanet	—	5-6	1.0	300	0.50	0.33	120	1,000

Source: William Monson, "Naval Tracts, in Six Books: The Whole from the Original Manuscript," in *A Collection of Voyages and Travels*, compiled by Awnsham Churchill, 3rd ed. (London: Henry Lintot and John Osborn, 1732), 313–14.

more useful sizes, those from 3 to 36 pounds of shot weight. By the early eighteenth century gun calibers had been standardized.

As mentioned, there were three families of guns, the culverins, cannons, and perriers. In the sixteenth century all three might have representatives of the same, or nearly the same, bore size. Toward the end of the century this similarity tended to disappear. While smaller weapons were quite long in caliber, the larger were usually no more than 18 calibers in length, and the family name referred more to bore size than to bore-to-length ratio.

As for the shape of the guns themselves, most appear to have been straight-line or formed of a single cone from the vent to the neck astragal, with a ring of some sort forward of the trunnions. For bronze cannon, metal thickness did not vary a great deal in the sixteenth century, although the breech gained somewhat and the chase grew smaller. The thickness of iron pieces was, however, reduced considerably as refining and casting techniques improved.

English guns in particular were noted for their lack of decoration and simple design, whereas in Italy, some founders engraved not only their guns but their shot as well, a practice that impaired performance. The overriding considerations in England seem to have been economy and efficiency.

The seventeenth century saw a continued swing from bronze to iron guns, an increase in the number of pieces per ship, and a shift to larger calibers. Although iron guns were still in many respects inferior to their bronze counterparts, the economic factor eventually won out. Improvements had also been made in casting iron ordnance, so that by 1626 England's Navy Board could note that John Browne had succeeded in producing iron guns that could endure double proof and were still lighter than bronze guns.

By the end of the seventeenth century, iron cannon emerged as the predominant ordnance aboard European naval vessels. In England, according to a report of 1671, only the large first-class warships were ordinarily armed with bronze cannon. One-third of the guns in second- and third-class warships were bronze. In 1677 two-thirds of the cannon in the Swedish navy were cast iron. In 1633, an observer noted in Amsterdam that less than one out of fifty Dutch ships had bronze cannon. An inventory taken in 1593 of Copenhagen's arsenal lists 158 bronze, 344 wrought-iron, and 426 cast-iron cannon. For some, tradition died hard—in 1759 the *Royal George* still carried bronze guns.

The first guns made specifically for the French navy were sixty cast-iron pieces ordered in 1624 and marked with an anchor showing that they were reserved for naval use. In 1661, the French navy had 760 regulation cannon ranging in size from 4 to 36 pounds. Of these, 394 were bronze and 348 iron. In 1700 the navy was armed with 8,973 guns, of which 1,177 were bronze and 7,796 were iron. By 1768, only 186 of 7,774 guns in the French navy were bronze. Notable also was the trend toward bigger guns.

Earlier, the French had been forced to purchase many of their cannon abroad. This arrangement was unsatisfactory to Jean Baptiste Colbert, chief minister to Louis XIV, who wanted to develop a domestic ordnance industry so that France would not have to depend on foreign suppliers. Colbert was particularly interested in increasing the production of satisfactory iron guns, not only because iron was so much cheaper than bronze but also because France had plenty of iron deposits, whereas it had to depend on imports for both copper and tin.

Colbert's efforts produced mixed results. At first many iron guns blew up in proof, but by 1680 foundries at Perigord and Angoumois were achieving satisfactory results. In 1660, a royal edict decreed that the proportion of bronze and iron guns be based on the size of the ship and the rank of the officer commanding. That iron guns were slow in winning the approval of ship captains is indicated in another decree of 1674 that ordered officers to accept iron guns supplied by arsenals.

Statistics presented in table 2 derive from a French edict of July 1670. For comparable statistics on English armament of the period, see table 3.

The French *Soleil Royal* was armed in 1689 with a lower battery of thirty 36-pounders. The *Royal Louis* of 1692 should have been the first French warship to carry 42-pounders, but they were not yet ready and she was armed with 36-pounders instead. These were exceptions, most naval guns of the

TABLE 2

French Establishment of 1670

		Cannon in Bronze						Cannon in Iron					
Rate	*Tonnage*	*24*	*18*	*12*	*8*	*6*	*4*	*24*	*18*	*12*	*8*	*6*	*4*
1	1,400 to 1,500	12	14	—	22	—	6	—	14	12	—	—	—
2	1,100 to 1,200	10	—	8	—	6	—	—	12	20	6	—	—
3	600 to 900	—	—	6	12	—	—	—	—	16	10	6	—
4	500 to 600	—	—	4	—	6	—	—	—	6	10	12	2
5	500	—	—	4	—	4	—	—	—	—	12	10	—

Source: Denoix and Muracciole, "Historique de l'Artillerie," *Mémorial de l'artillerie française,* 28, no. 1 (1964): 66.

period being much smaller. Dutch vessels of the seventeenth century, for example, seldom carried cannon larger than 24-pounders. Ships of the line did not use the 42-pounder until the 1790s, but it was unwieldy and recoiled too much. By the end of the eighteenth century the largest long guns in common use in European navies were 32-pounders. The *Victory,* which had fought the Battle of St. Vincent (1797) with a lower-deck battery of 42-pounders, was armed at Trafalgar (1805) with 32-pounders.

The carriages on which guns were mounted aboard ship had not changed appreciably by the turn of the century; they were still made of elm and equipped with free-moving wooden trucks. By means of breeching rope and tackle, guns recoiled safely and could then be brought back into battery at the gun port. The tackle, which ran through blocks, was secured to bolts on either side of the gun port.

By the eighteenth century, naval ordnance was being produced all over Europe. In the space of four and a half centuries the gun had come to be the decisive factor in naval warfare. Men-of-war were floating gun platforms, and the advantage in battle went more often to the side that could throw the heavier weight of metal in broadside. As Carlo Cipolla noted, "By turning

TABLE 3

English Establishment of 1677

Guns	*First Rates*	*Second Rates*	*Third Rates*	*Men per Gun*
Cannon (42-pdr)	26	—	—	8
Demi-Cannon (32-pdr)	—	26	26	6
Culverins (18-pdr)	28	26	—	5
(12-pdr)	—	—	—	4
Sakers (6-pdr)	28	26	—	3
(3-pdr)	2	2	4	2
	100	90	70	

Source: William Laird Clowes, *The Royal Navy, A History: From the Earliest Times to the Present*, vol. 2 (London: Sampson Low, Marston, 1898), 248.

TABLE 4

ENGLISH ESTABLISHMENTS OF 1716 AND 1757

	FIRST-RATES (100 guns)	SECOND-RATES (90 guns)	THIRD-RATES (80 guns)	(70 guns)
1716				
32-pdr (or 42s for first-rates only), lower deck	28	26	26	—
24-pdr, middle deck	28	—	—	—
lower deck	—	—	—	26
18-pdr, middle deck	—	26	—	—
12-pdr, upper deck	28	—	—	26
middle deck	—	—	26	—
9-pdr, upper deck	—	26	—	—
6-pdr, upper deck	—	—	24	—
quarterdeck	12	10	4	14
forecastle	4	2	—	4
1757				
42-pdr, lower deck	28	—	—	—
32-pdr, lower deck	—	28	26	28
24-pdr, upper deck	—	—	—	—
middle deck	28	—	—	—
18-pdr, middle deck	—	30	26	—
upper deck	—	—	—	28
12-pdr, upper deck	28	30	—	—
9-pdr, upper deck	—	—	24	—
forecastle	—	2	—	4
quarterdeck	—	—	—	14
6-pdr, quarterdeck	12	—	6	—
forecastle	4	—	—	—

Source: William Laird Clowes, *The Royal Navy, A History: From the Earliest Times to the Present*, vol. 2 (London: Sampson Low, Marston, 1898), 11.

whole-heartedly to the gun-carrying sailing ship the Atlantic peoples broke down the bottleneck inherent in the use of human energy and harnessed, to their advantage, far greater quantities of power."[14] Power not only in Europe but also the world over accrued to those states that made a greater shift to the concept of the ship as gun platform. Napoleon's observation about God favoring the side with the best artillery applied at sea as well.

CHAPTER II

Fighting the Guns aboard Ship

THE LARGEST WARSHIPS were ships of the line or line-of-battle ships, so called because they formed the main line in an age when naval battles were fought with rival fleets sailing parallel to each another. These vessels—two-, three-, or even four-decked, three-masted, and square-rigged—were rated at sixty-four to one hundred guns; first-rates carried one hundred guns or more. By the end of the American Revolution the main ship of the world's battle fleets was the third-rate, the seventy-four. The first American-built ship of the line was the seventy-four *America* of 1782, which was given to France and never saw service with the U.S. Navy. The first seventy-four in the U.S. Navy was the *Independence,* launched in 1814.

Smaller vessels such as sloops carried all their guns on a single deck, sometimes on the quarterdeck also. The term sloop of war was in fact applied to any vessel with its main battery guns on one deck. Usually these were ship-rigged vessels of less than twenty-four guns. But the workhorse of the American navy in the age of fighting sail was the frigate, a fighting vessel that belonged to a category between that of the sloop and that of the liner. The frigate was a two-decked, square-rigged ship with three masts, each having crossyards. One covered gun (main) deck carried the principal armament. The open spar deck, poop, and forecastle above carried the lighter guns. (By the late eighteenth century some frigates had, in effect, a single continuous deck at the forecastle/quarterdeck level.) Frigate armament varied greatly, depending on the size of the ship. Generally speaking, American frigates of the revolutionary period averaged about 125 feet in length and were rated at twenty-four to thirty-two guns. American frigates that fought in the War of 1812 were the largest of their class in the world. The *Constitution* measures 204 feet overall and 175 on the gun deck. Her extreme beam is 45 feet 2 inches, and she displaces 2,200 tons.

All warships were constructed in the same basic way, with the thickest oak planking and hull framing at the waterline. The *Constitution* and her sister frigates of the War of 1812 had an unusual degree of hull protection; with more than 20 inches of framing and planking in some places, they were as solidly constructed as some line-of-battle ships (hull protection could run to 30 inches on the biggest liners).

Armament varied greatly from ship to ship, even of the same class, for individual captains had their ordnance preferences and there were frequent changes of regulation. To this day historians argue about the respective numbers, types, and effectiveness of guns in American and British frigates of the War of 1812.

As an example of how armament changed in the period between the Revolutionary War and the War of 1812, the *Constitution*, commissioned in 1798, went from thirty long 24-pounders on her gun (main) deck, fourteen 12-pounders on her forecastle and what was once known as the gangways, and sixteen 18-pounders on the quarterdeck to an armament in 1812 of the same number of 24-pounders on the main deck, an upper battery of sixteen 32-pounder carronades on the quarter deck, and eight 32-pounder carronades and one 18-pounder on the forecastle. She also carried at least a dozen swivels, perhaps half of them mounted in her fighting tops. With such large batteries and hence large crews, conditions aboard fighting ships were quite cramped. The *Constitution* accommodated approximately 450 officers and men.

Batteries of guns on their carriages were located on both the port and starboard sides of a ship. On the gun deck, they pointed through square gun ports cut in the side of the ship, and on the upper deck, through ports in the bulwarks. On the *Constitution*'s gun deck, the captain's cabin aft housed four 24-pounder cannon. This deck—the broadest, strongest, and roomiest—had the heaviest guns.

The *Constitution* differed from British ships in having a berth deck immediately below the gun deck. The gun deck did not have to serve as living space. The orlop was the lowest deck in a ship; in the *Constitution,* the forward orlop contained the armory, sail storage, boatswain's stores, and paint locker. The after orlop held the cable tier, cockpit (four small staterooms and a like number of storerooms, along with the sick bay), and three bread rooms.

Many guns on the upper deck were shielded by strongly constructed bulwarks that also protected gun crews, at least from lighter shot such as grape and musket. Hammocks stored in the netting above the bulwarks provided additional protection.

The operation of guns, always carried out in a minimum amount of space, required trained crews and reliable equipment. Basic implements consisted of

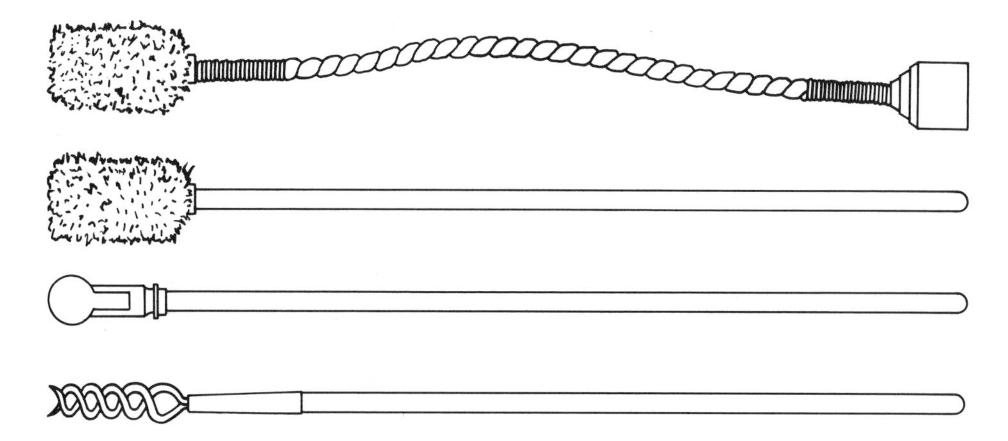

Fig. 7. Implements for Serving Guns. *Top to bottom:* Flexible sponge, sponge, ladle, and wormer.

the rammer, sponge, worm, ladle, boring bit, and priming wire.[1] The rammer was used to seat both the cartridge and shot. For chambered guns, it was tapered slightly at the end so that even a reduced charge could be seated. Later, the face of the rammer was hollowed to fit the shape of the shot. Rammer staves were one foot longer than the gun and had raised marks on them to show when ordinary and other charges were in place. When not in use, the rammer was stored on a beam to the right of the gun.

The sponge cleaned the bore of the gun between firings. For chambered guns, a longer head was used, its shape altered to fit the slope and chamber. In early days, sponge heads were sometimes covered with woolly lamb skin. By the 1820s American sailors were using a fabric, sometimes canvas with woolen yarn woven in full and thick and then trimmed down. Sometimes the rammer had a brush. Navy sponges all had a worm at the end to extract any fragments of the burned cylinder that might be left in the bore after firing. In 1860, the worm was made of flexible bronze or some similar composition and projected half an inch beyond the face of the sponge head. It was left-handed so that it acted when turned to the right. If a sponge carried no worm, the gun had to be wormed after every few shots. In 1815, the rammer and the sponge might be at either end of a piece of rope stiffened by spun yarn. This could produce a faster rate of fire, and freed crew members from the necessity of exposing themselves to enemy fire. The sponge had a cap made of canvas duck. When not in use, the wooden sponge was stored on a beam to the left of the gun.

The worm, or wad-hook, a metal corkscrew mounted at the end of a ramrod, was used to extract the wad and cartridge from the bore if necessary. The ladle was a cylindrical copper spoon that extracted loose powder from a torn cylinder or loaded the powder into the gun if there was no cylinder. Even by the time of the Civil War, when cylinders for powder were in use, ladles were available—one for each caliber of gun per vessel.

Priming wire, or priming iron, made of iron that did not bend too easily but was not brittle enough to break, was used to clear the inside of the touchhole so that it might be properly primed. Tempered boring bits were used when priming wire failed to remove obstructions from the vent. Boring bits had to be used with care, for if they broke off in the vent it was difficult to extract them, leaving the gun unserviceable for some period of time. If they failed to clear an obstruction, a vent punch and a vent drill and brace were available. Priming wires and boring bits were stored inside the brackets of the carriage, near the breech.

Included among service equipment were staffs to hold the match, match tubs, and crowbars. Handspikes (or handspecs) helped elevate the breech of a gun and move the carriage. By the time of the Civil War there were two handspikes per carriage, except for the Marsilly carriage, which had a roller handspike. When not in use, handspikes rested on the bed bolt of the carriage. There were also passing boxes for cartridges, fire buckets, lanterns, a wet swab for each gun, and battle axes. The number of axes varied according to the number of men at a gun.

After a gun was fired, the first step in reloading was to "stop vent and sponge." U.S. Army procedure was usually to leave the vent open, but there was disagreement in the U.S. Navy as to whether the vent should be stopped. It was thought that stopping it prevented circulation of air in the bore and therefore extinguished any lingering fire. The bore could then be sponged to remove fragments of remaining cylinder and to extinguish any fire. The sponge was rammed home against the bottom of the bore, turned from left to right for at least one revolution, then briskly withdrawn. This operation prevented sparks from prematurely discharging the cartridge as it was being rammed home. There were differences of opinion about whether the sponge should be wet or dry; by the time of the Civil War, U.S. Navy regulations called for a moist sponge. After every three firings it was usual practice to worm the gun, drawing out any unburned part of the cartridge. The charge of gunpowder was then loaded.

During the Civil War, gunpowder was still made by the old formula of seventy-five parts weight of nitre (saltpeter), fifteen parts carbon (wood charcoal), and ten parts sulphur. The first two materials produced the explosion, the third aided ignition and gave firmness and consistency to the grains of powder. Gunpowder was manufactured at a mill in Massachusetts as early as 1640, but subsequent restrictive legislation from London ended this. In 1774, on the eve of the American Revolution, there were no powder mills in America. In 1775 one appeared in Rhinebeck, New York, another in Hartford, Connecticut. Although incentives were offered for the manufacture of gunpowder, during the Revolution American gunpowder was inferior and scarce. It was not until 1802, after Éleuthère du Pont went into the business of making gunpowder near Wilmington, Delaware, that it was being manufactured in significant quantity. By the time of du Pont's death in 1834, the concern had become the largest of its kind in the United States and its product was sold the world over.

To prevent the absorption of moisture from the atmosphere, and hence deterioration, powder came to be compressed, granulated, and glazed. Known as press-cake powder, it was safer and cleaner to handle.[2] Priming powder such as that used for muskets was small grained; cannon powder was large grained. Small grains provided a large igniting surface and were consumed quickly; larger grains not only reduced the burning (ignition) rate, and hence the strain on a gun, but also imparted more velocity to the shot. Prior to about 1859, the standard-sized cannon grain ranged from 0.09 to 0.12 inch. Then Thomas Jackson Rodman of the Army Ordnance Corps began experiments to determine the best powder for the guns he had designed and for the navy's large Dahlgren guns. He learned that the heavier the charge, the larger the grains had to be. This led to the introduction of mammoth powder in grains of between 0.60 and 0.90 inch, allowing a heavier charge and greatly increasing projectile velocity. Further improvements, such as oriental-hexagonal and perforated-cake powder, arose during the Civil War and in the years immediately afterward.

Powder was proofed in an eprouvette, a short mortar set at an angle of 45 degrees and throwing a 24-pound solid ball. The number of yards an ounce of powder would throw a ball from the eprouvette determined its designation as 240-yard powder, 260-yard, and so forth. By mid-nineteenth century no powder designated below 225 yards was accepted; good cannon powder ranged from 280 to 300 yards.

At the beginning of the muzzle-loading era, gunpowder was loaded loose by means of a scoop mounted on the end of a ramrod. When it reached the end of the bore, the scoop was turned over and the powder emptied. A wad then rammed the powder home. Later, powder was put in cylinders or cartridges. During battle these were carried to the guns by ships' boys known as powder monkeys. There was one powder monkey to a gun, and he carried one charge at a time. Early cartridges were made of canvas, later ones of paper or parchment. Paper was certainly being used in the United States by 1797, but flannel cartridges were preferred because paper left a residue in the gun that sometimes continued to burn. With paper cartridges, guns had to be sponged after each shot, while flannel had the advantage of not retaining fire. Powder dust easily passed through a flannel cartridge, so a parchment cap covered it until it was loaded. In 1780 Muller recommended boiling the flannel in sizing, which sealed in the dust and stiffened the cartridge case, making it easier to handle.[3] In 1848 the regulation material for cartridges was twilled flannel, but by the Civil War tightly woven wool free of thread or cotton was recommended.

The cylinder consisted of a rectangular piece attached to a circular piece

TABLE 5

POWDER CHARGES OF U.S. NAVY GUNS, 1836

CANNON

Caliber	*Weight (cwt)*	*Charge Distant Firing (lbs-oz)*	*Full Charge for Single Shot (lbs-oz)*	*Full Two Shots or Reduction for Single Shot (lbs-oz)*
42-pdr	70 and upward	14-8	10-0	8-0
32-pdr	60 and upward	10-8	8-0	6-0
32-pdr	54 to 60	10-8	8-0	6-0
32-pdr	49 to 54	9-8	7-8	5-8
24-pdr	48 to 50	8-0	6-0	5-0
24-pdr	40 Congreve	8-0	6-0	5-0
18-pdr	31 light	6-0	5-0	4-0
12-pdr	28 to 30	4-0	3-0	2-4
9-pdr	22 to 25	3-0	2-8	1-12

CARRONADES

Caliber	*Weight*	*Full Charge*	*Second Charge*
42-pdr	35	3-8	3-0
32-pdr	22	2-8	2-0

Source: National Archives, Record Group 45, E464.

for the bottom. It was woven as tightly as possible to prevent powder from sifting out and igniting during the loading process. When filled, cylinders were tied with woolen rather than cotton or linen twine. The cartridge was inserted into the gun with the tie outermost and the seam facing away from the vent.

In early days, before grained powder was used, the weight of the charge was equal to the weight of the projectile; after the introduction of grained and improved powder, the charge was reduced to two-thirds, and in 1740, to one-half the weight of the projectile. By the early nineteenth century the normal powder charge was one-third.

Because a gun grew hot after firing, heating subsequent charges and increasing their strength, these charges had to be smaller. Another reason for reducing subsequent charges was to increase splintering in enemy vessels, which resulted in considerable casualties and was more feared than solid shot. The desired velocity was one that would just penetrate wood, creating the most splinters.

Powder charges evolved into three basic loads: distant, full, and reduced. In June 1812 the *Constitution* had a variety of charges on board for her 24-pounders: Service charges were available in 8-pound, 7-pound, and 6-pound sizes. There were also 4-pound charges for drill. By 1851 powder was packed in different-color cartridges: white for distant firing, blue for ordinary, and red for "near and saluting." These weighed, respectively, one-third, one-fourth, and one-sixth the weight of the shot.

During the Civil War, U.S. Navy guns used only two charges, normal and

TABLE 6

POWDER CHARGES OF U.S. NAVY GUNS, 1860

Ordnance		Charges of Powder (lbs)				
Caliber	*Weight*	*For Distant Firing*	*For Ordinary Firing*	*For Near Firing (two projectiles)*	*Diameter of Cartridge Gauges (in)*	*Saluting Charges (lbs)*
Guns					*Cylindrical*	
64-pdr	106 cwt	16.0	12.0	8.0	7.0	6.0
32-pdr	61 cwt	10.0	8.0	6.0	5.5	4.0
32-pdr	57 cwt	9.0	8.0	6.0	5.5	4.0
32-pdr	51 cwt	8.0	7.0	5.0	5.5	4.0
32-pdr	46 cwt	7.0	7.0	5.0	5.5	4.0
32-pdr	42 cwt	6.0	6.0	4.0	5.5	4.0
32-pdr	33 cwt	4.5	4.5	4.0	5.5	4.0
32-pdr	27 cwt	4.0	4.0	3.0	5.5	3.0
Shell Guns					*Conical*	
XI-in	15,700 lbs	15.0	15.0	15.0	11 × 5.5 × 11	7.0
X-in	12,000 lbs	12.5	12.5	12.5	10 × 5.0 × 10	6.0
IX-in	9,000 lbs	10.0	10.0	10.0	9 × 4.5 × 9	5.0
					Cylindrical	
8-in	63 cwt	9.0	8.0	6.0	5.5	4.0
8-in	55 cwt	7.0	7.0	6.0	5.5	4.0

Source: U.S. Navy Department Bureau of Ordnance, *Ordnance Instructions for the United States Navy* (Washington: G. W. Bowman, 1860), 141.

reduced, for distant and near firing. Normal charges were not loaded when a gun was hot. It was difficult to employ reduced charges in chambered guns. The chamber was made to hold a full charge, so if a reduced charge was used the shot would not touch it. The space between powder and ball had to be filled with a block of wood or cork tied in the cylinder's mouth.

Weight of charge varied according to gun size as well as caliber. For heavy cannon, 19 to 20 calibers long, the maximum charge might be one-half the weight of the shot; for light cannon of the same length, it was one-third to one-quarter.

Shipboard powder was kept in magazines guarded by marines and opened only on captain's orders. At first it was stored in barrels weighing approximately 100 pounds each, except for about 50 broadsides' worth, which was packed in cylinders laid on open shelves. The powder was "turned" every three to six months to prevent deterioration from the settling of saltpeter. By the time of the Civil War this practice had been deemed unnecessary and was discontinued. Gunpowder did often deteriorate in shipboard magazines, but from dampness rather than settling. As a result, it did not always produce enough force for shot to penetrate the hull of an enemy vessel. In the engagement between the British frigate *Shannon* and the U.S. frigate *Chesa-*

peake during the War of 1812, deteriorating powder plagued American efforts, as it would later in the same war when the brig *Argus* was defeated by the British. In the case of the *Chesapeake,* the shots' failure to penetrate may also have been caused by double-shotting, but as the range was not over 200 yards, this is doubtful.

By 1850, four-fifths of the powder aboard ship was stored in cylinders and one-fifth was in bags of 25 pounds each. These containers were stowed in copper tanks sealed with lids and rubber washers to protect against dampness and fire. Every ship of more than two decks had two magazines, located below the waterline at the vessel's extremities. Each magazine was provided with cocks to let water in during a fire. Conceivably, because of the metal tanks, this could be accomplished without damaging the powder. Empty powder tanks were stored on the upper shelves so that as many loaded tanks as possible could be kept below the waterline.

When three different charges were allowed aboard, one-tenth of the magazine's cylinders held charges for distant firing, six-tenths, charges for ordinary firing, and three-tenths, charges for near firing or double-shotting. Underproof powder was devoted to saluting charges. The cylinders were colored according to type, as were the lids of tanks in which they were stored.

In the magazines, extraordinary precautions were taken to prevent an accidental spark from setting off the powder and destroying the ship. Men wore a "magazine dress," a long shirt of worsted material with no metal buttons. They also wore soft-soled slippers.

The rammer pushed rather than drove the powder cartridge to the bottom of the bore, where it was then given two or three blows to make certain it was seated. It was judged to be so if it could be felt through the vent with a priming wire. If the cartridge was not seated properly, or the shot was not seated against the powder, the gun might explode.

By the mid-nineteenth century, two types of wads were in common use: the junk or hard wad, and the grommet wad. When guns were kept loaded during a cruise, it was customary to put a junk wad between the shot and the charge. A grommet wad was placed over the shot to keep it in place while the vessel was moving. If the shot rolled away from the charge, the gun might burst when fired. A loose shot in the gun might also cause friction and thereby set off the powder.

The junk wad was made from pieces of old cable or cordage compressed by means of a mall or a screw in an iron cylinder. Mall-driven wads were considered hard enough for small-caliber guns, but for heavy shot, and for those used behind the shot, wads produced by screw pressure were preferred. Junk wads tended to swell, were difficult to load, and occasionally jammed in the gun.

Rope grommet or selvagee wads were used only over the shot. The grommet wad was believed to improve accuracy by preventing deflections of the shot in the bore. When rammed home, it took position around the shot, transversing the bore. The grommet wad consisted of a piece of rope shaped like a ring with two crosspieces of rope to prevent it from collapsing. Its diameter was that of the bore of the gun; the two crosspieces projected slightly for a firm fit.

By the time of the Civil War, U.S. Navy regulations called for ten grommet wads to be kept at each gun. Being lighter than hard junk wads, they did not pose the threat of injury if struck by enemy fire. Only in rough seas were wads employed over shells, and they were always selvagee wads. During the war, regulations prohibited the use of wads between two shot or over grape shot.

After the gun had been loaded, priming wire was inserted into the touchhole. This not only pierced the cartridge but also ensured that the touchhole was open and free of debris. Then, to prime the gun, fine-grain gunpowder was placed in the touchhole until it accumulated at the top. The gun was now ready to fire. If it was necessary to unload the gun subsequently, and not advisable to undo its muzzle-lashing in removing the charge, the cartridge was pierced through the touchhole and a pint of vinegar was poured in.

Once the gun was loaded, handspikes trained it. These were levered under the horns (inner ends) of the carriage brackets. Men working the handspikes were assisted by those working the side tackles, which were fastened to bolts on the bracket horns and ran to the ship's side.

Carriages had to recoil, otherwise they would be destroyed. Therefore their weight was a matter of some concern. If too heavy, they would be damaged by recoil; if too light, they might lurch beyond the limited space allowed them in the ship's tight confines. The great recoil of light guns was hard on carriages, but it made the guns much easier to maneuver. Heavy guns produced lighter recoil but were harder to work. Thus a certain compromise in weight had to be reached.

It was originally thought that the amount of recoil affected the range of the projectile, and for that reason experiments were conducted with stationary carriages, all of which proved unsatisfactory. Finally it was established that the amount of recoil had no effect on the velocity of the shot.

Recoil could be eased by decreasing the diameter of the trucks and positioning the trunnions properly. English guns had less recoil because they were quarter-hung—with trunnions slightly below the axis of the bore—and thus produced downward pressure on the breech.

The stout rope known as breeching merely limited, did not arrest, recoil. Breeching was secured to the neck of the cascabel and through ringbolts (later the shackle) on the sides of the carriage; its ends were clinched to large ringbolts on bulwarks to either side of the gun port. (In French practice, breeching did not pass around the gun but through holes in the middle of the carriage cheeks.) When the gun was fired, it recoiled the full length of the breeching and was thus in position for loading, with the muzzle approximately one foot inside the port. Breeching, at least on the gun deck, was soon

Fig. 8. Tackle and Breeching in a British Ship of the American Revolution. A reconstruction. (Courtesy of the Colonial Historical Park, Yorktown, Virginia.)

damaged by continued exposure to moisture, so it was essential to have spares, already sized, on hand. Under optimum conditions, breeching could be expected to withstand two to three hundred firings before it had to be replaced.

Even with breeching, the recoil of the carriage was not always uniform or predictable, especially in oblique—off the beam—fire. As one writer noted in 1811, "It is a lamentable truth, that numbers of men are constantly maimed, in one way of another, by the recoiling of heavy ordnance used on board ships of war." Much of this resulted from the carriage's random recoil, which was "much affected not only by the motion of the vessel but also by the inequities of the deck; inasmuch that it is difficult for the people to know, within several feet, the point to which the carriage will come." Even with careful attention to tackles, it required "the greatest watchfulness on all hands to prevent accidents."[4] This was *with* breeching; the consequences were considerably worse if a gun broke free during recoil.

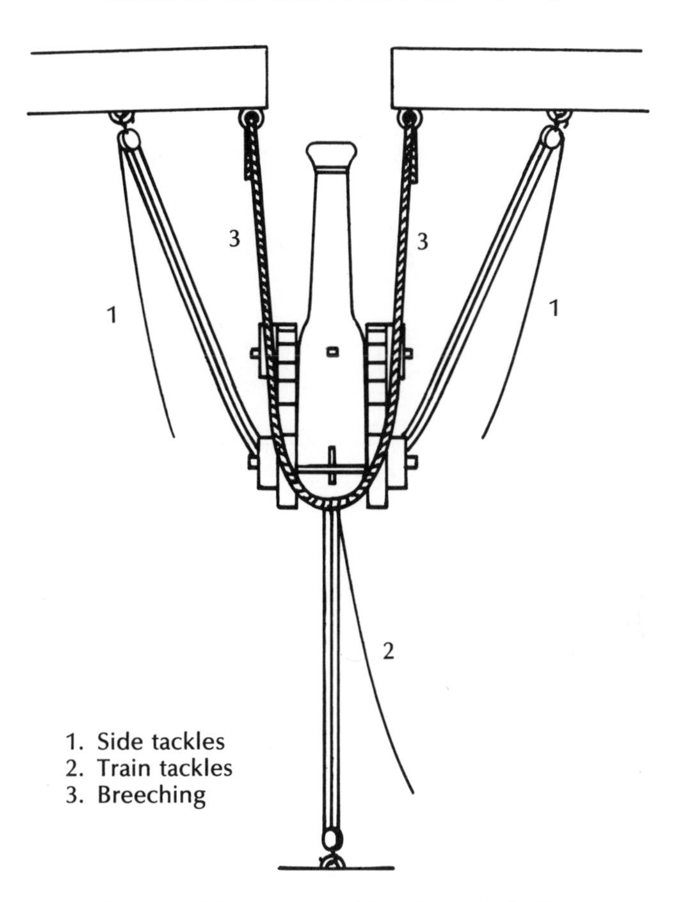

Fig. 9. Tackle and Breeching, Broadside Gun.

While the gun was "running out," train tackle, also known as in- or preventer-tackle, checked lateral movement. Train tackle could also bring the gun in if necessary and hold it in position during loading. The gun was run out by means of side tackles. These had a single block that hooked to the eye bolts on the carriage's side and a single block (double for 32-pounders) that hooked to other ringbolts on the gun port's sides.

The first small guns, which had little recoil, were probably fired by means of a hot wire leading to the touchhole. Later, cannon were fired with a match, also known as a common or slow match to distinguish it from the later quick match. The vent was filled with a fine powder, and on the vent piece toward the muzzle a powder train was laid so that the match would not be blown out by the blast.

Slow match was made of hemp or cotton rope about 0.06 inch in diameter. Three strands were twisted together to form the match, which burned at a rate of about 4 inches per hour. A length of match was supplied to each gun, the rope being wound around a wooden staff about 2 feet 6 inches tall known as a linstock. The linstock had a pointed metal end that was either stuck in the

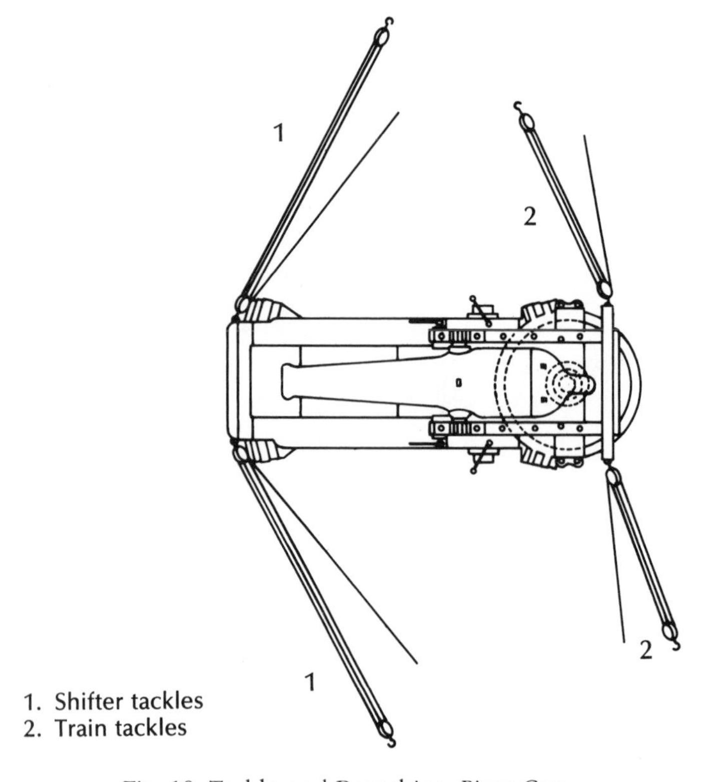

Fig. 10. Tackle and Breeching, Pivot Gun.

wooden deck or placed in a match tub, which was also supplied to each gun. The tub held not only the linstock but also water for the men to drink during action.

Before the end of the seventeenth century, port fire or quick match was introduced, slow match being retained to light it. Port fire was a short length of flammable material that freed the crew from the task of laying a powder train to the vent and thus greatly shortened the time between ignition of the priming and explosion of the charge. It was sixty parts saltpeter or nitre, forty parts sulphur, and twenty parts mealed powder. The flame was intense and could not be put out with water. A stock held the port fire, whose end, after firing, was nipped off by a cutter. Port fire came in a paper casing and was about 16 to 20 inches long by 0.5 inch in diameter; each piece would burn for 12 to 15 minutes. At the time of the Civil War port fire was still being kept aboard U.S. Navy ships.

Originally, gunners primed cannon by filling the vent with powder from a powder horn. This was a slow operation, and loose powder had a tendency to erode the touchhole (especially in bronze guns), resulting in a loss of shot velocity. This problem was partially overcome by the introduction of a tin tube, but it tended to fly out of the vent and could injure the crew. The best

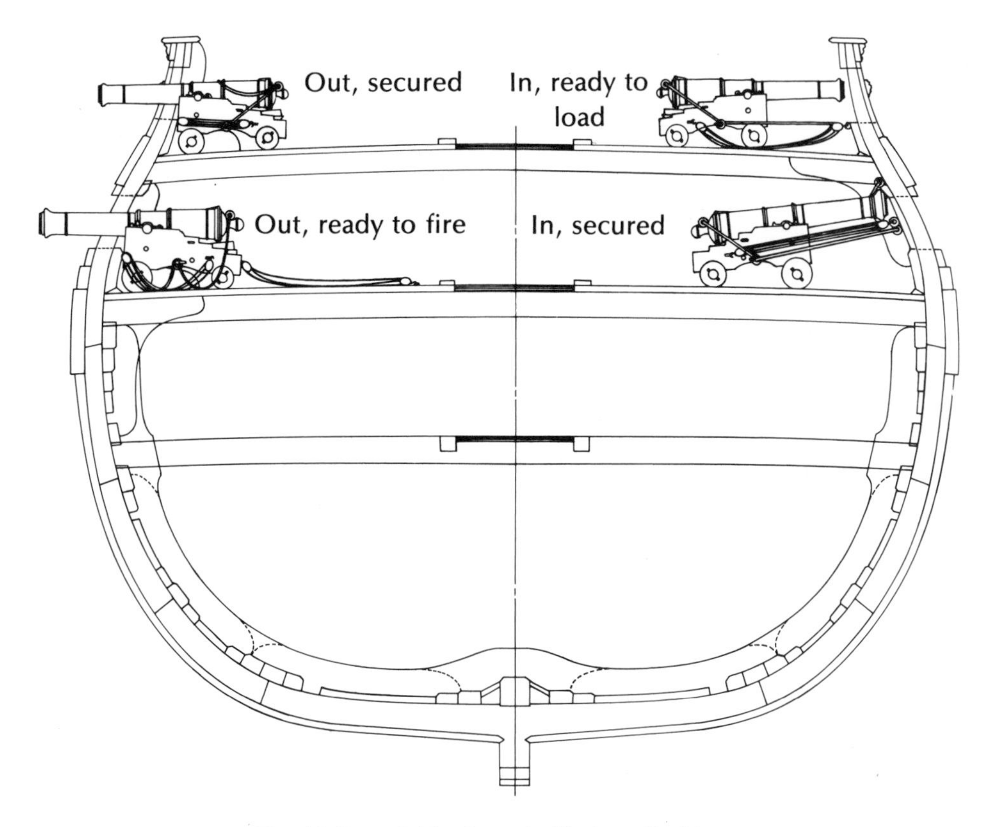

Fig. 11. Broadside Guns in Various Positions.

tool for priming was a goose quill, in general use by 1800. The large end of the quill was slit lengthwise about half an inch into seven or more parts, and these were bent back to form a cup. Fine woolen thread was then woven into the slits, making a sort of basket. A paste of mealed powder and camphorated

Fig. 12. Linstock.

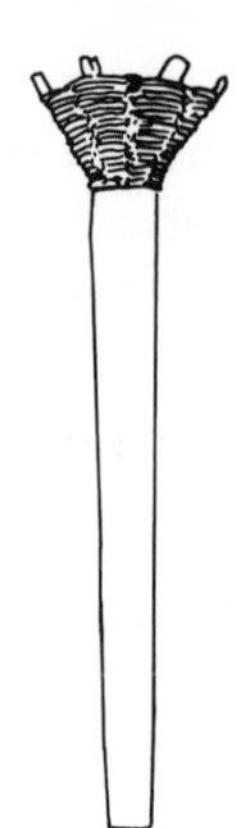

Fig. 13. Quill Tube.

alcohol was inserted into the quill, which was placed in the touchhole prior to firing and ignited with quick match. This system increased the certainty of fire but was still slow enough to allow a change in gun elevation before the charge went off.

The system of priming with a tube and igniting with a quick match was continued until the application of flintlocks to cannon. This advance is credited to Captain Sir Charles Douglas of the Royal Navy, whose recommendation in 1778 that they be adopted was rejected by the Admiralty. At his own expense Douglas, captain of the 98-gun ship of the line *Duke,* fitted out her guns with musket locks attached to pieces of wood and strapped with iron wire to the left side of the vents. He also purchased flannel bottoms for the paper cartridges and goose quills for tubes. Flintlocks not only produced a faster rate of fire, they were more reliable and gave the gun captain control of the timing of fire. This was especially important at sea, because a ship's rolling affected gun elevation.

In 1782 the value of flintlocks was clearly demonstrated in the Battle of the Saints, against the French. By that time, the guns of both the *Duke* and the *Formidable*—to which Douglas had been transferred in November 1781—had been equipped with them. Probably because this was the last fleet action of the War of the American Revolution and there was no sense of urgency, the Admiralty did not take immediate action to adopt flintlocks officially. It was not until 1790, when a new type of bronze lock became available, that they were officially adopted by the Royal Navy. Flintlocks were used during the Napo-

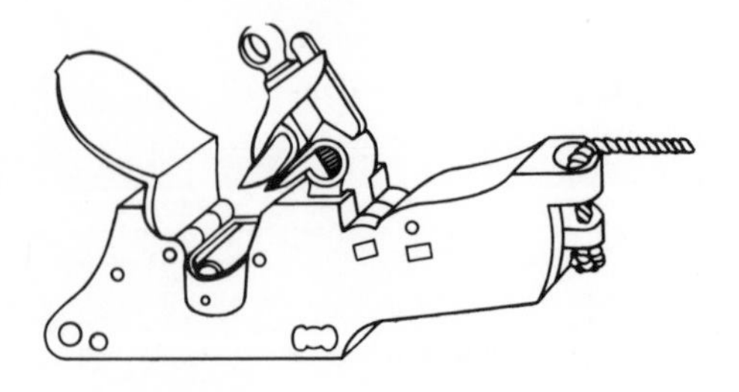

Fig. 14. Flintlock.

leonic wars. In 1818, a double-flinted lock, which increased the probability of ignition, replaced the older model. Other navies followed the British example. France officially adopted flintlocks in 1800. At Trafalgar, however, the French were still using the match, while the English merely kept it handy in case flintlocks failed. Later, the French adopted the double flintlock as well.

Just when flintlocks appeared in the U.S. Navy is uncertain. In 1814, during the War of 1812, a gun accidentally discharged on board the frigate *United States* when a seaman mishandled a lock lanyard. The guns of the *Constitution* were also fitted with locks when she engaged the *Java* and the *Guerriere*. These were probably musket flintlocks adapted to cannon. The first known navy contract for cannon locks was let in May 1814, when five hundred of them were ordered from Enoch Hidden, a New York City locksmith. Flintlocks were either kept on the guns or stowed separately and attached when needed.

The outstanding military invention of the first half of the nineteenth century may well have been the percussion cap. In 1807 a Scots Presbyterian minister, Alexander Forsyth, patented the use of fulminates of mercury as a new primer for firearms, thus rendering loose powder obsolete for that purpose. Mercury fulminates did not need fire to detonate them; they could be fitted over a firearm's touchhole and ignited when struck a sharp blow with a hammer, a device that worked almost instantaneously and was reliable in all weather conditions. They came in various forms and were known as friction primers, percussion caps, percussion wafers, or wafers.

The percussion principle was easily applied to small arms, and an effort was made to apply it to cannon. One problem was that the hammer struck directly over the vent, which exposed it to the force of the blast when the gun went off. Early locks, being spring operated, could not withstand this shock. The first percussion devices applied to the entire battery of a U.S. Navy ship—the *Vandalia,* in 1828—were spring-operated locks invented by Joshua Shaw of Philadelphia. Colonel Jure of the French Marine Artillery developed the first springless lock for shipboard use. The hammer recoiled on a stud when the gun went off.

Wafers, the earliest percussion primers, got their name from their shape. Although the vent was shaped to receive them, they were often dislodged by the shock of other guns being fired. To prevent this, a flat piece of metal was added; it pivoted on one end of the lock plate and lay over the wafer. As the hammer descended, the shank came into contact with a projection from the plate, which moved it horizontally and uncovered the wafer.

Another means of preventing dislodgment was to change the shape of the wafer. A percussion cap shaped like a cup, a half inch in depth and diameter, was substituted and placed on the nipple of the hammer. For some time this was the regulation primer of the U.S. Navy. Made of pasteboard coated with a small amount of fulminate and then waterproof varnish, it was pressed by thumb onto the head of the hammer. The percussion system may have been

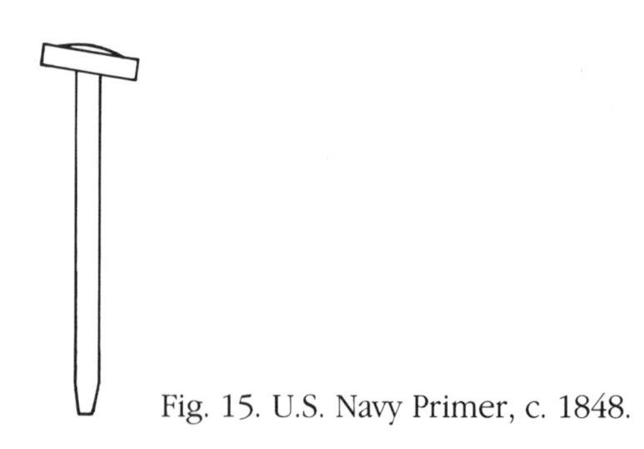

Fig. 15. U.S. Navy Primer, c. 1848.

developed by Shaw; in any case, the navy described it as being "at present used" in 1850.[5]

The percussion cap replaced all other ignition devices. But while the primer was satisfactory for small guns, especially the new boat howitzers, it did not work on larger guns because it was too far from the powder cartridge. They required a modified quill tube, which was still in use during the Civil War.

The percussion primer was essentially a quill tube capped by an explosive wafer. Instead of the basket of woolen yarn at the top of the quill, a perforated disk of paper was pasted under the prongs of the quill. Fine-grained powder replaced the pierced composition in the quill itself, and a piece of writing paper was put on the upper surface of the prongs. Above this was the detonating material, fulminate of mercury mixed with mealed powder. When pressed and dry, the wafer was coated with clear shellac to protect it from dampness. Grained powder was retained in the quill because of its greater ability to resist moisture. Since the lower end of the quill was sealed, itoccasionally obstructed the flame; to prevent this, it was pinched off before being seated in the vent. Primers were stored, fifty each in tin boxes with shellacked lids to keep out moisture.

Enoch Hidden continued to refine his locks with a view toward developing a hammer that could be withdrawn from the vent at the instant of firing, preventing damage. He patented one such lock in 1831, and in 1842 produced another known as Hidden's Patent Sliding Lock. (William R. Ashard probably had a hand in this invention, because in 1848 the navy purchased the rights to an improved lock from the two men.) Both the U.S. and British navies adopted the new lock. A pull on the "lock string" (lanyard) turned the hammer on its axial bolt in the lock lugs until it hit the primer; it continued moving away from the vent by means of a slot in the shank until the bolt came into contact with the opposite end of the slot. Thus the hammer exploded the primer in the vent and moved out of the way of the blast. This lock remained the standard type for the U.S. Navy through the Civil War.

In 1847, Lieutenant John Dahlgren developed a cannon lock with a perforated hammerhead so that the discharge from the vent passed through it without blowing it back. The lock operated successfully on guns of the

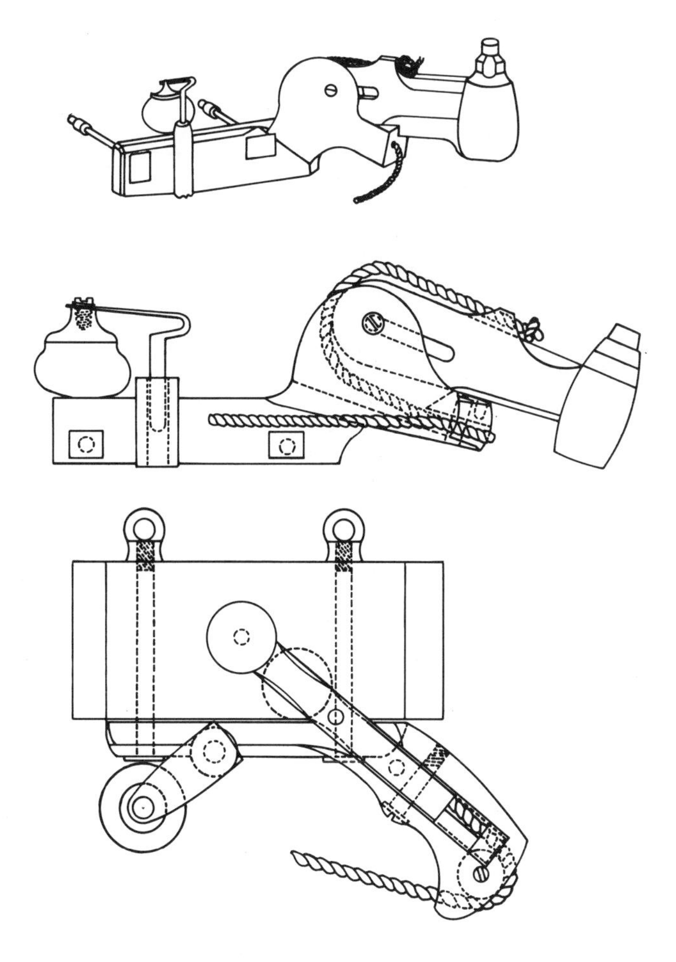

Fig. 16. Hidden's Lock, in Use on U.S. Navy Ships by the 1840s.

experimental battery at the Washington Navy Yard in 1848 and was adopted for use on boat howitzers of Dahlgren's design.

At the time of the Civil War, as Dahlgren recommended, the navy dispensed with the lock piece and lock lugs were cast on either side of the gun's vent. The lock thus became a simple hammer with a slot in the shank, secured by its axial bolt to the lugs of the gun. This was first carried on the new pattern 8-inch shell guns cast at the West Point foundry in 1851 and installed as the main battery on the razeed frigate *Macedonian.* When the gun was secured, the lock was left in place on it.

The friction primer was a tube filled with gunpowder. At its top was a spur containing friction powder, which was set off with a rough steel slider pulled by a lanyard. Friction primers were packed in sealed tin boxes similar to those storing percussion primers.

Artillerymen preferred the friction primer to the flintlock for use on land. In 1843 the U.S. Navy ordered 200,000 primers, and by 1860 they were

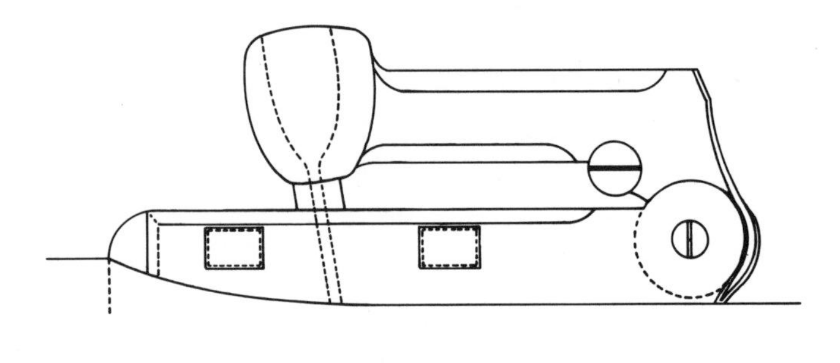

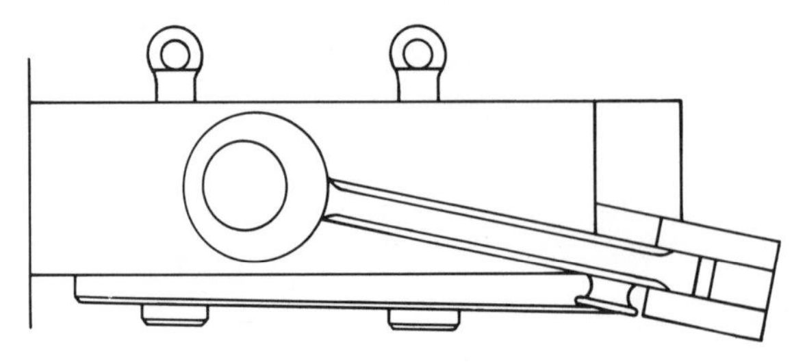

Fig. 17. Dahlgren's Perforated Hammer. (After an original drawing by John Dahlgren in National Archives, Record Group 74.)

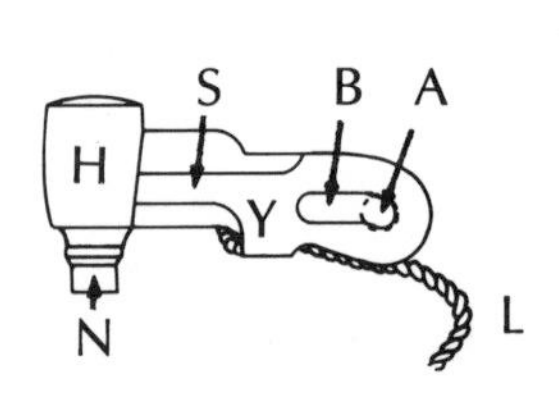

H: The head of the hammer, made of strong gun metal.
S: The shank, of strong gun metal.
N: An iron nipple with a case-hardened face, screwed into the head.
A: The hole for the axial bolt of the hammer.
AB: The extension of the hole, called a slot, running in the direction of the head. Its length allows the hammer to recede 1 inch, which takes it clear of the vent blast.
L: A Lanyard entering beneath the rear end of the shank, which is rounded for that purpose, then through a perforated stud *Y* on the underside of the shank.

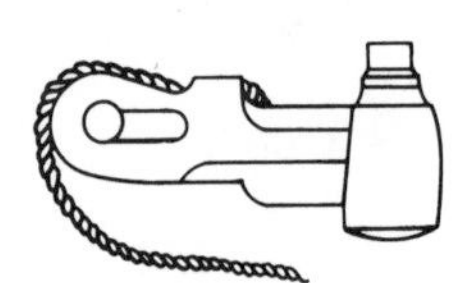

Ready to fire

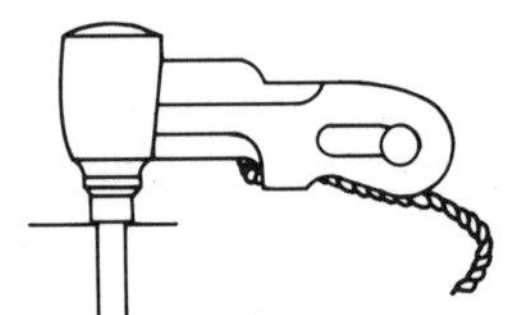

Ignition of primer on the vent

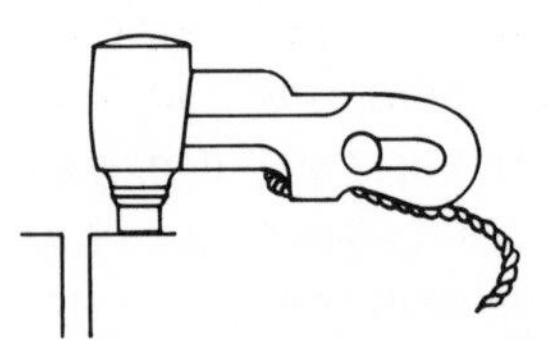

Withdrawal from the vent

Fig. 18. U.S. Navy Lock Lug and Sliding Hammer. (After a drawing in John Dahlgren, *Ordnance Memoranda: Naval Percussion Locks and Primers* [Philadelphia, 1853].)

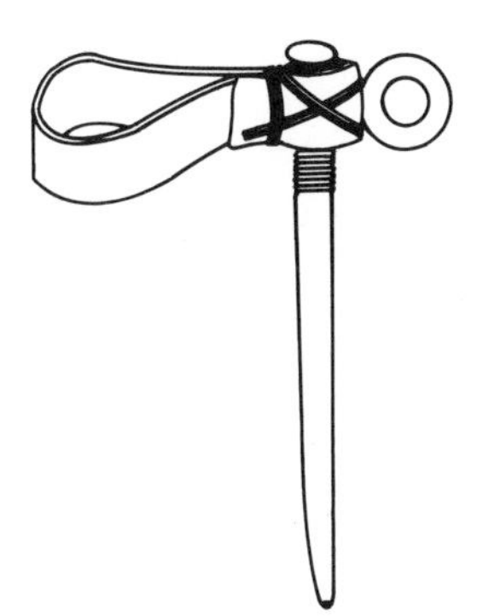

Fig. 19. Friction Primer.

included as standard issue in ordnance stores aboard vessels. At sea, the chief objection to them was that they could injure the crew, and for that reason they were used only when the lock did not work. If both lock and friction primer failed, recourse could always be made to the match.

Until the early nineteenth century, sights were virtually unknown. Gunners aimed by sighting along the axis of the gun; accuracy depended on proximity to the opposing vessel. Throughout most of the life of the muzzleloader, guns were usually fired at point-blank range, and many actions were fought yardarm to yardarm. When a proposal for a sight was sent to Admiral Nelson in 1801, he rejected it, noting, "The best and only mode I have found of hitting the enemy afloat is to get so close that whether the gun is pointed upwards or downwards forward or aft ... it must strike its opponent."[6]

Point-blank range in popular usage meant the point where, with the gun held horizontally, a shot fired from it hit the water. By the time of the Civil War point-blank range had come to mean, in the U.S. and British navies, the distance to the point at which a shot, fired from a level gun loaded with a full service charge, crossed the horizontal plane on which the trucks of the gun's carriage stood. To the French, point-blank referred to the distance from the gun to the point where the shot crossed the horizontal plane in which stood the gun's line of metal. In 1850, point-blank range was estimated at 275 yards for an 18-pounder and 400 yards for a 32-pounder. Shot fired beyond this range was "at random"—in French, *coup perdu*. Extreme range was at utmost random.

Because of light winds a ship might not be able to close with an enemy quickly, in which case guns were fired at long range. Long-range firing became more feasible as guns and powder improved. Accuracy of aim grew more crucial, making sights necessary. Pointing a gun meant giving a desired direction to the axis of its bore. This could be done horizontally (laterally) or vertically (with elevation).

In determining elevation, allowance had to be made for the fact that guns were smaller at the muzzle than at the breech. At short ranges, this produced the relatively common practice of firing too high. One writer calculated in

Fig. 20. How Sighting along the Top of the Gun Causes Shot to Go Too High.

1829 that if two frigates stood about 100 fathoms (600 feet) apart and a gunner sighted along the top of his gun, the shot would go 18 to 20 feet above the enemy's ports.[7] This was more likely with medium guns, which were shorter and had a greater dispart. A dispart sight on the top of the gun corrected the difference in thickness of muzzle and breech. Dispart sights were mounted on the second reinforce, almost in line with the trunnions, rather than at the muzzle, where they might be knocked off during loading or recoil. And yet disparts, like other sights, did not come into general use until the beginning of the nineteenth century.

The gunner's quadrant had been used since the sixteenth century to determine angle of elevation. Quadrants were made of bronze or wood and divided into degrees, with each degree divided into ten parts. One means of quickly setting the gun for elevation was to mark the quoin in degrees against the bed. In this fashion, all the guns in a battery could be laid for approximately the same elevation.

Tangent sights, graduated scales moving in a vertical plane at the breech of the gun, were a great advantage in distant firing. They vastly improved the training of guns, enabling a commander to set all of them at the same elevation regardless of their type of carriage. For range less than point-blank, it was necessary to decrease—rather than increase, as with the tangent sight—the angle of sight. The dispart or a fixed front sight performed this task.

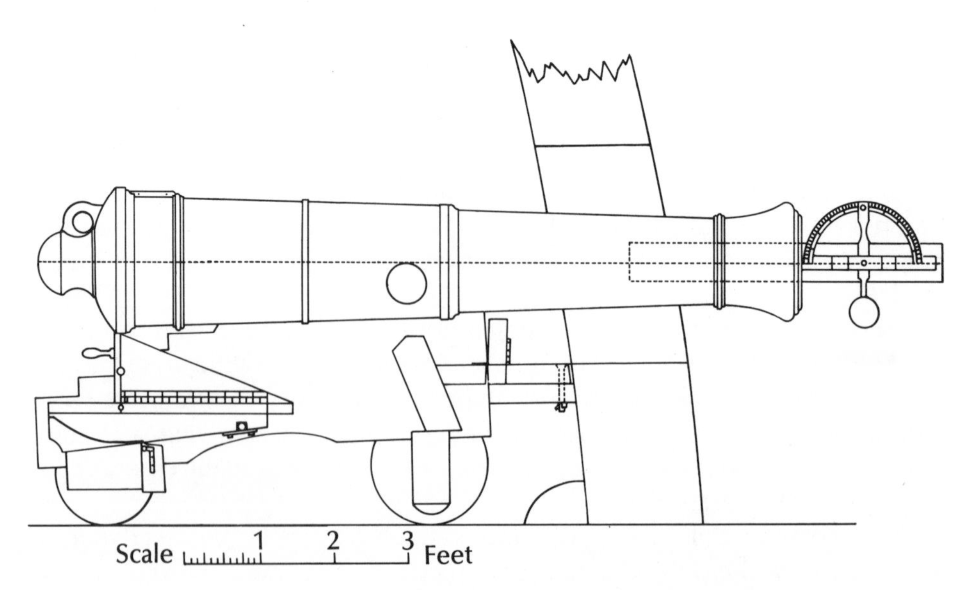

Fig. 21. Gunner's Quadrant and Quoin, Marked in Degrees.

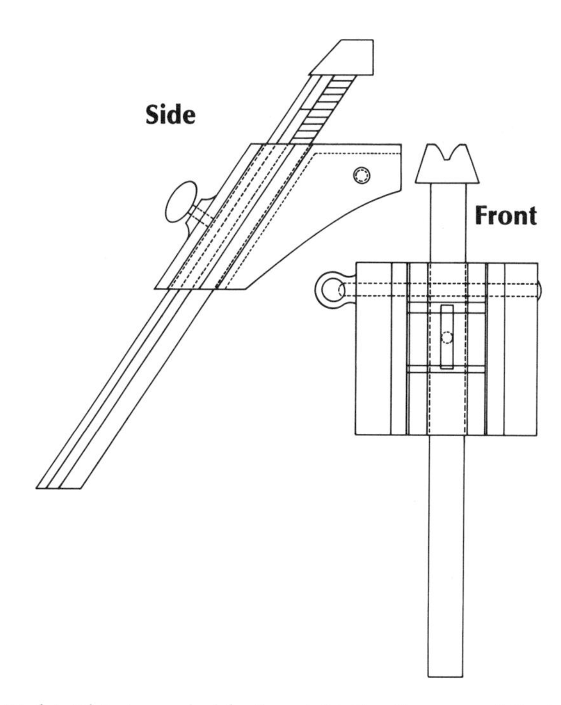

Fig. 22. Tangent Sight. This is probably the sight the Bureau of Ordnance ordered for all U.S. Navy guns in 1848. William Jeffers wrote in 1850 that it had been "lately adopted" from the English. He compared it unfavorably to contemporary French sights because it was calibrated only in degrees, and not for range and charge. (After a drawing in William Jeffers, *A Concise Treatise on the Theory and Practice of Naval Gunnery* [New York, 1850].)

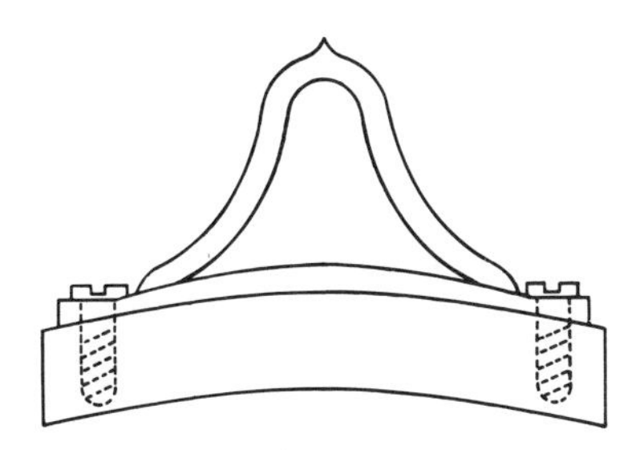

Fig. 23. Dispart Sight in Use in the U.S. Navy by 1850. (After a drawing in Jeffers, *A Concise Treatise*.)

The two elements of a front and rear sight were combined by Colonel Jure of France when he developed a system for pointing guns at sea. This consisted of a front sight near the end of the reinforce, and a sight—in essence, the tangent sight—at the breech. The latter consisted of an iron bar sliding in a bronze case, fixed perpendicular to the axis of the bore. The sight had six principal divisions, each representing one cable length, or approximately 608 feet; each division had four subdivisions.

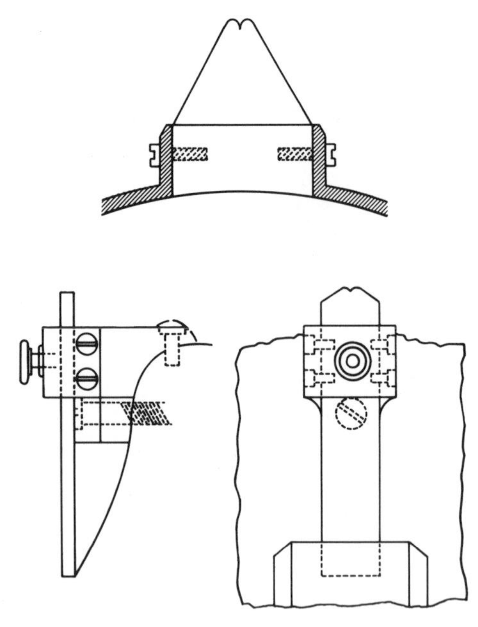

Fig. 24. Jure's System of Front Sight and Sight. (After a drawing in Jeffers, *A Concise Treatise*.)

Lateral aim was often taken with the aid of notches on the top of the gun, cut into the base ring and the side of the muzzle swell. These would be brought to bear on the target. Notches on the side of the breech, laid in quarter degrees, helped determine horizontal fire.

The improved sights of the nineteenth century were only slowly introduced aboard ship. It was not until 1848 that the navy's Bureau of Ordnance and Hydrography decided to equip all naval guns with them. By the time of the Civil War navy guns were fitted with two bronze sights, located at the breech and reinforce. Both were fitted with covers so that the sights might be left in place when the gun was secured.

The reinforce sight was a point fixed to the sight mass cast on the gun's upper surface, between the trunnions. The breech sight was a square bar or stem on the "head," which was the sight notch. The bar slid in a vertical plane, the sight box, fixed to the breech sight mass. A thumbscrew held the bar at the desired elevation. The sight was graduated in yards. When completely depressed, the line of sight was parallel to the axis of the bore.

Sights were not polished but left dark. If a metal sight was unavailable or damaged, a wooden dispart sight was lashed to the reinforce of the gun for tangent firing.

Pivot guns were supplied with trunnion sights to be used at elevations beyond those covered by ordinary sights. The trunnion sight, made of mahogany or some other hard wood, was about 18 inches in length, 2 inches wide, and 1 inch thick. It had a bronze notch at one end and a point at the other and was attached to the left trunnion with a thumbscrew. When the screw was slack, the sight could revolve. The face of the trunnion was marked in degrees so the sight could be read against it.

During the Civil War all new guns had notches on top of the lock piece or over the vent, on the reinforce sight mass, and on the muzzle, which marked the vertical plane passing through the axis of the bore at right angles to the axis of the trunnions.

The range to an enemy ship might also be calculated by determining the type of vessel it was. Since mast heights were approximately the same for the ships of each class, regardless of their nation of origin, determining the angle to the top of the mast would give the approximate distance for general firing. Under ordinary circumstances, however, the best means for determining range was to fire a shot at the target, note its impact, and adjust the sights accordingly.

There were many examples of poor shooting prior to the advent of sights. In their action of 25 October 1812, the frigates *United States* and *Macedonian* fired an estimated fifty broadsides each—a total of approximately 2,500 shot—and yet only a hundred hull hits were registered: ninety-five on the *Macedonian* and five on the *United States.*[8]

By the mid-nineteenth century, with advances in the science of ballistics, it was possible to calculate the ranges at which fire could be effective. The ability of a cannon ball to penetrate the side of a ship was closely related to its velocity. For example, to penetrate 30 inches of oak in a 74-gun ship, a 32-pound shot needed a velocity of 1,090 feet per second. This was obtained with a powder charge of ⅓ (10⅔ pounds) at 1,000 yards or of ⅙ at 500 yards. To penetrate 20 inches of a frigate's side, a 32-pound ball had to have a velocity of 850 feet per second. This was attained with a charge of ⅓ at 1,200 yards or ⅙ at 600.

Not only powder but also windage—the difference between the diameter of a shot and the diameter of the bore—affected velocity. Windage compensated for a shot's deviation from sphericity, for rust on the shot and in the bore, for bore fouling in continued firing, and for the expansion of shot when heated (estimated as being between 1/70 and 1/76 the diameter at white heat). If windage was too great, it allowed some of the powder's force to escape and therefore reduced the velocity of the ball. Experiments at Woolwich, England, before 1837 established that a windage of 1/20 allowed one-third to one-fourth of the powder's force to escape. Excess windage might also cause the ball to "bound" down the bore, an action known as balloting, and leave the muzzle in an uncertain direction. Balloting put a considerable strain on the bore and might eventually cause the gun to burst. Windage increased as the bore became enlarged by repeated firings, with the greatest amount of wear in the area of the charge.

When they were installed in a ship, guns were numbered consecutively on both the port and starboard sides, beginning with no. 1 at the bow. Normal

TABLE 7

RANGES, C. 1812

RANGE WITH CANNON (32-, 24-, AND 18-PDRS)

Elevation (degrees)	*Proportion of Powder*	*Species of Shot*	*Range (yards)*
2	1/3	With single shot to the first graze	1,200
2	1/4	With single shot to the first graze	1,000
2	1/4	Two shot, ranged close together	500
4	1/3	Single shot	1,600
4	1/4	Single shot	1,500
7	1/4	Single shot	2,150
7	1/4	Single shot	2,020
2	1/4	One round shot, and one round of grape with combined effect	600
4	1/4	One round of grape shot alone	1,000
2	1/4	One double-headed or bar shot to the first graze	800

RANGE WITH CARRONADES*

Elevation (degrees)		*Range (yards)*					
	Species:	*68*	*42*	*32*	*24*	*18*	*12*
	Charge (lbs-oz):	*5-8*	*3-8*	*2-10*	*2-0*	*1-8*	*1-0*
Point-blank		450	400	330	300	270	230
1		650	600	560	500	470	400
2		890	860	830	780	730	690
3		1,000	980	900	870	800	740
4		1,100	1,020	970	920	870	810
5		1,280	1,170	1,087	1,050	1,000	870

RANGE WITH 8-INCH SHELLS FROM 68-PDR CARRONADES

Weight of Shell (lbs-oz)	*Charge (lbs)*	*Flight (in)*	*Elevation (degrees)*	*First Graze (yards)*	*Extreme Range (yards)*
43-11	3	1.5	point-blank	302	1,365
43-11	8	—	5	1,140	—
43-11	4	1.5	1	358	1,843
43-11	—	5.0	5	1,137	1,250
43-11	—	—	11.5	1,767	—

RANGE WITH A 10-IN SEA MORTAR AT 21 DEGREES ON A HORIZONTAL PLANE†

Weight of Mortar			*Weight of Shell*	*Charge*	*Elevation*	*Flight*	*Range*
(cwt)	*(qrs)*	*(lbs)*	*(lbs-oz)*	*(lbs-oz)*	*(degrees)*	*(secs)*	*(yards)*
34	2	14	86	5-8	21	14.75	2,335
34	2	14	87	5-8	21	16.0	2,510

TABLE 7

(CONTINUED)

RANGE WITH SEA-SERVICE IRON MORTARS AT 45 DEGREES ON A HORIZONTAL PLANE					
13-in			*10-in*		
Charge (lbs-oz)	*Flight (secs)*	*Range (yards)*	*Charge (lbs-oz)*	*Flight (secs)*	*Range (yards)*
2-0	13.0	690	1-0	13.0	680
4-0	18.0	1,400	2-0	18.0	1,340
6-0	21.0	1,900	3-0	21.0	1,900
8-0	24.5	2,575	4-0	24.5	2,500
10-0	26.5	2,975	5-0	26.0	2,800
12-0	29.0	3,500	6-0	27.0	3,200
14-0	29.5	3,860	7-0	29.0	3,500
16-0	30.5	3,900	8-0	30.0	3,800
18-0	30.5	4,000	9-0	30.5	3,900
20-0	31.0	4,200	9-8	30.25	4,000

Source: Robert Simmons, *The Sea-Gunner's Vade-Mecum* (London: Steel, 1812), 201–3.
* The charge is one-twelfth the weight of the shot with one shell and one wad. The line of fire is from 6 to 9 feet above the level of the water.
† At 45 degrees the 13-in sea mortar went to 4,100 yards, the 10-in to 3,800 (the former with 32 lbs of powder, the latter with 12 lbs 8 oz).

practice was to have a full crew manning guns on only one side of the ship. If it was necessary to fight the guns on both sides at once, the crew would split up. Later, in the U.S. Navy, if both batteries had to be fought at once, the first part of the crew for no. 1 and the second part of the crew for no. 2 worked the no. 1 and 2 guns on starboard and the corresponding guns to port. In 1860, a new system was adopted that relegated crews to guns of one side rather than splitting crews between port and starboard.

There was no established gunnery drill in the Royal Navy until 1817. In the U.S. Navy, gunnery drills came even later. Commands varied widely, even on the same ship. One writer noted in 1850 that when he first entered the service, there were twenty-seven separate ones for exercising the guns in his division, whereas another officer on the same ship received only three commands—fire, load, and run out. In 1815 William Falconer and William Burney listed fifteen, and in 1851 General Sir Howard Douglas noted that, once the gun had been loaded and run out (without orders) the commands were prime, point (muzzle left or muzzle right), elevate, ready, fire, stop the vent, run in, sponge, load, run out, fire, cease firing, and secure. U.S. Navy ordnance instructions of 1860 gave ten commands, under the assumption that the guns were already loaded and run out: Silence, man the starboard (or port) guns; cast loose and provide; prime; point; fire; serve vent and sponge; load with cartridge; load with shot (or shell); run out; and secure.

Rapid firing depended on the manual strength of the gun crew and their ability to run the gun out as quickly as possible. In 1809, a 24-pounder might be manned by eleven men, an 18-pounder by nine, a 12-pounder by eight, and

TABLE 8

Ranges of Shot, 1852

Gun	*Distance of Bore above Water (ft)*	*Powder Charge (lbs)*	*Elevation* (degrees)*	*Flash to First Graze (secs)†*	*Yards*
32-pdr of 27 cwt (spar decks of third-class sloops of war)	7.0	4.0	Point-blank	0.7	250
		4.0	6	6.3	1,637
32-pdr of 32 cwt (spar decks of second-class sloops of war)	7.5	4.5	Point-blank	—	287
		4.5	5	—	1,598
32-pdr of 32 cwt (spar decks of first-class frigates)	15.33	4.5	Point-blank	1.10	366
		4.5	4	4.91	1,385
32-pdr of 42 cwt (spar decks of first-class sloops of war)	8.33	5.0	Point-blank	—	299
		5.0	5	5.8	1,651
		6.0	Point-blank	—	313
		6.0	5	6.0	1,756
32-pdr of 57 cwt (gun decks of frigates)	9.0	9.0	Point-blank	—	357
		9.0	10	10.7	2,731
		7.0	1	2.4	759
		7.0	3	4.4	1,353
8-in of 55 cwt (spar decks of sloops of war)	7.5	7.0	Point-blank	—	283
		7.0	10	—	2,600
		8.0	1	—	602
		8.0	8	—	2,308
8-in of 63 cwt (main decks of frigates)	9.0	9.0	Point-blank	—	332
		9.0	5	6.32	1,769
10-in of 86 cwt (discontinued aboard U.S. Navy ships replaced by newer and heavier 10-in shell gun)	7.75	10.0	5	5.5	1,535

Source: U.S. Navy Department Bureau of Ordnance, *Instructions in Relation to the Preparation of Vessels of War for Battle* (Washington: C. Alexander, 1852), and John Dahlgren, *Shells and Shell Guns* (Philadelphia: King and Baird, 1856), 28–35.

* Figures do not include all elevations given, merely point-blank and maximum.

† Figures include the first graze of the shot, not subsequent grazes (ricochets).

a 6-pounder by five. These figures varied considerably in practice, however. The size of the crew working a gun came to be determined by its weight. By 1850, it was estimated that one man was required for every 500 pounds of metal in a gun on a truck carriage, and one man for every 450 pounds if the gun was on a slide carriage. In addition, there was one powder boy to each gun. A shell gun had one man more than a shot gun of similar weight; the practice of allowing further supplies of ammunition to sit next to the gun was forbidden with shells, thus requiring an extra person to convey ammunition.

The normal crew for a heavy 32-pounder was fourteen men and a powder boy. Man no. 1. was the first captain, positioned to the rear of the gun, facing the port. No. 4, the sponger, and no. 6, the assistant sponger, stood to the right of the gun, close to the ship's side; no. 5, the assistant loader, stood to the left

Fig. 25. Gunnery Practice aboard HMS *Excellent*. (From Lieutenant-General Sir Howard Douglas, *A Treatise on Naval Gunnery* [London, 1851].)

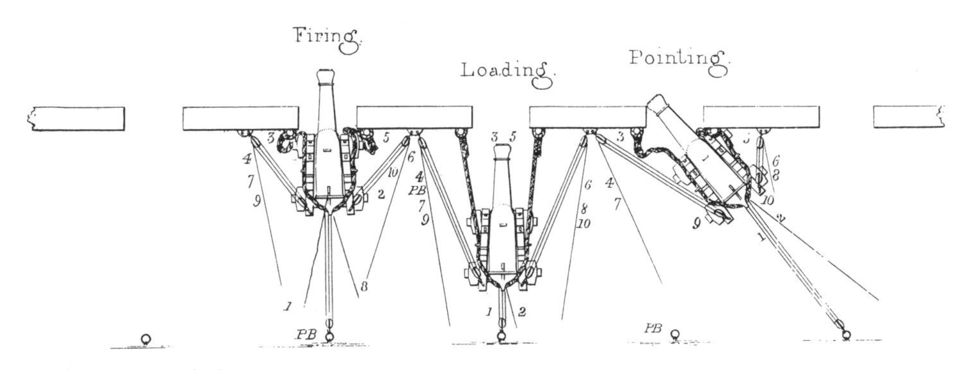

Fig. 26. U.S. Navy Gun Crew of Ten Men and a Boy, Working a 32-Pdr of 42 CWT, 1852. (Bureau of Ordnance, Navy Department, *Instruction in Relation to the Preparation of Vessels of War for Battle* [Washington, 1852].)

of the gun, next to no. 3; and no 2, the second captain, was to the right of no. 1, facing the ship's side but clear of the recoil. Men nos. 7, 9, 11, and 13 were auxiliaries or tacklemen to the left of the gun, while nos. 8, 10, 12, and 14 were auxiliaries to its right. The handspikemen, also known as the crowmen, were nos. 9 and 10. These numerical designations were the same for both the U.S. and Royal navies.

The captain of the gun was responsible for seeing that the gun crew

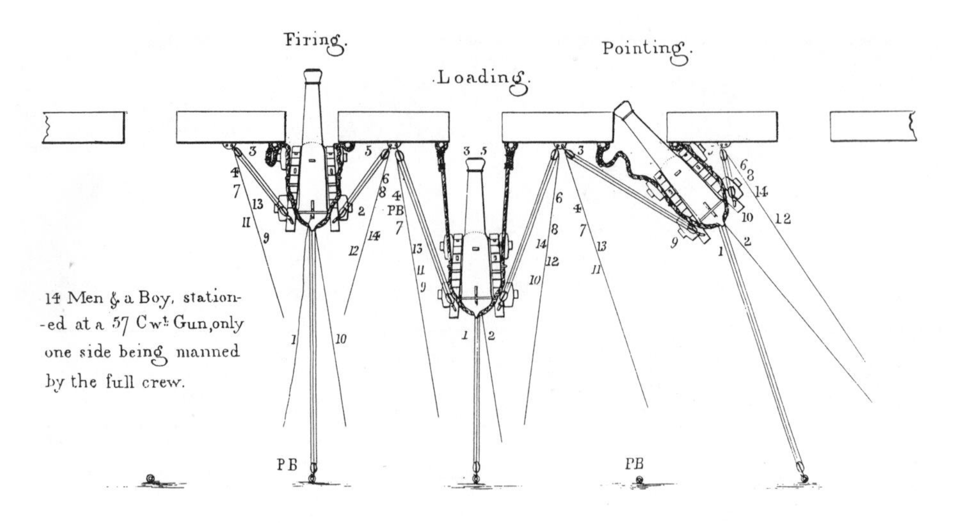

Fig. 27. U.S. Navy Gun Crew of Fourteen Men and a Boy, Working a 32-Pdr of 57 CWT, 1852. (Bureau of Ordnance, *Instructions*.)

carried out its proper duties, including the laying and training of the gun. The no. 4 man sponged the gun after each round and then rammed home the cartridge, shot and wads, with the assistance of no. 5; no. 6 handed no. 4 the sponge and rammer and then placed them on the deck after they were used. No. 3 loaded cartridge and shot. The powder boy brought the cartridge case to the gun. No. 5 handed the shot to no. 3. No. 2 moved the quoin into proper position when the gun was elevated. He also put the quill in the vent and cocked the lock.

The beat of a drum called gun crews to quarters. Preparing for battle, they stowed hammocks and furniture. This might take as little as 5 minutes for a frigate and up to 15 for a line-of-battle ship. When the order was given to clear for action ("Cut loose the battery"), each gun crew cleared two guns, their own and the one abaft. Once the guns were ready for action, the order was given to man the starboard (port) battery.

With the exception of the first and second captain and the powder boy, the gun crew stood facing obliquely toward the loaded gun and its port. All men were to stay clear during recoil. The vent was shown clear and the cartridge pierced with the priming wire. Next, to the order "Pick and prime," the vent was primed with loose powder from a powder horn, later from a tube. The gun was then aimed to the right or left, depending on the captain's orders. The handspikemen raised or lowered it using the steps of the carriage for leverage. The gun captain indicated which direction by the use of his hand, and when satisfied, he called out, "Well." No. 2 then positioned the quoin, and as soon as he felt the weight of the gun, he gave the word to the handspikemen. When he was clear of the gun, no. 2 said, "Ready."

At this point, the quill was inserted in the vent and the lock was cocked. Lee guns had to be fired quickly to keep water from getting down the bore or wetting the priming. The next order was to drop tackles and fire. (In the Civil War, the no. 1 man simply raised his hand high for this signal and then called out, "Fire!" as he pulled the lanyard.) The tackle falls were dropped and the train tackles picked up. The captain pulled strongly on the lanyard to the lock (or match was applied to the priming by the second captain), and the gun was fired. The next orders were to stop vent, sponge, load, and then run out. When firing was over, the men were ordered to secure their guns.[9]

Where possible in the U.S. Navy, the gun was fired while the vessel rode the top of a wave and had just begun to roll toward the target. This practice partially accounted for the high number of hull hits registered by American vessels in the War of 1812. The aim was to sink the enemy ship by hitting it amidships, near the waterline.

There were two types of fire: direct, where the gun was laid so that the projectile struck the target without grazing, and ricochet. Ricochet firing was used both on land and at sea. At sea, the gun would have to be elevated not more than 2 degrees above the water. In smooth seas, ricochet firing offered greater range than direct firing, but it had less striking power because of the force lost when shot hit the water. Thus it was employed primarily for long ranges against small craft or troops.

Concerning the ranges achieved by direct and ricochet firing, these calculations were made in 1829: the first graze of a 24-pounder, 9½ inches in length, at 1 degree of elevation, with a charge one-third the weight of the shot, was 800 yards. The same shot could ricochet out to 2,500 yards.[10] Ricochet firing was always more effective with the larger and heavier projectiles.

Quick firing, used in close action, meant rapid firing at will without the use of the tangent sight. The crew loaded guns by seating the cartridge and shot and ramming them home together, in one motion. During the Civil War, this could be done with all guns except the pre-1851 8-inch of 63 cwt pattern. It was not recommended, however, for IX-inch and larger guns.

There were also different methods of battery fire: independent firing, also known as firing at will, firing in succession, and broadside or concentrated firing. In the first case, the captain of a gun laid and fired it independently. Firing in succession referred to firing on command after the next gun had fired. In broadside or concentrated firing, all guns were laid for the same point and then fired simultaneously on order from the upper deck. This was not easy to carry out in the din of battle, and the heavy shock of discharge made it additionally objectionable.

In concentrated firing, elevation was determined by means of either the degree marked on the quoins or a wooden scale held vertically, one end on the deck so that a mark on the gun could be brought in line with the degree on the scale. The gun used as the reference point, usually amidships, was known as the director. With the director as reference, calculations were made to determine the exact direction of aim for each of the other guns at given ranges. Men trained the guns by following the principle of converging lines. This might be done by marking the beams over each gun, denoting points before or abaft. A piece of line was hooked over the center of the port, the other end held by the gun captain immediately under the required mark on the overhead beam. The gun was then trained until the axis of the bore and the line were parallel. Concentrated fire was not attempted beyond 400 yards. One great objection to it was that the initial aim had to be accurate or the entire broadside might miss.

Because of the disadvantages of simultaneous discharge, U.S. Navy ordnance instructions of 1860 stated that in concentrated firing, each gun captain should be allowed the discretion to fire his gun at will.

More than anyone else, Captain Philip Broke of the Royal Navy was responsible for the development of improved gunnery practices. Not only did he train his gun crews to carry out concentrated fire, but at his own expense he also fitted the guns of the frigate *Shannon* with dispart sights and gunners' quadrants. He developed a ballistics pendulum for regulating gun position in horizontal firing. And he insisted on realistic gunnery training reinforced by frequent drills with live and simulated firing. The positive results of his efforts were evident in the engagement between the *Shannon* and the *Chesapeake* in June 1813. Although there were other factors at work, the *Shannon's* superior gunnery played an important role in her victory over the American frigate.[11]

Partly as a result of this celebrated battle, much more attention was paid to the sighting of guns and to regular drills after the War of 1812. Captains trained their gun crews regularly, for in the confusion of battle, procedures had to be as automatic as possible.

When a vessel first opened fire, the object was to wound the enemy ship by destroying masts and rigging. In close action, especially using shell guns and carronades with their great smashing power, the object was to hit the enemy's hull—the target was the waterline—and damage it mortally. Another objective at close range was to sweep the opponent's deck. A good example of this procedure properly carried out was the engagement between the *Wasp* and the *Avon* in September 1814. The *Wasp* crippled the British vessel by damaging her rigging with dismantling shot and then directed fire at her hull, which caused her to sink.

Rate of fire varied considerably. By the time of the Civil War, in ideal circumstances, trained crews might discharge a shot from their guns every 75 seconds. One source credits a rate of one shot per minute for the U.S. and British navies as early as 1805, with the French lagging far behind at one shot per 3 minutes.[12] By mid-nineteenth century, the usual rate of fire was a round every 2 minutes or less. This included the use of wormer and sponge after each round, though the sponge might be applied only once every three rounds.

Training was essential to achieving a high rate of fire. In 1856, a trained crew working the new Dahlgren IX-inch gun on a Marsilly carriage fired five shells in 2 minutes 39 seconds for a rate of one shot every 40 seconds. Crews were able to fire broadside guns faster than the larger pivot pieces, however.

In bad weather, the battery was housed to prevent the guns from breaking away. A loose gun could cause frightful damage and even sink the ship. Housing a gun had the advantage of easing strain on a ship's side; gun weight was divided evenly between the frame and keel instead of resting on the frame alone, as was the case when guns were secured. One contemporary described the process this way:

> To house a gun, run it in, and let the breech down upon the rear axletree; the muzzle rests against the ship's side above the port (placing a mat to prevent chafe), and is to be lashed to the housing-bolt; the side tackles are to be set well taut, racked and the ends expended; the train-tackle is to be hooked to the housing-bolt, the single block to a strap over the nob of the cascable set well taut; the parts of the breeching are to be frapped together under the breast of the carriage, and the chocking-quoins placed in the rear of the outer trucks. The lower-deck guns are kept in a taut breeching and the *housing chocks,* placed in front of the outer trucks, kept in their place by bolts.
>
> They are sometimes secured by setting taut a stout hawser, or the stream cable, at the bow and stern, seizing it to the cascable ring, and the ship's side by setting taut the train-tackle, and placing the chocking-quoins before the outer trucks.[13]

The quoin, crow, and handspikes were placed under the gun, and other items were returned to their proper places. When not in use, the muzzle was stopped with a plug of wood or cork, known as a tampion, and a thin piece of lead known as an apron was tied over the touchhole to keep it dry.

In good weather, when guns were not being used, they were stored in cleared parks on brick walls topped by iron skids, with the muzzle lower than the breech. Masonry had to be high enough to keep the trunnions from touching the ground. The vent hole was either up or on the side; it and any screw holes were filled with beeswax dissolved in turpentine and then plugged with a piece of greased or waxed wood. The muzzles were left open to prevent condensation; if a tampion was inserted, a score half an inch wide and deep was cut in it for drainage.

After being cleaned of rust, guns were lacquered inside and out. It was said that foulness produced by firing a gun was the best preventive against rust. Thus it was common practice to "scale" a ship's guns at regular intervals. The scaling charge was generally one-twelfth the weight of the shot.

In 1860, U.S. Navy ordnance instructions decreed that the bore of a gun struck below or transported be washed with fresh water, sponged, dried, and coated with melted tallow. A wad dipped in tallow was connected by a lanyard to a tampion, which was securely inserted into the bore. The vent was stopped by a greased leather vent plug and puttied over.

Iron guns were usually painted. Black was probably the most common color, though English guns, at least in Nelson's time, were generally a gray-blue steel color with a scarlet band around the muzzle. Some English pieces were red or chocolate; one captain even had his painted white.

By 1850, U.S. Navy guns were scraped, their blisters were filed away, and holes were puttied. Two thin coats of red lead ground in oil were then applied, followed by two coats of black paint. By 1860, the production of lacquers had become somewhat more complicated; generally, they consisted of black and red lead, lampblack, and linseed oil, along with other ingredients.

The following is a method for "bronzing" iron cannon that appeared around 1845. Four ounces of red lead, 4 of litharge, and 2 of umber were added to 1 gallon of linseed oil and boiled for approximately four hours. The guns were freed of paint or lacquer of any kind and rubbed smooth with sandpaper. The oxide of iron mixed with the prepared oil produced "a most beautiful dark bronze, which effectively preserves the gun and gives it a beautiful appearance. It is also a good preparation for the bores when stored away, preserving them effectively from corrosion."[14]

Many variables affected the life of a gun, including its metal type and thickness, length, and method of manufacture, as well as the size of powder charges, types of shot, and length of time between firings. The lifetime of a gun was approximately 1,000 discharges, but this was with normal service charges and one shot. Firing heavier charges or double shotting shortened the life of a gun, as did firing consistently at higher elevations to obtain greater range. Some guns lasted much longer than expected. In 1812, several British 24-pounders were fired nearly 3,000 times without incurring accident or injury.

The first sign of wear on a gun was usually an enlarged vent. Later, bounding shot enlarged and dented the bore itself. When bronze cannon were fired rapidly, the chase might actually bend. In sustained fire, iron guns were more likely than bronze to be damaged in the vent, and it was usually a fractured vent that caused a gun to burst.

The two simplest ways to disable a gun were to spike it or knock it off its trunnions. In spiking, a steel rod was rammed down the vent and broken off. The rammer could also be used to bend back the point inside the bore; then the vent would have to be painstakingly rebored by an armorer. A shot might also be lodged in the bore when a rammer pushed in steel or iron wedges. A sledgehammer could disable a gun by knocking off its trunnions, but a cannon was permanently disabled only if it burst. This would happen if it were fired with a heavy charge of powder while its bore was filled with sand and it was at a high angle.

CHAPTER III

Founders and the Casting of Cannon

MOST MUZZLE-LOADING ordnance of the eighteenth and nineteenth centuries was of cast rather than wrought iron. By the time Americans began casting cannon in any quantity, iron had already won the battle against bronze for naval guns. The first step in casting was to extract iron from its ore by smelting. In this process, ore was roasted to volatilize any arsenic and sulphur, dry out moisture, and burn away carbonic acid. Smelting required a blast furnace, a vertical structure 30 to 40 feet high lined with firebrick and open at the top for feeding ore and fuel. A receptacle at the bottom caught molten metal as it flowed down. Wood charcoal, coal, or coke served as fuel, carbonate of lime—either oyster shells or limestone—as a flux.

The blast furnace was supplied from the top with alternating layers of kindling, coal or coke, and ore and flux together until the furnace was filled or "charged." Next a fire was lit at the bottom, a steam engine or water power encouraging combustion by producing a blast of air. The blast might be cold or hot. Cold blast could mean anything up to about 500 or 600 degrees. It was found that guns cast by cold blast had greater tensile strength, so by 1842 that process was the one required in the production of U.S. Navy guns.

During blast, the carbon of fuel united with the oxide of ore and burned it off. Some carbon united with the iron to form iron carbide. Nonferrous materials (slag or scoria) and iron flowed together, passing through an aperture at the bottom of the furnace into the receptacle below. Slag floated to the surface, where it accumulated and flowed out through holes left open in the upper sides of the receptacle. When iron reached the level of the holes,

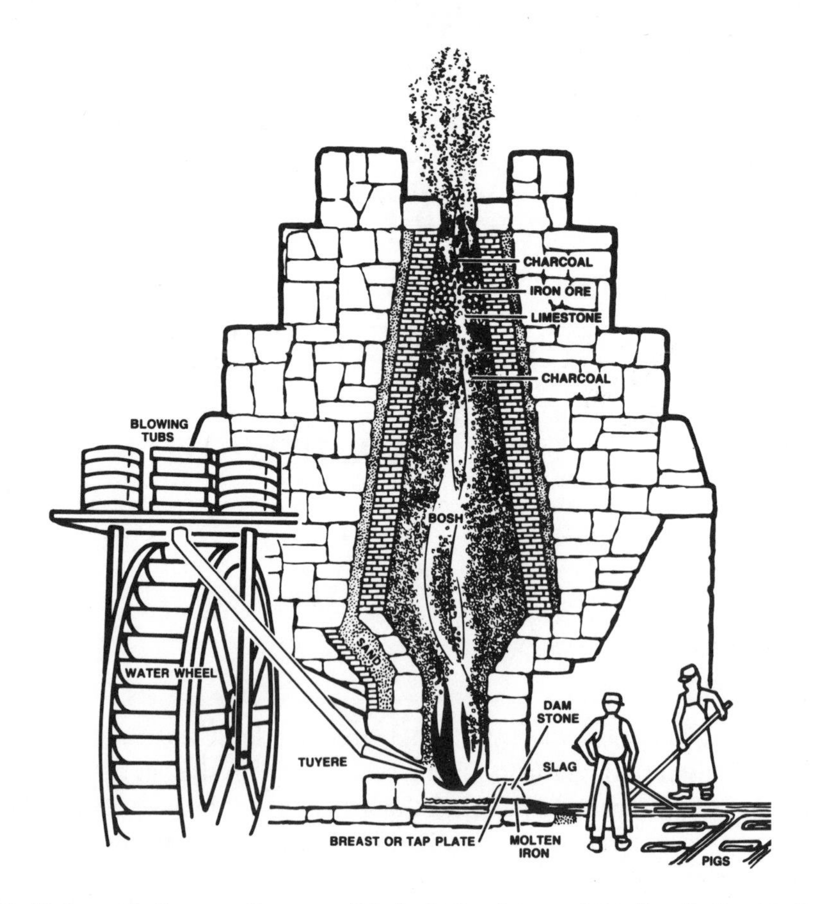

Fig 28. Eighteenth-Century Furnace. (Clyde A. Sanders and Dudley C. Gould, *History Cast in Metal: The Founders of North America* [American Foundrymen's Society, 1976].)

the receptacle was "tapped" at the bottom and the molten iron flowed into a sand-bed mold, where it cooled as pig iron.

When the pigs had cooled they could be broken up for testing. Iron with a dull-gray, coarse-grained fracture had the hardness and tenacity needed for guns. Founders learned that a number of techniques could be used in the smelting process, including the union of different types of ore in the blast, to produce the desired type of iron. Even weather could be a factor.

In 1861, it was calculated that smelting required two parts (in weight) of fuel, two of roasted iron, and one or less of flux. The founder then knew that the resulting metal would be less than half the weight of the roasted ore.

Wrought iron was cast iron reduced to the purest possible metallic state through burning and working out any remaining carbon and oxygen. In this process, known as puddling, molten iron was stirred while it collected in sand pools or puddles. The stirring brought together the carbon and oxygen and burned them off. What carbon was not burned off was consumed by oxygen in the air. Cooling iron thickened into balls, called puddle balls, which were placed under a triphammer and then in a rolling mill.

By hammering, reheating, and rolling, most slag and other impurities were worked out. The result was the purest possible metallic bar and rod iron. In this form the iron was malleable, but care had to be taken that residual slag, which appeared as grain, always moved in a direction longitudinal to the work.

The casting of cannon was obviously an expensive and time-consuming process requiring highly skilled workmen. In the eighteenth century, a pattern for the finished gun was built on a wooden core or spindle. The spindle was wrapped with rope to approximate the size of the piece and then covered with a clay mixture. This was turned on its axis and shaped to conform to the gun pattern. Next a clay mold was applied over the pattern, in sections. The inside wooden core was knocked loose and the rope unwound. Finally, this hollow mold, conforming on the inside to the desired shape of the gun, was inspected, cleaned, dried, and made ready for casting with its several sections bound together.[1]

In 1715, in Bergdorf, Switzerland, Johann Maritz introduced a new system of manufacturing cannon, a technique his sons soon took to France and Spain. Instead of being cast around a core, the guns were cast in solid form with the cascabel facing downward, resulting in greater density where the shock of discharge was greatest, at the breech. The bore was then cut out horizontally while the guns were turned on their axes. Turning the gun instead of the cutter yielded a cannon bored true to its axis. The Maritz technique thus produced a smoother and more accurate bore. This system was greatly improved by Jan Verbruggen of Holland, who with his son Pieter later headed the foundry at Woolwich, establishing there perhaps the finest boring equipment in Europe.

The technique of boring in the solid was probably not introduced to the United States until after the Revolution. Louis Tousard, who inspected artillery cast for the U.S. government, wrote in 1809 that American founders had vastly improved on the European boring machines, so that of about two thousand cannon of different calibers that he had inspected, he "never was compelled to reject a gun on account of a defect in the bore. . . ."[2]

By 1750 sand molds had come into use. The form of the gun was now obtained by impressing a pattern in sand and then withdrawing it. The pattern was made of well-seasoned hard wood or, for greater durability, of metal. Hollow patterns of iron or bronze, turned and polished in a lathe, could be used for years and would produce guns of uniform size and shape, but they were expensive. The disadvantage of wooden patterns was their vulnerability to weather; they contracted in heat and expanded in humidity.

Sand was packed around the pattern, which was contained in a box divided into two or more parts for ease of withdrawal. The pattern itself was made of five or more pieces. The first part comprised the body from base ring to chase ring. The second comprised the muzzle swell and sprue, the third the breech, and the fourth and fifth the trunnions.

The sprue (or head) was an additional length given to the gun. Its purpose was to receive slag as it surfaced and to furnish any extra metal required as the cast shrank in cooling. Its weight was thought to compress metal in the cannon proper, increasing the density of lower portions of the piece where the strain was greatest during fire. For casting, a square projection further lengthened the breech, which enabled the piece to be held while it was turned and bored.

The flask was the wood or metal box containing the sand. It consisted of several pieces, each of which had perforated flanges so they could be bolted together. To form the mold, the pattern for the sprue and muzzle was coated with pulverized charcoal or coke moistened with clay and water to prevent adhesion. The pattern was then positioned vertically, carefully surrounded by corresponding parts of the jacket. Previously prepared sand—also moistened with water and clay for adhesion—was then rammed around the flask. The pattern for the body of the gun was placed on top of this, and corresponding pieces of the flask were secured and filled in succession with the molding composition. Patterns for the trunnions and rimbases were bolted to the pattern for the body, the bolts being withdrawn once the flask had been packed with sand. End plates were then screwed onto the trunnion molds. The rest of the mold for the body was finished section by section. After the pattern for the cascabel had been installed, the mold was complete.

The pattern was carefully covered with coke wash, and dry sand was sprinkled on top of each piece of the jacket to prevent adhesion and allow portions of it to be separated. A channel was also made in the mold cavity for the introduction of metal.

When the mold was completed, the flask was taken apart and the pattern withdrawn. After inspection, any damaged part of the mold was repaired. The interior was then coated with coke wash. The parts were placed in an oven to be gradually dried, then carried to the pouring pit, where they were joined together and secured in a vertical position, usually breech down. Meanwhile, the interior of the mold was inspected and covered with coke wash to prevent sand from adhering to the melted metal.

After being placed in the pouring pit, the flask was surrounded with sand, which filled the pit as high as or higher than the trunnions. This ensured against too rapid cooling.

The metal was poured into the prepared channel of the mold—in short guns, from the top, in long guns, where the fall of metal might damage the mold, from the bottom. As molten metal rose in the mold, a workman agitated it with a long pole, sending impurities to the surface but preventing them from entering the trunnion cavities.

Sand was not removed from around the flask of a 24-pounder for three days. With heavier guns, it was allowed to remain longer—with the 10-inch columbiad, for example, for seven to eight days. Once the metal had cooled, sand was removed. The gun, still in the flask, was hoisted out. The flask was then taken away and the gun cleaned of sand.

The piece was now ready to be bored. This was the most important and time-consuming part of the manufacturing process. In 1850 it took six to ten days, according to the hardness of the metal, to bore a 24-pounder. The gun was carefully positioned in a rack to keep the axis perfectly horizontal. Machinery for revolving the gun was attached to the square knob on the cascabel. The sprue was first cut off by turning the gun and bringing a cutter to bear from the side.

A succession of cutters were fixed to the boring rod. The first of these, known as the piercer, was used until it reached the end of the bore. A second cutter, the reamer, drilled to the rounded bottom of the bore. If there was to be a chamber, the reamer bored only to its edge; a chamber cutter then shaped that portion of the bore. If the gun was cast hollow around a core, a piercer was not needed.

The exterior of the gun was turned during the boring process, except for the portion between trunnions. This was planed later with another machine. The trunnions were also turned. Care had to be taken that they were the same diameter, perfectly cylindrical, and that their axes were perpendicular to the axis of the piece. The vent was bored by hand or machine.

The entire process of producing cannon was a long one. Even by the mid-nineteenth century, it took three to four weeks to make a 24-pounder and six weeks to make a 10-inch gun.

All guns were inspected and test-fired before being accepted into service. First they were tested for preponderance (excess of weight behind the pivotal axis) and subjected to a minute examination to see if they were without flaw and conformed to the drawings furnished to the founder. External measurements were made, and the length and exact diameter of the bore were calculated. The bore was also examined for cavities with a mirror. Then an instrument known as a searcher was introduced into the bore. It had steel points attached to springs; if there were any cavities, the points would get caught in them and the gun would be rejected. Exterior cavities exceeding a quarter inch in depth were also grounds for rejection. In another test, conducted by hydrostatic pressure, water was forced into the bore to reveal flaws such as cracks in the casting that the searcher had not detected earlier.

Then the gun was fired to see if it was strong enough to sustain service charges. At the end of the eighteenth century, each cannon was subjected to two successive proof firings: the first with powder equal to two-thirds the weight of ball, the second with powder equal to half the weight of ball. The gun was double-shotted, with wads over and under the projectile.

By the mid-nineteenth century, gun inspections had become much more effective. The strength of gun metal was tested by measuring the traverse strength of a 2-inch square bar cast from the same pour as the gun. Another method was to cut a plug from the face of the gun and put it on a machine that gripped both ends and pulled it apart. Tensile strength was to exceed 22,000 pounds per square inch. To test for torsion, the piece of metal might also be pulled and twisted at the same time, the resulting fragments then evaluated. By the time of the Civil War, these processes were regarded as sufficient for judging a gun's service reliability, "without risking injury by an excessive and conclusive powder-proof to every gun."[3]

During the war, established navy procedure was for the founder to submit a sample of the iron he intended to use. Once the metal had been tested and approved, the founder laid in a quantity sufficient to make all the guns on that contract. One of the first five guns produced was then subjected to a powder proof of ordinary service charges up to 1,000 rounds. If it passed, the gun was set aside and referred to as the standard. All remaining guns on the contract had to conform to it, and each was proved by firing only ten service rounds with shot. The only exception to this procedure was the XV-inch Dahlgren.

Cannon rejected for imperfections were marked ⊕ near the foundry initials. If rejected for dimensions only, no proof marks were put on it; if rejected in water proof, one trunnion was knocked off. Guns withstanding proof but damaged in testing through no fault of the founder were marked ⊖ Guns passing inspection were marked with their weight, their date of construction, and the initials of the foundry and proving officer. Weight was indicated with three figures separated by dashes or dots—the first expressing how many cwts (112 pounds), the second how many quarter-cwts (28 pounds), and the third how many pounds. For the largest guns there were four weight figures—the first being tons of 2,240 pounds—usually on top of the breech or the cascabel. Later, weight was expressed solely in pounds. By 1845, foundry initials and weight in cwts were stamped on the base ring, the letter *P* and the inspecting officer's initials on the left trunnion, and the caliber of gun and date it was cast on the right trunnion.

Perhaps the first attempt to establish an iron forge in the New World was in 1619 at Falling Creek, Virginia, on the James River just below Richmond. In 1622 the first blast furnace to produce pig iron was destroyed, the workers killed, in an Indian raid. The first permanent furnace was established in 1644 at Braintree, near Boston. The principal figure in the venture, John Winthrop, Jr., had the assistance of both artisans and capital from England.

The impetus behind the rapid development of an iron industry in America came from Britain. Iron cannon were replacing bronze guns in the eighteenth century, and the number of wars being fought during the period created additional demand. The production of British furnaces, already far short of demand, was declining as forests rapidly disappeared and charcoal became scarce. In this century, it took 3 tons of ore and 250 bushels of charcoal to make a ton of iron. The ready availability of timber, limestone (for flux), and water power dictated the location of a furnace.

The British looked to America, abundant in natural resources, to take up the slack. The colonial iron industry made little progress in the late seventeenth century, but by the time of the Peace of Utrecht in 1713 it was firmly established. It seems to have been concentrated in New England, particularly in Massachusetts, where there were large shipbuilding interests. Large-scale iron manufacturing was also permanently established in Virginia about this time.

In the course of the eighteenth century, thanks to the steadily increasing demand, the iron industry burgeoned. Between 1715 and the Revolution, "there was an almost phenomenal expansion. . . . Furnaces, forges, and bloomeries were erected in almost every colony, with the industry being most highly concentrated in southwestern Pennsylvania. By 1775 the continental colonies were producing about one-seventh of the world's supply of iron, and their production of pig and bar exceeded that of the mother country."[4]

Though anxious to secure iron, England was also concerned about the growing strength of an independent American iron industry, accompanied as it was by rising belligerency about natural rights. As a result, Parliament passed the Iron Act of 1750 limiting the sale of iron products to the colonies where they were made and prohibiting the erection of slitting or rolling mills, plating forges, and steel furnaces. The colonists successfully evaded the act. In 1730 they exported 1,130 tons; by 1770 this had risen to 7,500 tons.

Harry Leonard of Lynn, Massachusetts, may have cast the first cannon in North America in 1647. In 1673 Edward Randolph, who was examining Massachusetts affairs for the English government, reported that in New England "there be five ironworks which cast no guns."[5] By 1702 this situation had apparently changed: a furnace in Plymouth County was producing cannon balls along with holloware, and in 1710, near Abington and Hanover, Massachusetts, a works was built in which Colonel Aaron Hobart cast cannon and shot during the Revolution.

One of the first American gun manufacturers was a young Scot by the name of Hugh Orr, who arrived in 1738. Orr, who had been trained as a gun- and locksmith, set himself up in the iron trade in Bridgewater, Massachusetts. He manufactured axes and scythes and may well have monopolized edge tool production in that part of America. In about 1748 he produced five hundred muskets for the Massachusetts Bay Colony, most of which the British subsequently carried off when they evacuated Boston during the Revolution. A strong advocate of the American cause, Orr, assisted by a Frenchman, managed a cannon foundry known as the State Furnace. He installed boring machinery and produced a number of iron and bronze guns, 3- to 42-pounders, along with shot.

In 1774, on the eve of the Revolution, Great Britain prohibited the exportation of firearms, gunpowder, and other military stores, to which the colonies responded by recommending local manufacture in defiance of imperial legislation. There were at that time, however, few furnaces in

America capable of casting cannon, and until production could be expanded, the colonials had to rely on imports from the French and Spanish West Indies.

One problem that plagued the colonials was a shortage of bronze for guns of that metal. In September 1776, the Continental Congress authorized General Washington to requisition bells from churches and public buildings in New York City, and the New York Convention authorized the confiscation of bronze knockers from houses.

Soon, domestic production of small arms sharply accelerated, although high demand made muskets scarce. The production of cannon was slower, but gains were made. In February 1776 John Adams could note in a letter to James Warren, "Measures are taking to make Cannon both of Brass and Iron—Some Experiments have been made in Maryland, Philadelphia and New York, with success."[6] Perhaps three dozen founders produced cannon during the Revolution, but the quantity and ultimate disposition of these pieces are unknown. The Continental Marine Committee planned to have all the guns for thirteen frigates cast in Pennsylvania, work that fell to the Reading, Warwick, Cornwall, and Hopewell furnaces under the overall supervision of Captain Daniel Joy. Problems arose in casting the guns, but sources do not make clear the nature of the difficulty.[7]

In the years following the Revolution, orders for cannon declined as the standing army and navy were partially replaced by militia. By the mid-1790s cannon were again being produced for the federal government. Over the next fifty years the manufacture of cannon in America came to be highly specialized, the monopoly of a handful of foundries.

On 27 March 1794, Congress authorized the construction of six frigates for the navy. Together they required several hundred cannon, the majority of them long 24-pounders. To secure the guns the commissioner of revenue let several contracts, the earliest extant documents of their kind. The first of these was let on 28 June 1794 to Samuel Hughes of Cecil Furnace. He was to produce one hundred cannon for fortifications and ninety 24-pounders for the frigates (for a list of subsequent navy ordnance contracts, see appendix C), the government agreeing to pay an allowance for the extra expense if the guns could be bored from solid metal. Hughes later noted that they had been cast in clay, and that this "was the first experiment in the United States of boring from the solid and made by contract at this risk. . . ." Thirteen years later, he complained that he had still not been indemnified for the extra expense.[8]

In July 1796, Captain Thomas Truxtun of the *Constellation* accepted twenty-eight short 24-pounders cast by Hughes under this contract. After the capture of the French frigate *Insurgente,* Truxtun removed the guns because they were too short and heavy. In 1808 Hughes wrote that the principal fault was in their design, which compared unfavorably with the guns "since cast in dried sand. . . ."[9]

Inability to adhere to contracted production deadlines was a constant problem for Hughes. By April 1798, he had delivered only eighteen 24-

pounders for fortifications and thirty-six 24-pounders for frigates. Nor could he fill a contract to produce 6- and 9-pounders for the tribute frigate being built for the dey of Algiers. Despite the backlog, contracts continued to be let with Cecil Furnace. It wasn't until August 1810 that the contractual disputes were finally settled.

Even though it was the senior ordnance established for the navy, Cecil Furnace was deficient in many respects. When John Clarke, a cannon maker from Virginia and later proprietor of the Bellona foundry, visited northern ordnance establishments in 1798, he inspected Cecil Furnace and was surprised to find it "so badly planned, so temporarily built, and the guns so badly made."[10]

Shortly after the original contract of 1794 was let to Hughes, the commissioner of revenue contracted with "Messrs. Brown and Francis and others" of Hope Furnace in Rhode Island for sixty 24-pounders to be used in the frigates. Hope Furnace was much more successful than Cecil Furnace in fulfilling the terms of its contract. By April 1798, it had delivered all but one of the cannon. In 1798, however, the navy had trouble with some of the guns cast by Hope. In September, as a result of the extraordinary need for vessels occasioned by the Quasi-War with France (1798–1800), arrangements were made to purchase the ship *George Washington* from Hope Furnace founder John Brown. Brown was also to furnish twenty-four 9-pounders and six 6-pounders. The latter were apparently successful, but most of the 9-pounders burst in the proving, and Captain Fletcher of the *George Washington* was reluctant to receive the others on "account of the general bad quality of the metal."[11]

About this time, there was talk in Congress of establishing a national foundry to cast cannon for the army and navy. Secretary of the Treasury Oliver Woollott, Jr., had recommended such a course to President Washington in 1795, and in December 1797 Rufus King, U.S. minister to Great Britain, had urged the government to accept the proffered services of American-born Sir Benjamin Thompson, Count Rumford, who had experience in cannon founding. In the midst of the problems with France, the idea of a national cannon foundry was revived by the Federalists and buoyed by the slogan Millions for Defense, but Not One Cent for Tribute. The Senate Naval Committee, headed by Benjamin Goodhue of Massachusetts, drafted a bill appropriating $100,000 for the establishment of a federal foundry. The bill passed the Senate at the end of March 1798, and the House Naval Committee recommended its passage without amendment.

The Republican opposition resorted to stalling tactics, demanding detailed information about the number of heavy guns the United States had acquired since 1 January 1794. The Federalists supported the proposed foundry, claiming it would keep prices low. Republicans replied that if the government intended to make its own guns, already established founders would cease manufacture in the hope of selling their plants to the government at a good price. Nonetheless, the bill was approved, on 4 May 1798. By then it had burgeoned into a major arms program, appropriating up to $800,000 for cannon, small arms, ammunition, and military stores. President John Adams was authorized to lease or buy foundries if he found it difficult to purchase guns.

Former President Washington now began to lobby for the erection of a foundry on a site the government already owned. This would eventually become Harpers Ferry arsenal and armory. Secretary of the Navy Benjamin Stoddert also endorsed the idea of a permanent "National Establishment for the casting of Cannon & Shot" at Harpers Ferry.[12] Despite this, no national cannon foundry was established in the United States at the time.

The next founder known to have supplied cannon to the navy was David Waterman, owner of a foundry in Salisbury, Connecticut. The cannon were intended for one of the 44-gun frigates authorized by Congress in 1794, possibly the *Chesapeake* or *Congress,* which were launched in 1799 and 1800, respectively. In return for the guns, the navy offered the founder £55 per ton. The going rate in Philadelphia at this time was £55 a ton for small guns and £50 for large. But the same rate did not apply everywhere. In November 1798, Secretary of the Navy Benjamin Stoddert noted that guns were "dearer in Providence" and probably also in Philadelphia.[13] The federal government would furnish the shot and powder for proof unless a gun failed, in which case the founder would bear the expense.

In November 1798, Secretary Stoddert stated that the navy needed 396 guns in all, and he proposed to contract with William Lane of Philadelphia and William Salter of New Jersey for one-third or more of them. The first contract was signed next month for $23,000 worth of cannon. The pieces were to weigh about 200 pounds for every pound of ball.

The key figure in the manufacture of cannon in the United States at that time, however, was undoubtedly Henry Foxall, who had learned the iron trade in Britain before coming to the United States. Foxall was superintendent of the Eagle Foundry on the Schuylkill River at Philadelphia, in partnership with Robert Morris, Jr., son of the financier of the American Revolution. He began casting at the Eagle Foundry in the fall of 1796.

In the spring of 1797, Foxall learned that the United States needed a considerable quantity of cannon ball and bar shot for tribute to the dey of Algiers. It had to be of higher quality than the ammunition previously supplied by American founders. Foxall cast the shot in iron molds. Secretary of State Timothy Pickering, pleased with his work, informed Foxall that the government also needed some small cannon to arm warships as tribute for the Barbary Powers. The founder apparently supplied these guns as well.

Later, during the Quasi-War with France, when a lot of cannon larger than those cast by the Eagle Works were required, a boring mill was erected near the Schuylkill's lower bridge. This mill was built at Foxall's own expense but with advances from the government to expedite construction.

In addition to being the first American founder to perfect boring machinery, Foxall is thought to have cast the first carronades in the United States. His importance to the navy as a supplier of ordnance is expressed in a letter from Secretary of State Pickering to Secretary of the Navy Benjamin Stoddert in January 1799:

> Sir, Mr. Foxall called on me this morning about his cannon contract; when I wrote, on his paper of proposals, what occurred at the moment. Justice to him requires that I should add—That he was the first person who produced, in the United States, cannon of unexceptionable quality, in the *casting & boring*—the first that made perfect machinery for the latter important operation: that the other founders, Lane & Godfrey (or Salter) and lately Colo. S. Hughes, have constructed, or are constructing similar machinery, by means of workmen *previously instructed by Mr. Foxall*—enticed away by means well understood among Iron-Masters: that Mr. Foxall is the only founder on whom we can depend for further improvements, and particularly for casting that very useful gun called the *Carronade*: & that it was certainly contemplated to allow him a price superior to that agreed to be given to Lane and Godfrey (now Lane & Salter).
>
> Upon the whole, since the U. States are bound to take of Mr. Foxall guns to the amount of fifty thousand dollars, if those sizes above twelve pounders are wanted, I think he has an equitable claim to have them substituted at the same price agreed to be allowed him for smaller guns. The U. States are really indebted to him for the improvements he has introduced amongst us.[14]

Foxall cast in both bronze and iron, producing long guns as well as mortars and carronades. Most of the bronze guns were 3-, 6-, 12-, 18-, and 24-pounders. He also cast 10-inch bronze mortars at his subsequent Georgetown location, as well as a considerable number of 32- and 42-pounder carronades of English pattern.

Foxall, casting guns for the navy by 1798, was obviously the preferred founder. Subsequent contracts with other founders stipulated that their guns be similar in all respects to his. His first known contract with the navy, let in January 1799, called for the delivery of $23,000 worth of guns at the boring mill on the Schuylkill.

In the spring of 1799, the navy experienced problems with cannon cast at Salisbury Furnace. Five of twenty-four 12-pounders cast for the 28-gun frigate *Adams* were found defective. The secretary of the navy noted, "I fear the Guns made at Salisbury cannot be depended upon, and you will please to inform me particularly as to this point, for as we know certainly that good Guns can be cast here in Philadelphia, it will not do to depend in future on the Salisbury Furnace if their Guns will not stand proof or are defective in any respect."[15] Subsequently, at least some of the 12-pounders for the *Adams* came from Foxall. In addition, his works probably provided part of the ordnance required for the 20-gun sloops *Maryland* and *Patapsco,* as well as the frigates *John Adams, Essex,* and *Congress.*

If Salisbury Furnace was having difficulty with its guns, other founders were not. By 1800, the government was apparently satisfied with the production of iron guns in America. Secretary of State Pickering—who was also acting secretary of the navy for part of 1798—wrote in November of that year, "It shall be unnecessary to send to Europe for Cannon & Powder, which can be supplied in this Country in sufficient quantities and of as good quality as can be imported."[16] In January 1800, Pickering wrote to U.S. Consul General Richard O'Brien in Algiers that twenty bronze 24-pounders requested by the dey could not be obtained in the United States, "nor probably elsewhere during the present war." Iron guns of that size, "and of the neatest and best kind," could be substituted. "Our iron is of a superior quality, and our founderies now very perfect. The guns will be light, as well as strong and smooth." Pickering extolled iron guns over bronze: "For every kind of real service, in ships and garrisons, iron guns of strong metal, and light, are, in the opinion of good judges, superior to brass. I have said thus much to obviate the common prejudice in favour of brass guns; seeing we have it not in our power to furnish them."[17]

During this period progress was also made in establishing reliable suppliers of gunpowder. The earliest extant navy contract for powder is dated 14 March 1800. On that date Stephen Decatur of Philadelphia and William Lane, the cannon founder, contracted for 100 tons of gunpowder at the rate of $6 per 100 pounds. The navy was to furnish the saltpeter, and an ounce of the resulting gunpowder was to be strong enough to propel a 24-pound ball a distance of 180 feet from an eprouvette set at a 45-degree angle.

In 1799 and 1800, separate contracts for 148 guns were signed with Hughes, Lane, and Foxall. This represented the ordnance for six 74-gun ships. In 1800, Foxall ended his connection with Morris and established a new foundry, the Columbia or Columbian. It was located in Georgetown, between the Potomac River and what would later be the Chesapeake and Ohio Canal. The reason for Foxall's move from Philadelphia is unclear. Perhaps he welcomed the chance to establish his own firm in the area to which the federal capital was transferred from Philadelphia in 1800.[18] The Eagle Foundry was subsequently purchased by Samuel Richards but did not cast ordnance for the navy until 1807. From 1801 to 1849, the Columbia Foundry produced both iron and bronze guns for the navy.

In 1810, when Secretary of the Treasury Albert Gallatin reported to the House of Representatives on the status of American manufacturers, he noted only three cannon foundries capable of casting the largest caliber guns, "together with the proper machinery for boring and finishing them." These he identified as Hughes Works of Cecil County, Maryland, Columbia Foundry, and Virginia Manufactory of Arms in Richmond. "Each of the last two," Gallatin noted, "may cast 300 pieces of artillery a year, and a great number of iron and brass cannon are made at that, near the seat of government."[19]

In fact, the Virginia Manufactory of Arms, which Foxall helped set up, had a relatively short life casting cannon (1809–13), and those guns it did produce were small, mostly 6-pounders.[20] Certainly at the time of the Gallatin report, Columbia was the major foundry in the United States.

In 1807, interest in a national cannon foundry revived. Secretary of War Henry Dearborn conferred with Foxall, seeking to persuade him to establish such a concern at Greenleaf's Point, in Washington. Foxall might have been expected to oppose this proposal, pushing instead for the expansion of his own facility at nearby Georgetown, but instead he supported it. Despite reservations, chiefly over the government's plan to have him construct the foundry at his own expense, he offered a number of suggestions, including the acquisition of a steam engine for turning and boring and metal models for casting cannon. Foxall subsequently invested in metal patterns and flasks for the sand molds in his own foundry.

He agreed to undertake all the work of setting up a national foundry except for that entailed in the installation of a steam engine, which someone else would have to oversee. In return, he wanted free use of the establishment and a contract sufficient to keep it going for a two-year period after its completion.

Since the foundry was to be located on government-owned land, Foxall estimated its completion costs—including steam engine, foundry, boring mill, and shops—at $30,000. This figure did not, however, include the metal patterns for the guns or the iron flasks for the molds. In 1836, a much higher estimate was proposed for a Washington foundry (exclusive of land): $284,823.07.[21]

Although nothing came of this project, Foxall did set up the cannon foundry at the Virginia Manufactory of Arms in Richmond in 1808–9. The cost was $5,000. John Clarke, the superintendent originally charged with establishing the manufactory, had visited various Northeastern foundries and evidently been impressed by what he saw at Georgetown. He imported tools from England and constructed some of the machinery himself, commissioning Foxall to design and build the machinery for the foundry and boring mill.

The manufactory's first cannon, an iron 6-pounder, was ready for proving at the end of June 1809. No cannon for the federal government were ever produced there, only several hundred 32-pound shot. The manufactory ceased operations in 1813.

The next known contracts were let in 1807, one with Samuel Hughes.[22] Meanwhile, in August 1807, two individuals approached the navy about casting guns. One was William Lane—back in the iron business near Pittsburgh—who offered to cast a quantity of cannon balls. Lane's dealings with the navy are hard to unscramble. He signed his last formal contract in 1800, but in November and December 1807 and January 1808 he delivered to the navy 44 guns, probably part of a contract or contracts for the casting of 168 cannon. Thus he may have cast a number of guns in Pittsburgh. In any case, problems with his contracts continued until 1824. He claimed to have delivered all the guns ordered, but the navy could find no record of them. The confusion was attributed in large part to Lane's inadequate record keeping.

In 1807, the navy agreed to purchase 100 guns and 4,000 shot from Samuel Richards of the Eagle Foundry. Richards cast at least a sizable portion of the guns.[23]

Navy contracts of this era were let intermittently, a fact that troubled founders. In December 1808, Richards wrote Secretary of the Navy Robert Smith: "I have thought proper to retain the Workmen I had employed in casting Cannon, until I knew from you, whether more cannon would be wanted or not. If I am not favoured with a new contract, I shall be under the necessity of discharging a number of hands, which I should be extremely sorry to do at this season of the year, as they are all poor and would not be likely to find employment untill spring."[24] The works, he added, could be kept in operation through the winter if the navy ordered ten to fifteen cannon of each kind he had been making.

Meanwhile, Foxall was busy casting guns for the navy. He continued to produce carronades, including twenty additional 32-pounders for the *Constitution,* ordered in March 1808.

Perhaps surprisingly, there are no orders for cannon recorded in the contracts let in the early months of the War of 1812. There were, however, a number of large orders for shot. References to cannon cast for the navy do not appear until February 1813, and these were carronades rather than long guns. Up to fifty 32-pounder carronades, all of Foxall's manufacture, were ordered for shipment to Pittsburgh in response to a request by Isaac Chauncey, commander of naval forces on lakes Ontario and Erie, to arm two brigs. The demand for carronades continued. In May 1813, a contract was let with William, Walter, and John Dorsey of Baltimore—referred to after 1815 as Etna Furnace—for one hundred 32-pounder carronades.

In February 1814, the navy's first contract with Joseph McClurg of Pittsburgh was signed, for one hundred carronades. The firm may have been established as early as 1804. In the 1840s it became known as Knap and Totten, but was popularly referred to as Fort Pitt Works. It would be a major supplier of ordnance to both army and navy in the years ahead.

According to tradition, McClurg supplied Perry with the cannon, balls, and grape shot used in the Battle of Lake Erie in September 1813. Certainly the proximity of the firm to Lake Erie was of great benefit to the United States. Subsequently, a contract was signed for carronades and the construction of a boring mill utilizing horses. Three or four years later, steam power replaced horses.

Meanwhile, Secretary of the Navy William Jones was trying to get a cannon foundry reestablished in the Northeast. In June 1814 he wrote to John M. Holley, one of the owners of Salisbury Furnace in Connecticut, offering to place a sizable order for cannon and shot. The contract was declined, perhaps because of price. The rate of $133.33 a ton for cannon had not changed since

1798. Jones noted in a report of February 1814, "The cannon foundries are few in number, and [there are] none of any note north of the waters of the Chesapeake."[25]

The only reference to guns cast by Foxall for the navy during the War of 1812 was the 32-pounder carronades of 1813, and they were not part of a contract. Although no hard evidence exists, and available records show few cannon ordered in this period from any founder, it is believed that Foxall continued to cast cannon for the navy.

In January 1815, a contract was let with Peter Townsend of Orange County, New York, for cannon and carronades. Two months later, a contract was let for 175 cannon and carronades with John Clarke and William Wirt of Richmond, Virginia. The principal figure in this latter venture was Major Clarke, whose works is referred to in subsequent contracts as John Clarke and Company, later as Bellona Furnace or Foundry. It was located in Powhatan County, twelve miles from Richmond.

Clarke, who does not seem to have been the most adroit of businessmen, had supervised the construction of the Virginia Manufactory of Arms. Possibly some of the machinery had been sold to him, for he left the foundry in 1809 to return to Powhatan County and establish his own works. He continued to operate the Bellona Foundry until the mid-1840s, when he sold it to Dr. Junius L. Archer.

In 1815, Henry Foxall sold the Columbia Foundry to General John Mason. The first contract with Mason, let in June 1816, is noteworthy for making the first reference to the new smooth gun form. The contract specified that the moldings were to be turned and the rest of the exterior was to be chiseled and perfectly smooth.

There is extant an inventory of cannon the Columbia Foundry delivered to the Washington Navy Yard between 1817 and 1822. It amounts to 355 long guns and carronades, 97,218 round shot, grape, and cannister—proof that Columbia continued to be the navy's major foundry during this period.

In 1816 a group of New York industrialists—John and Robert Swartout, Joseph G. Swift, Gouverneur Kemble, and James Rees—established the Cold Spring Foundry on the Hudson, opposite West Point. The first navy contracts with the firm, later known as the West Point Foundry Association (WPFA), were let in December 1816. This contract and the one signed in 1816 with Mason were each to provide the entire armament for one 74-gun ship (part of a postwar naval building program that consisted of six improved 74-gun ships, nine 44-gun frigates, and ten large sloops). Two of the 74s, the *Ohio* and *Delaware,* were laid down in 1817.

Between 1819 and 1824, the navy let a total of seventeen contracts for ordnance to meet the need of ships built under the Gradual Increase Act. Clarke got one contract; the rest were evenly divided between Mason and WPFA.

In 1825, many of the cannon from John Clarke's Bellona Foundry failed to pass proof and inspection. Despite this the inspector, Captain Thomas Ap Catesby Jones, noted that the long guns and carronades were "beautifully cast & I think the handsomest guns I have ever inspected."[26] Indeed, the problems seem not to have affected Bellona's contracts with the navy. In May 1825, the Board of Navy Commissioners signed another contract with Clarke for carronades, cannon, and shot.

In 1826, contracts were signed with WPFA, Mason, and Clarke for a total of 240 medium 24-pounders, ordnance for ten new sloops.[27]

There are no surviving contracts for navy guns between 1827 and 1837, the year the next extant contract appeared. It is unlikely that guns were cast for the navy in this period; ordnance expenditures were only about $15,000 a year, and this must have gone to items such as gunpowder, carriages, and magazine upkeep.

Fortunately for founders, the army ordered ordnance in the meantime. Between 1826 and 1840, Mason alone turned out hundreds of guns plus shot, shell, and casemate carriages for the army, including a number of 8-inch seacoast howitzers. Navy contracts were also being let, for gun carriage timber (of white oak), priming and cannon powder (E. I. Dupont de Nemours; J. P. Garesche; Staney, Reed and Company; and Oliver M. Whipple), and cannon locks and percussion primers (Enoch Hidden, Joshua Shaw, and Samuel Ringgold).

The first shell guns were ordered in 1841, 8-inch pieces referred to in most contracts as "Paixhans." Some 42-pounders were bored to a diameter of up to 8 inches but had the chamber of a 32-pounder. New 8-inch guns with 32-pounder chambers were also cast. The first contract for 10-inch shell guns (with 42-pounder chambers) was let in 1842.

An 1841 contract for 8-inch guns was Cyrus Alger's first with the navy. His firm, variously known as The South Boston Iron Company, Cyrus Alger and Company, and South Boston Iron Works (the latter probably after the Civil War), was founded in 1809 and would become one of the major American cannon foundries of the nineteenth century. It is said that Alger's father had learned the foundry trade in Bridgewater from Hugh Orr.

Fort Pitt Works (Knap and Totten) was also producing ordnance in this period. In 1841 the works was sold to Charles Knap, Jr., and W. J. Totten, men previously involved in its operation. A navy contract of 1842 called for the production of one hundred 32-pounder cannon. By the time of the Civil War, Fort Pitt Works was one of the largest and best equipped foundries in the world. In 1864, it was turning out an average of seven 9-inch navy, six 10-inch army, three 11-inch navy, one and a half 15-inch army, and one and a half 15-inch navy guns per week.

In July 1842 the Tredegar Foundry in Richmond, Virginia, signed its first navy contract for 100 guns, the first 60 of which were accepted but the final 40 of which were rejected after 5 burst during proof. Tredegar had been formed in the late 1830s of two companies, Tredegar Iron and the Virginia Foundry.

The new firm was in financial straits when the Panic of 1837 ended the railroad boom in Virginia. In March 1841, after a commercial agent had failed to extricate the company from financial difficulty, the job was given to an ambitious retired army officer, Joseph R. Anderson. He may have negotiated a contract with the navy in 1841 for chain cable, shot, and shell; by the end of 1842, he had sold the government almost $90,000 worth of iron. His success in this market led the owners to approve his request to erect equipment for manufacturing heavy ordnance; soon he had his own contract for navy guns.

Anderson, who experimented with casting techniques and mixes of iron, established a high reputation for his cannon. Between 1844 and 1860, the company cast 881 pieces of ordnance for the federal government. Anderson claimed that, since Tredegar's 1842 failure, not one gun failed to pass proof firing.[28]

In the 1840s, Tredegar became one of the largest casting facilities in the United States. In addition to manufacturing for both the army and navy, it cast sixty-four pieces for the state of South Carolina in 1850 and 1851. By 1859, Anderson had gained control of the company, renaming it J. R. Anderson and Company.

All founders were concerned about getting a regular flow of government contracts. In August 1842, after the passage of the new naval appropriations bill, Alger inquired whether the Navy Board was ready to enter into contracts for guns, shot, and shell. Kemble, at WPFA, raised the same question in a letter in which he appealed for a contract: "The present state of our orders is such, that unless you can give us some employment, I see little hope but that I shall be obliged to close the establishment. . . ."[29] Much of the agitation was no doubt caused by a new law providing that government gun contracts go to the lowest bidders.

In the 1840s, the navy began extensive experiments with new types of cannon. A contract was signed in October 1843 with Daniel Treadwell, a professor at Harvard, for the manufacture of four cannon at $1,000 each. These "hooped" guns, delivered at Boston in January 1845, were made of iron and had steel bands reinforcing the breech.

After the *Princeton*'s wrought-iron "Peacemaker" gun burst in February 1844, the government began a series of experiments on the properties of metal for cannon and the means of strengthening guns. These were carried out between 1844 and 1851 at South Boston Foundry, at Fort Pitt Foundry, and in Washington. Tests, which dealt primarily with tensile strength and specific gravity, resulted in a procedure for testing metal from the gunhead; whenever the tensile strength of a sample fell below 20,000 pounds per square inch, it was declared unfit for service. The tests also led to the discovery that density, hardness, and tenacity could be increased if iron was melted twice or even three times from the pigs, and that keeping iron in fusion—retaining it in the furnace and exposing it to continued heat—for a longer period increased tensile strength.

Additional experiments were carried out on hydraulic pressure and on the comparative strength of gun metal cooled slowly and that cooled rapidly. Hot-blast smelted iron was found inferior to cold blast in density and tenacity, and as a result the government prohibited it in future contracts. The Peacemaker tragedy thus had the positive effect of procuring higher quality guns for both the navy and the army.

From 1844 to 1849, a substantial number of guns were ordered and completed. The usual practice was to split contracts among the navy's six principal cannon founders. During this period Tredegar contracted for 346 cannon, WPFA for 398, Knap and Totten, 404, Cyrus Alger, 310, John Mason, 60, and Bellona, 184. Quantities of shot were also produced by these founders and others.

The Washington Navy Yard was putting out small pieces. In December 1850, the U.S. Navy formally adopted Dahlgren boat howitzers. These 12- and 24-pounders were cast and turned at the Washington yard under Dahlgren's supervision. By 1852, some forty had been produced, thirty of which were in service. Also cast at this yard, in Dahlgren's experimental department, were a number of guns that included rifled 12- and 40-pounders.

Others in addition to Dahlgren were testing new methods. The bursting of the Peacemaker induced Lieutenant Thomas Rodman, later brigadier general and chief of army ordnance, to experiment with casting techniques that would improve gun endurance. Rodman had joined the army in 1841 and in 1845–46 supervised the casting of guns in Richmond and at Fort Pitt Foundry. In 1845, he proposed to the Ordnance Bureau a new method for casting guns which was rejected by its chief, Colonel Bomford, and later by his successor, General Talcott. Having been informed by Talcott that there would be no objection to his working through private sources, Rodman obtained such a patent in August 1847 and made arrangements with Knap and Totten at Fort Pitt to try his method of casting on a hollow core cooled from the interior. The founders agreed to run the financial and physical risks, which were considered great—Rodman testified in 1864 that Knap and Totten thought his new technique might burn down the foundry—of carrying out the Rodman theory in practice. They also helped him secure the patent, in return receiving 50 percent interest in it. Ultimately, Rodman received half a cent per pound on all guns Fort Pitt cast utilizing his method. This arrangement lasted until 1861, when Knap secured full rights to the patent, although he continued to give Rodman the same price for guns cast by his method. Dahlgren never received any royalties on his ordnance inventions, and this was probably one cause of the friction that later developed between the two men. Knap said he cast the first hollow-bore guns on the Rodman principle in 1845, but the government did not use it until 1858 or 1859.

On 5 August 1849, at Fort Pitt, Knap cast two experimental 8-inch columbiads at the same time and from the same metal, one in an open pit in the solid, to be bored, the other in a covered pit around a core, cooled from the interior. The iron for the two castings was melted in two separate furnaces but mixed in the pouring process. Both guns were completed and inspected on 6 September and then subjected to proof. They were fired alternately eighty-four times, and on the eighty-fifth, the solid-cast columbiad burst. The hollow-cast gun did not burst until it had been fired 251 times.

On 30 July 1851, two more 8-inch columbiads were cast at Fort Pitt under similar circumstances. This time the iron remained in fusion at high heat for two and a half hours. On 21 August, two 10-inch columbiads were also cast, one solid and the other hollow; the molds were placed in the same pit.

In provings, the 8-incher that had been cast solid broke on the seventy-third fire. The one cast hollow sustained 1,500 firings and remained unbroken and capable of more. The solid-cast 10-inch gun broke on the twentieth fire, the hollow-cast 10-incher after 249 firings. The latter's lack of endurance was explained by the fact that its flask had not been externally heated while the cast was cooling; it had been placed in sand, which, it was mistakenly thought, would retain the heat sufficiently.

Rodman's technique of casting is described in a contemporary account as follows:

> On the Rodman principle the flask is sunk in the pit as in solid castings; a tube closed and water-tight at the lower end, and fluted on the exterior for the escape of the gas generated by the metal, forms the base of the core. This tube is wrapped closely, along its entire length, with a sash cord, over which is plastered mud to the depth of three-fourths of an inch. Inside of this tube is a copper pipe for the purpose of conducting water to the bottom of the larger tube, from whence the water rises, filling the entire tube or core, and the surplus passes off from a pipe at the top. After the metal has been poured into the mold of the gun, water is allowed to run through the pipes for twelve hours, when it is stopped off for a half hour or so, during which time the heat of the yet uncooled huge mass of molten metal causes the cord, already mentioned as wrapped around the tube, to be consumed . . . [T]he entire core . . . is easily withdrawn. Water is then allowed to run into the . . . cleared bore of the gun, until it is sufficiently cooled to be hoisted from the flask.[30]

The time for cooling varied. For the 8-inch columbiad, the core was withdrawn twenty-five hours after casting, but water continued to flow for forty more hours. For larger guns, cooling times were increased.

The Rodman technique had a number of advantages. Guns cast by this method were stronger, their bores were less liable to enlargement under continued firing, and less time was required for manufacture. This meant that safe guns could now be made larger than before. By 1859, the U.S. Army Ordnance Department specified the Rodman method for all heavy artillery.

There was opposition to this stipulation, however, from founders Joseph Anderson, R. P. Parrott, Cyrus Alger, and Junius Archer, mostly because of the new equipment the Rodman method required. Anderson was particularly adamant; after a year-long feud with the Ordnance Department, he almost gave up casting altogether. As has been noted, his obstinacy cost the South dearly in the Civil War.[31] Archer also refused to adopt Rodman's method.

The technique improved heavy ordnance manufacture, as northern founders later admitted. In 1864, the Union's chief of ordnance stated that the army counted on getting three times as many firings from guns cast by the Rodman technique as from cannon of similar caliber cast solid.

It is not known when the navy became interested in the Rodman method, but in October 1851, Charles C. Turner reported to the chief of the Bureau of Ordnance and Hydrography on the experimental columbiads at Fort Pitt. He described their casting and proving as well as their bursting, and speculated about how the technique would affect shipborne guns. But despite its demonstrated success, the navy did not adopt the Rodman technique right away. The largest Dahlgren guns, even XI-inchers weighing 16,000 pounds, continued to be cast solid because with their extraordinary thickness about the breech and curving shape, none had ever burst in service. This was not the case with the large columbiads cast for the army. Not until late in the Civil War was the Rodman technique specified, and then only for the largest navy guns. Despite this, the XV-inch Dahlgren was the only U.S. Navy Civil War gun cast hollow that saw active service. Some experimental X-inch Dahlgrens of 16,000 pounds and one IX-incher of 12,000 pounds—both intended for service against ironclads—were cast solid, but they were not placed in service.

Before the Civil War, the 15-inch cast gun was close to the limit in size. Twenty-inch cannon were cast at Fort Pitt for the army and navy, but these did not see service until after the Civil War.

Another individual experimenting with new ordnance and foundry techniques was a former captain of ordnance in the army, Robert P. Parrott. He was inspecting guns at WPFA in 1836 when Gouverneur Kemble prevailed on him to resign his commission and take over as superintendent of the foundry. In 1851, Parrott became sole proprietor. It was at Cold Spring that he developed the Parrott gun. Despite an attempt to dissociate his gun from Treadwell's, it was based on the principle of Treadwell's built-up gun developed in the 1840s. It was essentially a cast-iron rifle with a wrought-iron band reinforcing the breech.

Contracts continued to be let in the 1840s and 1850s for gun carriage timber and cannon powder. Principal suppliers of timber were L. Y. Beger, H. S. Ward, and John Petty, while gunpowder came from E. I. Du Pont de Nemours; Loomis, Swift, and Masters; and I. P. Garesche.

The most influential figure in mid-nineteenth-century U.S. Navy ordnance design was John Dahlgren. His work is discussed elsewhere, but the first prototype IX-inch gun of his design was cast by WPFA and delivered in May 1850. The first XI-inch Dahlgren was cast by Cyrus Alger and delivered in October 1851. The first service contracts for the new IX-inch and XI-inch Dahlgren shell guns were let in December 1854 for the screw frigates authorized that year. They were to be cast by Parrott as part of a larger order.

Apparently, WPFA was the only foundry that had initial success with the

Dahlgren guns. In December 1854, a contract was let with Knap and Wade for fifty IX-inchers, but not a single one was accepted. Parrott produced twenty-five of them for Knap and Wade and delivered them in October and November 1856. Contractual records state that Tredegar delivered twenty-four of the remaining guns, although neither the date of delivery nor the amount of payment is given.

But Tredegar as well as Cyrus Alger had difficulty producing Dahlgrens. One problem was certainly that many of the larger ones could not withstand proof. Although Dahlgren's first XI-inch gun, cast by Alger and delivered in 1851, did not burst until round 1,959, that was not the case with many others. In 1855, Dahlgren noted in his journal that six columbiads had burst at WPFA "in common proof," and shortly afterward five out of nine guns burst in Boston "by the common proof or its repetition." He was concerned enough to write to the Bureau of Ordnance and advise extreme proof for the new guns.[32]

Dahlgren believed that the trouble was with the foundries rather than his gun design. He pointed to deficiencies in casting metal, noting that a procedure to test that used for new shell guns was no longer being performed in Pittsburgh and Boston. In Pittsburgh, three of the IX-inch guns burst, resulting in the rejection of forty-three others. Two-thirds of these had defective trunnions that broke off before bursting—which alone would have been fatal to the guns. In Boston a IX-inch gun burst on the first fire; so did an XI-incher, which condemned the rest. But one IX-incher endured 950 service rounds. At WPFA there was no difficulty, but in Richmond several of the guns had "objectionable iron" and so all were condemned. Dahlgren noted that Knap and Wade and Alger and Company were displeased with Commodore Charles Morris's decision that either the guns be condemned or new inspection procedures be instituted. Alger finally agreed; Knap and Wade argued their case at length without success.[33] It was later determined that many of these guns had failed because the density of their iron was too high.

Dahlgren also had problems with founders making modifications on his designs. As Charles Knap of Fort Pitt Foundry explained in testimony given in February 1864, the founders objected to Dahlgren's insistence that his guns be cast as cylindrically as possible—that is, with the chase almost as large as the breech—to obtain uniform cooling. Once cast, the gun had to be put in a lathe and the excess metal turned off. Knap said that the founders—Alger of South Boston, Parrott of WPFA, Anderson of Tredegar, and himself—met with Commodore Morris in 1847 or 1848 (the date is certainly in error) to decide on a fair price for the guns. Since there was the extra expense of turning and metal was lost in the process, it was agreed that the founders would receive 10 or 15 percent more for their Dahlgren guns than for comparable army columbiads cast with the Rodman technique. Knap himself, closely tied to Rodman, said there was "very conclusive evidence everywhere that the Rodman is the better gun."[34]

In March 1857, the navy issued a specifications booklet for the manufacture of cannon.[35] This and other procedures helped end problems with the casting of heavier guns.

Before the Civil War great strides had been made in ordnance manufacture in the United States, and production expanded significantly during the conflict. From the outset of war until mid-August 1862 Knap, Alger, and Parrott delivered to the navy more than 748 mortars, howitzers, and cannon. In addition, the same three founders, along with Hinkley and Williams, and Brown and Company, produced more than 35,694 shells of all types. At this time James T. Ames cast twenty-six 12-pounder and seventy-two 24-pounder boat howitzers for the navy.

At the beginning of 1861, the U.S. Navy had 2,966 heavy guns and howitzers. By 1 November 1864, 4,333 new guns had been added, most of the heavy guns cast by the three founders who had captured the ordnance market in the North—Knap, Parrott, and Alger. Seyfort, McManus of Reading, Pennsylvania, Builder's Iron Foundry of Providence, Rhode Island, and Hinkley, Williams and Company also cast heavy ordnance.[36] Northern manufacturing was extensive and well developed.

The South was not in a like position, as Lieutenant Colonel J. W. Mallet, superintendent of Confederate States Ordnance Laboratories, noted:

> In 1861 the Southern States were almost wholly occupied with agricultural pursuits, and their resources immediately available in the way of manufacturing establishments were poor indeed. There were two small private powder mills in Tennessee, two in South Carolina, one in North Carolina, and a little stamping mill in New Orleans. There were but two first class foundries and machine shops—the Tredegar works in Richmond and the Leeds' Foundry at New Orleans; the loss of the latter was one of the sorest consequences of the fall of that city. There were several fairly respectable machine shops of the second class period.[37]

Tredegar, the last of the pre–Civil War "Big Four," became the principal supplier of heavy ordnance to the Confederacy. The war was, in fact, Tredegar's salvation. In a difficult financial position, in part due to Anderson's rejection of the Rodman technique required by the Army Ordnance Department, orders from Southern states before the outbreak of fighting enabled Tredegar to survive. These included three bronze 6-pound rifled field pieces for Georgia ordered in December 1860, two 10-inch columbiads for Alabama's Fort Morgan ordered on 31 December 1860, and a significant number of shot and cannon for South Carolina's batteries at Charleston, ordered between January and April 1861.

During the Civil War, Tredegar produced between 1,043 and 1,099 pieces of ordnance of all types. Approximately 1,050 pieces—all but 33 of them field—were manufactured by eleven other Southern firms during the conflict.[38] One estimate is that even by 1863 the entire production of Southern foundries did not exceed 16,000 tons a year. Paucity of industry and an undeveloped raw materials' base were key factors in the defeat of the Confederacy.

CHAPTER IV

U.S. Navy Ordnance and Ship Armament to 1812

CANNON CAME to the New World with Columbus, and within a century there were numerous forts along the Spanish Main armed with ordnance. These often large and highly ornamented guns included reinforced cannon. The English also brought cannon to the New World, but the earliest ones were light pieces such as falconets, falcons, minions, and sakers. English heavy cannon apparently did not make the trip over, culverins only occasionally, and demi-culverins slightly more frequently.

Cannon were used early in the history of intercolonial strife. They were involved, for instance, in an engagement between French ships and a Spanish squadron in 1565. Ordnance was required for the many merchant vessels and warships built in colonial America, especially the merchantmen conducting the risky business of international trade. In 1748, the *Bethell* of Boston carried fourteen guns. Later she captured a Spanish treasure ship of twenty-four guns.

Colonial seamen participated in several military expeditions in American waters, beginning with the 1690 attack on Quebec. For the capture of Louisburg in 1745, the colonists fitted out a large fleet. Colonial vessels also took part in expeditions against Havana (1748), Louisburg (1757–58), and Quebec (1759).

During the War of Jenkins' Ear, several colonies built vessels to protect their coasts against Spanish privateers. When the Seven Years' War began, Massachusetts built a 26-gun ship and other colonies built privateers, including one in 1758 that carried thirty-six guns.

Colonial ships purchased by the British were given English-made ordnance. American warships, because the British government discouraged the production of ordnance in the colonies, acquired most of their ordnance from England or other countries.

During the War of the Austrian Succession, London merchants Elias Bland and Company ordered a ship, the *Tetsworth,* built under the direction of John Reynell of Philadelphia. In 1746 her cannon (ten 4-pounders and two 6-pounders), along with shot, were sent from England.

By the time of the American Revolution, ordnance in the hands of the colonials represented a motley collection of every sort and caliber—mostly English guns, but also some from France, Spain, and even Scandinavia. This state of affairs continued well beyond the Revolution.

Although suffering at the outset of the Revolution from a state of neglect, the Royal Navy nevertheless enjoyed overwhelming superiority at sea, a situation not significantly altered until France entered the war in 1778. A powerful fleet was, in fact, Britain's most obvious advantage over the colonies. In 1775, when the Revolution began, the Royal Navy had 270 ships. In the fall of 1776, American naval strength amounted to twenty-seven ships carrying an average of twenty guns each. Few of these vessels were at sea, however, owing to lack of crews. At the same time, on the American station the British had, in addition to smaller craft, seventy-one ships mounting on the average twenty-eight guns. Among these ships were two sixty-fours, one sixty, seven fifties, and three forty-fours. Guns in these heavier ships were much larger than those carried by American vessels.

Naval superiority meant that the British could shift troops at will from Britain to America and almost at will from one American port to another. Control of the coastline alone did not ensure victory, and in any case, the Royal Navy did not have the ships available to bring this about. Still, given the appalling state of land communications, control of the seas was a great advantage.

The colonial effort against the British was even more diffuse at sea than on land. There was the army's navy at Boston and New York, established by George Washington; the army's navy on Lake Champlain, Benedict Arnold commanding; a force of converted merchantmen; and the Continental navy, begun with the Marine Committee and the frigate construction program. Eleven colonies also had small navies of their own for local defense, the largest being those of Massachusetts, Pennsylvania, Maryland, Virginia, Connecticut, and South Carolina. In addition, a large number of privateers were commissioned by Congress and most state governments.

General George Washington authorized the creation of a saltwater navy in the summer of 1775. On 24 August he hired the schooner *Hannah;* commanded by Nicholas Broughton and manned by volunteers from the army, she sailed on 5 September to open the naval war against Great Britain. Washington created two fleets, one at Boston and later one at New York. Together there were a dozen armed schooners whose purpose it was to capture supply vessels bound for enemy forces. They took a total of thirty-five prizes, and some of them operated until 1777.

Obstacles to building a navy existed not only because of the expense but also because of opposition to war. It was not until 13 December 1775 that Congress authorized a program of naval construction. Thirteen frigates were to be built at a total expenditure of $8,666,667. All the material for outfitting the frigates, with the exception of canvas and gunpowder, was to come from America.

The frigates were three-masted square-rigged vessels about 125 feet long on the average. Three were rated twenty-four guns, five were twenty-eights, and five were thirty-twos. Four of the thirteen vessels were destroyed on the stocks to prevent capture by the British, and not until the spring of 1776 were the *Warren* and *Raleigh* launched and ready for sea. The *Randolph* was the first to reach open sea, on 6 February 1777.

All of the earlier converted navy was destroyed or captured by the end of 1779, and virtually the same was true of the newly built navy. In 1783, the Continental navy consisted of only one ship—the 32-gun *Alliance,* larger than an armed schooner—and there were in all only five vessels. The British had 608 vessels of all classes, 62 of which were on the American station and more than that number in the West Indies.

Given the overwhelming superiority of the Royal Navy during the war, the colonials were limited largely to harassing tactics that nonetheless secured badly needed ordnance supplies. Early captures included the schooner *Diana* (four 6-pounders and a number of smaller weapons), the schooner *Margaretta* (four "double-fortifyed" 3-pounders and fourteen swivels), the schooner *Diligent* (eight to ten guns), and the tender *Tapuaquish* (sixteen swivels).

There was a much more important haul of ordnance supplies during Commodore Esek Hopkins' expedition to the British West Indies. In March 1776, his eight converted merchantmen took New Providence (now Nassau) in the Bahamas. From its forts came eighty-eight cannon of different sizes (9- to 32-pounders), fifteen bronze mortars (4- to 11-inch), more than 16,500 round shot and shells, various other ordnance stores, and twenty-four barrels of powder. It took two weeks just to load these captured supplies. One writer called it America's most successful naval operation of the Revolution.[1]

During its return voyage, on 27 March 1776, Hopkins' fleet took the six-gun schooner *Hawke,* the first British prize of a Continental navy vessel, and the bomb brig *Bolton,* carrying two mortars as well as eight smaller guns. Much of the captured ordnance and supplies were handed over to Washington's forces as they moved from Boston to New York.

In the most important colonial acquisition of British arms, the sloop *Lee* captured the ordnance transport *Nancy* on 29 November 1775, when she was bound for Boston with supplies for the British army. The brigantine yielded a fantastic quantity of ordnance for the colonial cause, including 2,500 muskets, 40 tons of musket shot, a considerable quantity of cartridges, a number of bronze and iron cannon (with carriages) ranging in size from 4- to 24-pounders, and a bronze 13-inch mortar subsequently named The Congress by its captors.

On 17 May 1776 the *Franklin,* commanded by James Mugford, captured the armed transport *Hope.* She carried a large cargo of military stores, including 1,000 carbines, five gun carriages, and 1,500 barrels of gunpowder. Next to the *Nancy,* the *Hope* was the most valuable munitions prize taken by the colonials during the war. From September 1775 to October 1777, the schooners of Washington's tiny navy took fifty-five British prizes in all. When the Royal Navy was able to bring its full weight to bear, however, these depredations virtually ceased.

Throughout the Revolution the colonial navy repeatedly lost skilled seamen, shipbuilding resources, and supplies to the more lucrative business of privateering. Indeed, in 1776 few ships of the navy were ready for sea because they lacked crews. The number of privateers operating during the conflict, though it varied from year to year, was quite large. Congress issued letters of marque to 1,697 vessels carrying at least 14,872 guns. In 1781, there were around 405 privateers manned by more than 20,000 men and carrying 6,700 guns, while at its peak in 1777, the Continental navy consisted of thirty-four ships and fewer than 5,000 men.

Between 1775 and 1783, 64 revolutionary navy vessels with 1,242 guns and swivels captured 196 enemy vessels. Lloyds of London reported that during the same period American privateers captured 3,087 British merchantmen and privateers. Of these, 879 were retaken or ransomed, leaving a total of 2,208. For their part, the British took 1,351 vessels (including 216 privateers), of which 28 were recaptured or ransomed. During the war 203 vessels of the regular British navy were lost to all causes; 18 were retaken.[2]

All classes of vessels participated in the privateering effort, most of them small, averaging less than 70 feet in length and 100 tons in carrying capacity. Late in the war vessels of as much as 600 tons appeared, but the majority ranked below 50 tons in size, and some privateers were less than 10.

The number of guns they had also varied. The 80-ton sloop *Commerce* carried six guns and twenty-five men, while the brigantine *Flying Fish,* which was the same size, carried twice the number of both. The 500-ton privateer *Velisarius* mounted twenty guns and had a crew of 200.

Like navy guns the pieces in privateers were for the most part small, the 9-pounder being about the maximum size. Six-pounders were more common, 4-pounders and smaller guns the most. Much of this ordnance was obtained from abroad because American commissioners in Paris and agents in the West Indies also authorized privateers.

Perhaps the most successful of the American privateers was the *Holker,* which took six prizes on her first cruise, including one vessel transporting eighty cannon destined for the British army in America.

The capture of British ordnance was not limited to the sea. The colonials

Fig. 29. Bow View of the Gondola *Philadelphia*, Showing a 12-Pdr on a Slide Mount, Two 9-Pdrs on Truck Carriages in Broadside, and a Swivel Gun on the Rail. (Courtesy of the Smithsonian Institution.)

made a tremendous haul when they took Fort Ticonderoga and Crown Point in May 1775. Colonel Henry Knox listed fifty-eight pieces in all—forty-two cannon and sixteen mortars and howitzers. A number of these, including many of manufacture other than British, reached the fleet of Brigadier General Benedict Arnold on Lake Champlain. It numbered seventeen small vessels manned by 936 men. In October 1776, in one of the war's decisive battles, Arnold's fleet forced the British temporarily to abandon their thrust from Canada.

Perhaps the most famous of American revolutionary cannon are those that belonged to the gondola *Philadelphia,* part of Arnold's flotilla and now preserved at the Smithsonian Institution as the oldest American naval vessel in existence. Her three Swedish-manufactured cannon—one 12-pounder on a slide in the bow, two 9-pounders mounted amidships and firing to port and

Fig. 30. Swivel and Broadside 9-Pdr on a Truck Carriage in the Gondola *Philadelphia*. (Courtesy of the Smithsonian Institution.)

starboard—are all believed to have come from Ticonderoga. The *Philadelphia* also mounted a number of swivels, only one of which survives.

Gunpowder also had to be obtained from foreign sources. The first powder mills in the American colonies were not established until 1775, and the powder produced during the Revolution was of poor quality and unreliable. Large quantities were purchased abroad. An order in council of 19 October 1774 prohibited the export of powder to the American colonies, and royal governors were exhorted to enforce it. Despite the ban, Americans were able before the outbreak of fighting to buy powder, ammunition, and other supplies from England, western Europe, and the West Indies.

This traffic intensified because of the ineffective British blockade in the early years of the war. American and neutral vessels penetrated the blockade with comparative ease, landing needed supplies from Spain, Holland, France, and the Caribbean in exchange for colonial goods. As has been noted, during the first year 90 percent of the gunpowder used by American forces came by sea. The Revolution could not have proceeded without such aid.[3]

Typical of early voyages was that of the sloop *Molly* to Martinique, where her master Richard Conway openly purchased 500 muskets, sixty barrels of gunpowder, six 4-pounder carriage guns, and twelve swivels in February 1776. More than one hundred ships loaded with needed supplies reached America in the first two years of the Revolution.

At first the American procurement of military stores was haphazard. The bulk came from private merchants, and Congress was obliged to pay exorbitant sums for the supplies, in some cases whether they reached America safely or not. The procurement process was systematized somewhat with the appointment on 18 September 1775 of the Secret Committee charged with contracting for the importation of gunpowder, cannon, and small arms. In November 1775, it was empowered to export produce to the West Indies in exchange for war material.

The chief source of arms, including cannon, was France. French aid to America was a state secret, if an open one, handled by Pierre Augustin Caron de Beaumarchais. In April 1776, Louis XVI issued an order to rebuild the French navy and provide new equipment for the army. This released a considerable stock of old military supplies to the trading company of Roderique Hortalez, which Beaumarchais had established and which was the conduit channeling French aid to America. In May 1776, another royal decree made a fund of a million livres available to Beaumarchais. From 1776 to 1783, he dispensed 21 million livres.

The French government's position was difficult. France was not ready for war with England and so had to avoid any responsibility for Beaumarchais's activity. The minister of foreign affairs, Count Charles Gravier de Vergennes, insisted, therefore, that French markings be removed from bronze cannon in the royal arsenals before they were given to the Americans. If this could not be done without weakening the guns, new ones were to be cast. Despite such precautions, English Ambassador Lord Stormont "haunted Vergennes's chamber with complaints, almost always well founded. . . ."[4]

Meanwhile, Beaumarchais was accumulating supplies at French ports. He obtained more than 200 cannon, 25,000 small arms, 100 tons of gunpowder, 20 to 30 bronze mortars, and clothing and tents sufficient for 25,000 men, mostly from French arsenals.

Many of the cannon from France were quite old—some sold to the state of Virginia went all the way back to 1678—and not all were of French manufacture. A pair of iron guns bought from France in 1778 are now at the state capitol in Raleigh, North Carolina, and one is unmistakably English. At least 112 4-pounder cannon and 21 9-inch mortars were Scandinavian.

In December 1776, the British ambassador protested the planned sailing of three of Beaumarchais's ships from Le Havre. Perhaps forewarned by the French government, Beaumarchais got off one brig, the *Amphitrite,* which managed to elude British cruisers and reached Portsmouth, New Hampshire, with 75 bronze cannon, 15,000 uniforms, and 10,000 muskets.[5] Despite the temporary setback, Beaumarchais continued to equip merchant ships and get them to sea with stores for America. He also financed the fitting out of a man-of-war, the *Fier Roderique.* After the *Amphitrite,* eight other vessels of Beaumarchais's were reported to have reached Portsmouth in the spring of 1777. In March 1777 the *Mercury* brought 1,000 barrels of powder and 11,987 muskets from Nantes.

Others were also involved in the trade. Le Ray de Chaumont sent a shipload of powder to Boston with instructions not to insist on repayment unless the Americans won. He was never repaid, and neither was Beaumarchais.

A number of American warships—notably, the *Bonhomme Richard, Hogue,* and *Queen of France*—were fitted out in French ports. The quality of ordnance they received varied greatly. While the latter two vessels obtained first-rate pieces, two of the old 18-pounders on board the *Bonhomme Richard* burst during the battle with the *Serapis.* French aid was nonetheless invaluable and is credited with making possible the Continental army's victory at Saratoga.[6]

Arms trade developed with other countries as well, chiefly Spain and Holland. It was usually indirect. Dutch goods, for example, were sent to France or to the Dutch West Indian island of St. Eustatius, whence they were shipped to America. Some Swedish iron came to America's shores directly from Gothenburg, but that was an exception.

Because the Atlantic crossing was hazardous (the British captured perhaps one in nine ships), the bulk of the trade came by way of the French, Dutch, and Spanish Caribbean islands. The islands most active in this trade were Hispaniola (Haiti), Martinique, Cuba, St. Croix, St. Martin, and St. Eustatius. The most important of these was undoubtedly the tiny island of St. Eustatius. As the war continued, the volume of trade increased substantially. During one thirteen-month period, 3,182 vessels were said to have cleared Port Orange. A good deal of them carried gunpowder or its components, including saltpeter from the Dutch East India Company. A principal item of exchange was tobacco. When Britain finally declared war on Holland and Admiral George Rodney's forces took St. Eustatius in December 1780, it yielded a fantastic treasure of supplies awaiting shipment. Rodney found 125 vessels at anchor at Port Orange, twelve of them English.

Most American navy vessels of the revolutionary period were quite small. The largest of them was the ship of the line *America,* rated at seventy-four guns and authorized by the Continental Congress in 1776. Construction began at Portsmouth, New Hampshire, in 1777 but was delayed by lack of funds, skilled artisans, and materials. Armament was reported as thirty long 18-pounders on the lower deck, thirty-two long 12-pounders on the upper deck, and fourteen long 9-pounders on the quarterdeck and forecastle. Finally launched in November 1782 at Portsmouth, this ship, which John Paul Jones had hoped would be the pride of the American navy, was turned over to France as a gesture of gratitude for help in the war and as compensation for the loss of the French ship of the line *Magnifique,* wrecked in Boston Harbor that year.

The next largest vessel was the 42-gun *Bonhomme Richard,* a converted Indiaman purchased in France. Her largest guns were 18-pounders. Other American vessels ranged in size from the *Indien (South Carolina)* of forty guns—she carried Swedish 36-pounders on her main deck, making her a formidable frigate—to the *Mosquito* of only four guns.

The seventeen vessels in General Arnold's flotilla on Lake Champlain mounted a total of 102 guns and 186 swivels. The majority of these vessels were gondolas such as the *Philadelphia* carrying three guns. The sloop *Enterprise* and schooner *Royal Savage* carried the largest number of guns—twelve cannon plus ten swivels each. The cannon in Arnold's fleet ranged from 2- to 18-pounders.

The schooners of Washington's little navy in 1775 carried between two and six guns each, all 2- and 4-pounders. Most of these vessels had ten swivels, and each carried twenty rounds per gun.

The armament of the thirteen frigates authorized in 1775, which were to form the backbone of the American navy, was as follows: thirty-two guns in the *Hancock, Randolph, Raleigh, Washington,* and *Warren* (twenty-six 12-pounders and six 6-pounders), twenty-eight guns in the frigates *Trumbull, Effingham, Congress, Virginia,* and *Providence* (twenty-six 12-pounders and two 6-pounders), and twenty-four guns in the frigates *Boston, Delaware,* and *Montgomery* (twenty-four 9-pounders).

It is difficult to ascertain the number of guns carried by a vessel at any particular time. Ships could easily exceed their rate, and usually did so if possible. A 32-gun frigate would, for example, usually carry thirty-six guns. Armament also changed a good deal throughout the life of a vessel.

The cannon for the thirteen frigates were intended to be of standard design, but this proved impossible. Throughout the Revolution nonstandardization was the rule for American naval vessels. It was reinforced by borrowing between the army and navy of cannon, ammunition, and stores, a practice that continued at least into the War of 1812. There are many examples of nonstandardization. The frigate *Warren,* which should have carried twenty-six 12-pounders and six 6-pounders, had twelve 18-pounders, fourteen 12-pounders, and eight 9-pounders, making her quite formidable for her size. Her 18-pounders were the heaviest cast for naval use in the colonies during the Revolution.

Occasionally all guns in a vessel were of the same make. For example, each cannon for the *Virginia* was cast at the Hughes furnace near Baltimore.

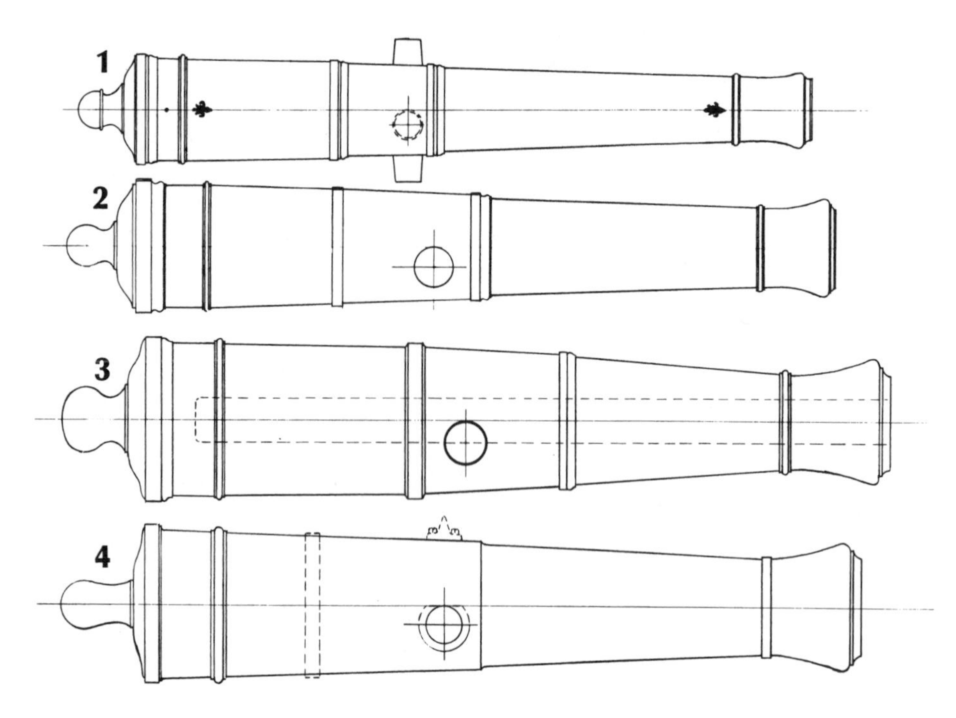

Key:

Gun no. 1: A 12-pdr raised from Lake Champlain. At Fort William Henry.
Gun no. 2: Four of these are at Fort Ticonderoga, marked "French 24's from Nicaragua." Close to the French design of 1766.
Gun no. 3: From a drawing of a French 36-pdr cast in 1778. Note the location of the trunnions near the beginning of the second reinforce rather than at the end, as in gun no. 2. From the late seventeenth century to around 1830, the French 36-pdr was the heaviest standard gun carried by naval vessels.
Gun no. 4: A 36-pdr of the establishment of 1786. Later models were given a first reinforce ring, an almost complete rimbase, and a front sight mounted above the trunnions with screws.

Fig. 31. French Iron Cannon, c. 1750–86. (Drawing by C. S. Tucker.)

But instead of the twenty-six 12-pounders and two 6-pounders with which she was to be armed, the *Virginia* went on her first cruise with twenty-four 12-pounders and six 4-pounders.

It was difficult to secure ordnance throughout the Revolution. The Plymouth Committee of Correspondence, when asked to supply guns for the schooner *Triton,* came up with four 3-pounders as well as "Seven Swivels of different Size Bour *[sic],* one of which is Brass, one Excellent Wall piece and two Cohorns."[7] When Jovial Coit took command of the *Harrison,* he wryly described her armament as follows: "4 four pounders, brought into this

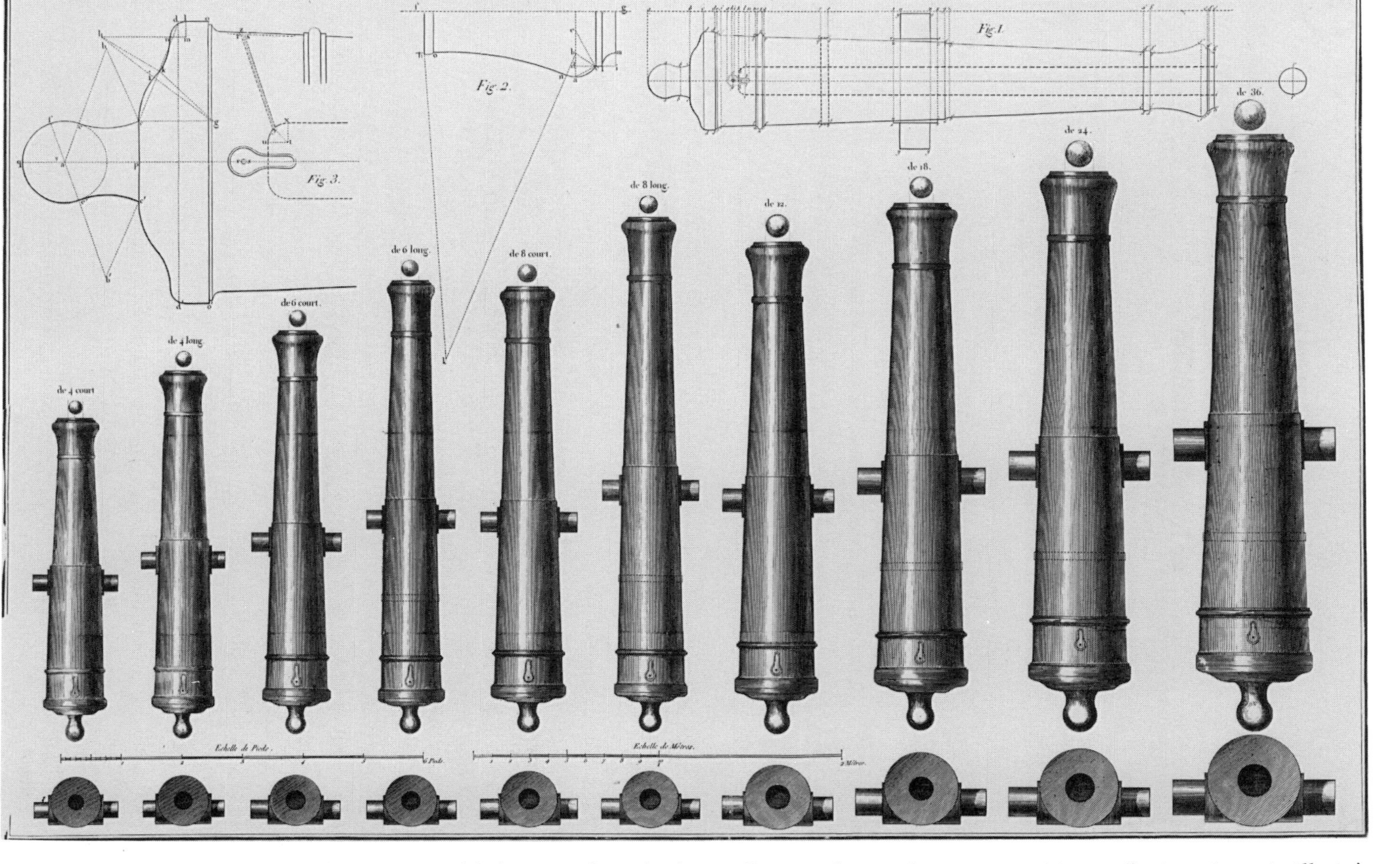

Fig. 32. French Iron Guns for the Navy, Establishment of 1786. These, illustrated in a plate in Louis Tousard's *American Artillerist's Companion*, are often mistakenly thought to be U.S. Navy guns of the period. (From Gaspard Monge, *Description de l'art de fabriquer les canons* [Paris, 1974].)

TABLE 9

ENGLISH BRONZE AND IRON GUNS, 1753

	LENGTH*		WEIGHT*		
POUNDERS	*Feet*	*Inches*	*100 Pounds*	*Quarters*	*Pounds*
Bronze cannon					
42	9	6	61	2	10
32	9	5	55	2	7
24	9	5	51	1	12
18	9	0	48	1	0
12	9	0	29	0	0
9	8	5			
6	8	0	19	0	0
3	6	5	11	0	0
Iron guns used in the sea service					
42	10	0	55	1	12
32	9	6	53	3	23
24	9	5	48	0	0
18	9	0	41	1	8
12	9	0	32	3	3
9	8	5	23	2	2
6	7	0	17	1	14
4	6	0	12	2	13
3	4	6	7	1	7

Source: William Falconer, *An Universal Dictionary of the Marine* (London: T. Cadell, 1789), 66.

country by the company of Lords Say and Seal, to Saybrook when they first came, a pair of cohorns that Noah had in the Ark; one of which lacks a touch-hole, having hardened steel drove therein, that she might not be of service to Sir Edmund Andros—Six Swivels, the first that ever were landed in Plymouth, and never fired since."[8]

The *Alliance* and *Confederacy,* frigates built in 1777, were to have all their guns made at Salisbury Furnace in Connecticut, but it was unable to deliver them and the full contract was given to John Brown of Rhode Island instead. Brown also failed to produce all the guns. The *Confederacy* went to sea armed with fourteen 12-pounders supplied by Brown, two 6-pounders taken from the wreck of *Columbus,* a 12-pounder borrowed from the army, and other 12-pounders taken from the captured British galley *Pigot.*

Both the *Alliance* and the *Confederacy* were rated at thirty-two guns and were supposed to be armed with twenty-eight 12-pounders and eight 6-pounders. But the *Alliance* carried twenty-eight 12-pounders and eight 9-pounders, and the *Confederacy* mounted twenty-eight 12-pounders and eight 6-pounders.

The dearth of such pieces during the Revolution makes any statement about American-made cannon of dubious value, but it is believed that most were copied from British designs. French patterns are said to have been used

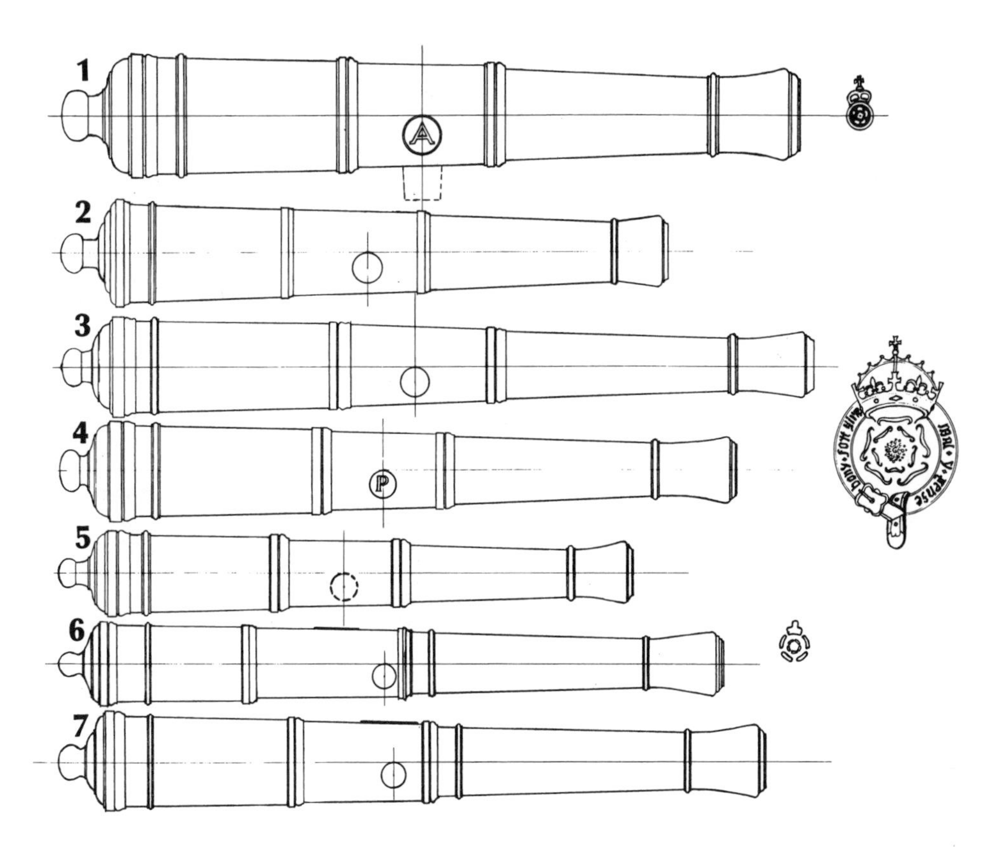

Gun no. 1: A 24-pdr of ca. 1660, 9′ 7″. Cambridge Square, Cambridge, Massachusetts.
Gun no. 2: An 18-pdr, 8′. Memorial Park, Lewes, Delaware.
Gun no. 3: Possibly a 12-pdr of 1690–1700, 10′. Fort Ticonderoga, New York.
Gun no. 4: Possibly a 12-pdr of 1690–1700, 9′. Cambridge Square.
Gun no. 5: A 6- to 12-pdr, 7′ 6.5″. Fort Phoenix, Fairhaven, Massachusetts.
Gun no. 6: A 6-pdr, probably of 1710–14, 9′ 2″. Governor's Palace, Williamsburg, Virginia
Gun no. 7: Size of a 12-pdr, but not bored full size, 9′ 6″. Mariner's Museum, Newport News, Virginia.

Fig. 33. English Cannon of the Rose and Crown Design, Seventeenth and Eighteenth Centuries. All of these cannon bear the royal cipher of the crowned rose, in some cases encircled by the sign of the Order of the Garter. The cipher went from a crown about a rose in a circle (garter) to something like a keystone arranged above a ring of fragments. The cannon probably predate 1714, the beginning of the reign of George I. All lengths are measured from the rear of the base ring to the face of the muzzle. (Drawing by C. S. Tucker.)

infrequently; there is no record of French ordnance on board American naval vessels other than that in ships fitted out in France.

All cannon used at sea by the colonials were relatively small, and all of them were long guns (carronades, utilized by the British, appeared too late to

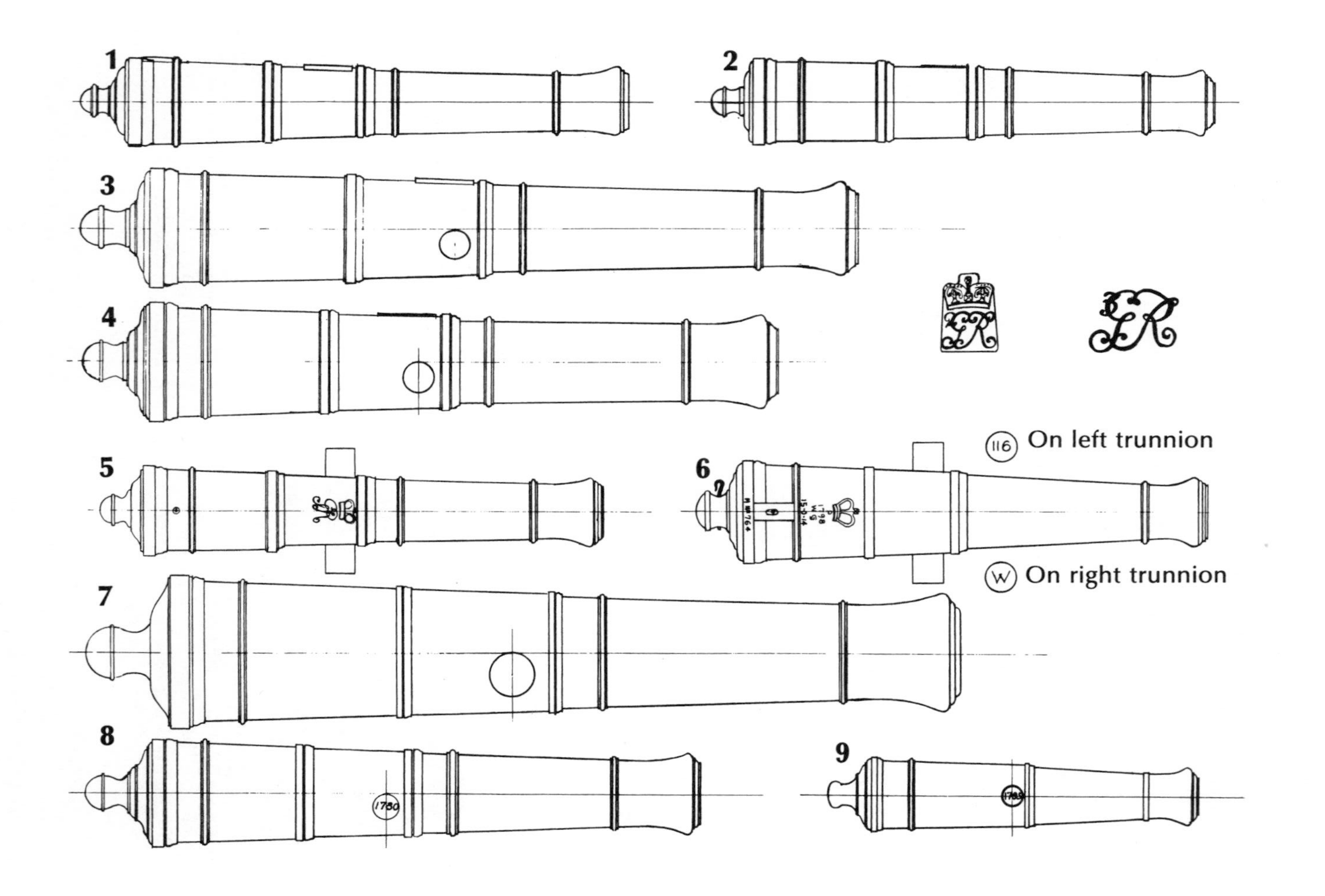
1
2
3
4
5
6
7
8
9
116 On left trunnion
W On right trunnion
1780

Key:

Gun no. 1: A 6-pdr bearing the cipher of George II. Astragal molding on the cascabel knob indicates a date of about 1740. At Fort Ticonderoga.

Gun no. 2: A 6-pdr with the monogram of George III. One of the cannon mounted at Fort Ticonderoga in 1775. At Fort Ticonderoga.

Gun no. 3: A 12-pdr with the monogram of George II. Now mounted in the restored Fort Erie. One of the guns of that fort in the War of 1812.

Gun no. 4: A 12-pdr bored up to an 18-pdr. In Valley Forge Park.

Gun no. 5: This piece has a bore of 4.25" but is smaller than gun no. 6. Said to have been part of the armament of HMS *Augusta* during the American Revolution. At the U.S. Naval Academy, Annapolis.

Gun no. 6: A 6-pdr. One of four cannon around the foot of the monument to the capture of HMS *Macedonian*, described as 18-pdrs of the *Macedonian*'s main battery. Marked WG 1798, this piece probably belonged to the guns purchased for the armament of the early U.S. Navy beginning in 1798. At the U.S. Naval Academy.

Gun no. 7: A 32-pdr of the lower battery of the *Royal George,* which sank in 1782. Part of the collection in the Tower of London.

Gun no. 8: One of a pair of 9-pdrs at Valley Forge. Dated 1780 on one trunnion. While not strictly an Armstrong design, it is apparently American manufactured and copied largely from the Armstrong type.

Gun no. 9: A 4-pdr. Another American-made piece, dated 1795 and marked HF. Though influenced by the Armstrong design, the first and second reinforces have been run together and the muzzle astragal has been simplified. At Crompton, Rhode Island.

The insignia indicating the reign of George II was set in raised letters on a plaque cast on the gun. Since all markings are incised, it is believed that initials were not put on pieces sold abroad, the crown signifying only that the piece had been proofed and met royal requirements. The three pieces similar to no. 6 lack the 6 and P alongside the crown. All three have W on the right trunnion and the numbers 97, 103, and 113 on the left trunnion.

Fig. 34. English and American Cannon of the Armstrong Design, 1736–95. Most of the cannon employed in the two wars between the United States and Britain were the so-called Armstrong design of 1736, which superseded the Rose and Crown type. (Drawing by C. S. Tucker.)

TABLE 10

JOHN MULLER'S PROPOSAL FOR NEW SHIP GUNS

General construction for iron ship guns. Let the length of the piece be 15 diameters of the shot; the diameter of the bore 25 parts of the shot's diameter divided into 24, as before; the distance *AD*, 40 parts; the breech *AC*, 24; the thickness of metal at the vent 24, and half that thickness at the mouth; the diameter and length of the trunnions 24 each, and the rest of the construction the same as before. By the same way of computing as before, we shall find 140 pounds of iron, or a hundred and a quarter, for every pound weight of the shot—supposing that 108 cubic inches of cast iron weigh 29 pounds, according to our table of specific gravities.

Old Pieces			New Pieces		
Caliber (pdr)	*Length (ft-in)*	*Weight (cwt-qrs-lbs)*	*Caliber (pdr)*	*Length (in)*	*Weight (cwt-qrs-lbs)*
3	4-6	7-1-7	3	3-6	3-3-0
4	6-0	12-2-13	6	4-4	7-2-0
6	7-0	17-1-14	9	5-0	11-1-0
9	7-0	12-2-2	12	5-6	15-0-0
12	9-0	32-3-3	18	6-4	22-2-0
18	9-0	41-1-8	24	7-0	30-0-0
24	9-0	48-0-0	32	7-6	40-0-0
32	9-6	53-3-23	42	8-4	52-2-0
42	10-0	55-1-12	48	8-6	60-0-0

Source: John Muller, *A Treatise of Artillery* (London: Printed for John Milan, Whitehall, 1780), 56.

be adopted by the Americans). The largest in common use in the Continental navy were 12-pounders.

Briton Benjamin Robins, who did so much to advance ballistics, had argued in the 1740s for a reduction in both gun length and weight to enable ships to carry larger-caliber ordnance. His ideas were supported by John Muller, a professor of fortifications and artillery at Woolwich who published *A Treatise of Artillery* in 1757. The book went through a number of printings and appeared in America in a pirated edition in 1779. It is thought that this was the only artillery manual available to the colonists during the Revolution and that they adhered more to its precepts than the British did.[9] American adoption of a simpler form for guns and the new practice of placing trunnions on the centerline indicate that Muller did indeed influence American gun design.

In addition to these measures, Muller called for more scientific analysis in gun design and practice, lighter guns, chambers for cannon larger than 24-pounders, and the elimination of bronze in favor of iron. Muller wanted guns to be 140 pounds (1.25 cwt) for every pound of shot in weight and fifteen calibers in length. The resultant saving in weight, he calculated, would allow ships to carry nearly double their caliber of guns.

The actual length of guns of this period was, however, much greater than that proposed by Muller. French regulations of 1766 called for a 6-pounder to be approximately 23 calibers in length, a 36-pounder about 19. British guns of the revolutionary period ranged from 22.9 calibers for a 6-pounder to 17.09 for a 42-pounder. This is based on Muller's calculations of iron ship guns in service at the time his book was written. He gives 7 feet as the length of a 6-pounder and 10 feet for a 42-pounder; 12-, 18-, and 24-pounders were all 9 feet long. It should be pointed out, however, that the same-caliber guns were often made in several lengths (this was particularly true in British service), depending on their use and place in a ship.

When discussing Muller's proposals it is well to remember that he was not trained at sea. In 1807, the American artillerist Louis Tousard quoted an unidentified officer "of rank and character in the American navy" who said that the guns made for frigates such as the *United States* and *Constellation* were too short, although they were longer than 18 calibers. They were easier to load but ran the great risk of injuring the ship's side when discharged obliquely.[10] Founder Samuel Hughes wrote in 1808 that the first short 24-pounders he had cast were 8 feet in length (16.5 calibers) but that all naval officers who saw them felt they were too short. In fact, they were a foot longer than Muller's proposed 24-pounder.

In most respects, ship carriages of the period were similar to iron garrison carriages except that they were made of wood, preferably the best white oak, which was less likely to break and splinter and was considerably lighter than iron. A wooden carriage for a long 24-pounder weighed about 860 pounds, while the same carriage in iron weighed 2,268 pounds. In design, U.S. Navy carriages closely resembled those of the Royal Navy. The wooden parts were the axletrees, arms of axletrees, fore and hind trucks, brackets, transom, stool bed, and quoin. The iron parts included the bed bolt, transom bolt, cap squares, joint bolts, breeching bolts, and loops.

Carriages were built in proportion to the dimensions of a particular gun. As dimensions varied, it was normal practice not to make carriages until guns were delivered. In form, carriages were little changed from their predecessors of the century before. A writer in 1862 noted that the common sea-service truck carriage had "continued in its present form and proportions, without material alteration, for nearly three hundred years."[11] This statement is fairly close to the mark.

Muller explained the process for determining the size of ship and garrison carriages in use in 1748 (see figure 35). On the line *AB,* two points—*C* and *D*—were the distance from the center of the trunnions to the extremity of the breech (that is, three-fourths the length of the gun). From *C* and *D* two lines were drawn at right angles to line *AB*. *EF* (which passed through *C*) equaled the diameter of the second reinforce ring; *GH* (passing through *D*) equaled the diameter of the base ring. Lines drawn through *E* and *G* and *F* and *H* determined the inside width of the carriage.

All carriage dimensions were proportioned to the gun for which they were intended. For example, the brackets of the carriage were 1 shot-diameter in thickness. The distance from *D* to *B* was the length of the cascabel. From *C* to *A* the distance was half the diameter of the trunnions and half the diameter of the fore trucks (later expressed simply as 2 calibers).

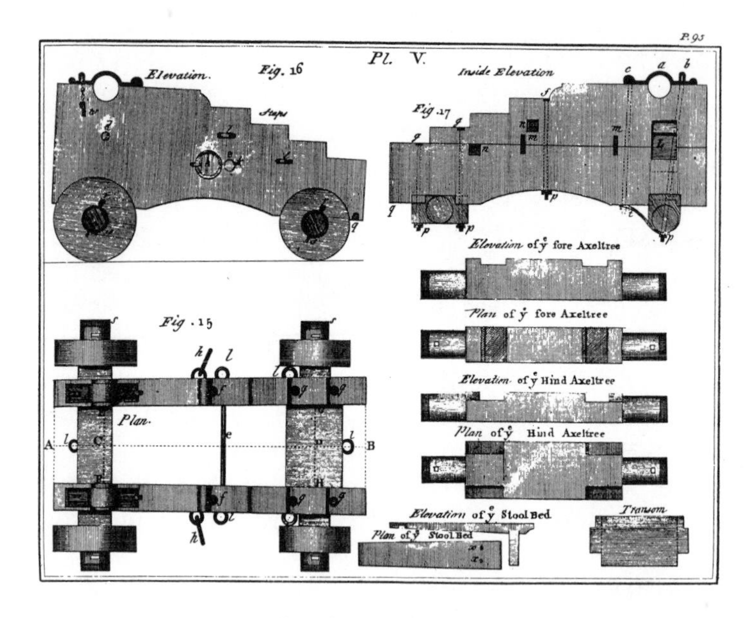

Irons for Ship Carriages

a.	Cap squares	2	m.	Dowel pins	4
b.	Eye bolts	2	n.	Square riveting plates	8
c.	Joint bolts	2	p.	Rings with keys	10
d.	Transom bolt	1	q.	Traversing plates	2
e.	Bed bolt		r.	Linch pins	4
f.	Bracket bolts	2	s.	Axletree hoops	2
g.	Hind axletree bolts	4	t.	Axletree stays	2
h.	Breeching bolts with rings	2	w.	Keys, chains, and staples	2
k.	Burrs	2	x.	Stool bed bolts with riveting plates	2
l.	Loops	6			

Fig. 35. English Ship Carriage of 1748. (From Muller, *A Treatise of Artillery*.)

The trunnion holes were 1 shot-diameter, with the center located at *C,* a quarter of an inch below the top surface of the side pieces. On each side of line *GH,* 6 inches were allowed for the breadth of the axletree, which was always 12 inches. The fore part of the trunnion hole was the centerline for the fore axletree.

The height of the side pieces in front was 4.75 diameters of the shot and half that height behind. The steps, or offsets in the brackets, were each one-eighth the length of the side pieces or, taken together, one-half of the side piece beginning in the rear. The quarter-round, which finished off the steps, was taken from the fore part of the carriage. The steps in the carriage provided a fulcrum for the handspikes elevating or depressing the gun.

The lower part of the brackets was hollowed out in the form of an arch, making them somewhat lighter without reducing their strength. The axletrees were sunk into the side pieces, and a strong piece of timber known as the transom, which was a shot-diameter in breadth and two high, was placed so that the fore part passed through the center of the trunnion holes and thus

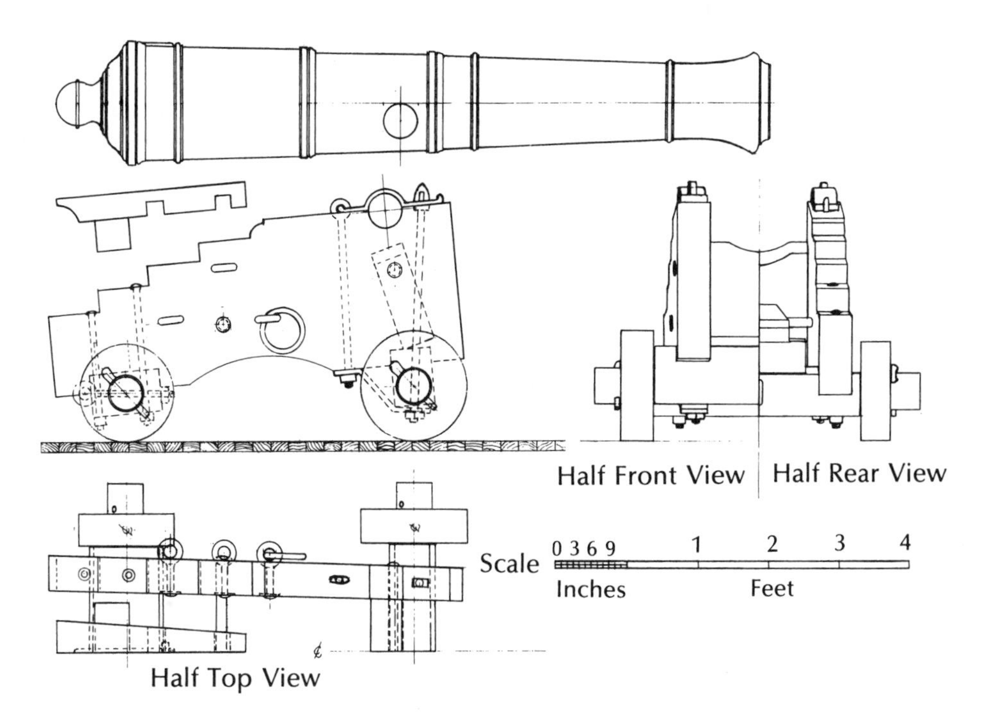

Fig. 36. English 24-Pdr and Ship Carriage, 1775. (After John Robertson, *Treatise of Such Mathematical Instruments as Are Usually Put into a Portable Case* . . . [London, 1775]. Redrawn by C. S. Tucker for "Introduction of Cannon at Sea.")

protected the axletree by 1 inch; the lower edge touched the axletree (Muller advocated placing the transom so that it was directly over the fore axletree and exactly in the middle of the height of the side pieces).

The trucks were always equal in breadth to the side pieces. Usually, the fore trucks were larger than the hind ones by half a diameter. (Muller gave dimensions of 4 bore-diameters for the size of the fore and 3.5 for the hind; others give 3 and 2.5. But as Muller himself noted, "we have observed before, that if the port-holes in ships are made higher or lower, these dimensions must be increased or diminished.")[12]

The metal cap squares were hinged to permit easy removal of the gun. The other end of the bolt holding the cap in place secured the fore axletree against the bracket by means of washers and iron pins. A transom bolt and bed bolt (the latter supporting the stool bed) were riveted over burrs. There were also two ringbolts for breeching and six metal loops for tackles. The one in the breast transom was used for transporting the carriage about the deck. The one at the rear was for the train tackle.

The breeching for a navy gun had a circumference one and a quarter times the diameter of the bore, and it was made of three-stranded hemp. It was three times the length of the gun except in the case of lower-deck guns, where there was more room; then it had three and a third or three and a half as much length. Tackles were one-half the diameter of the bore in circumference and

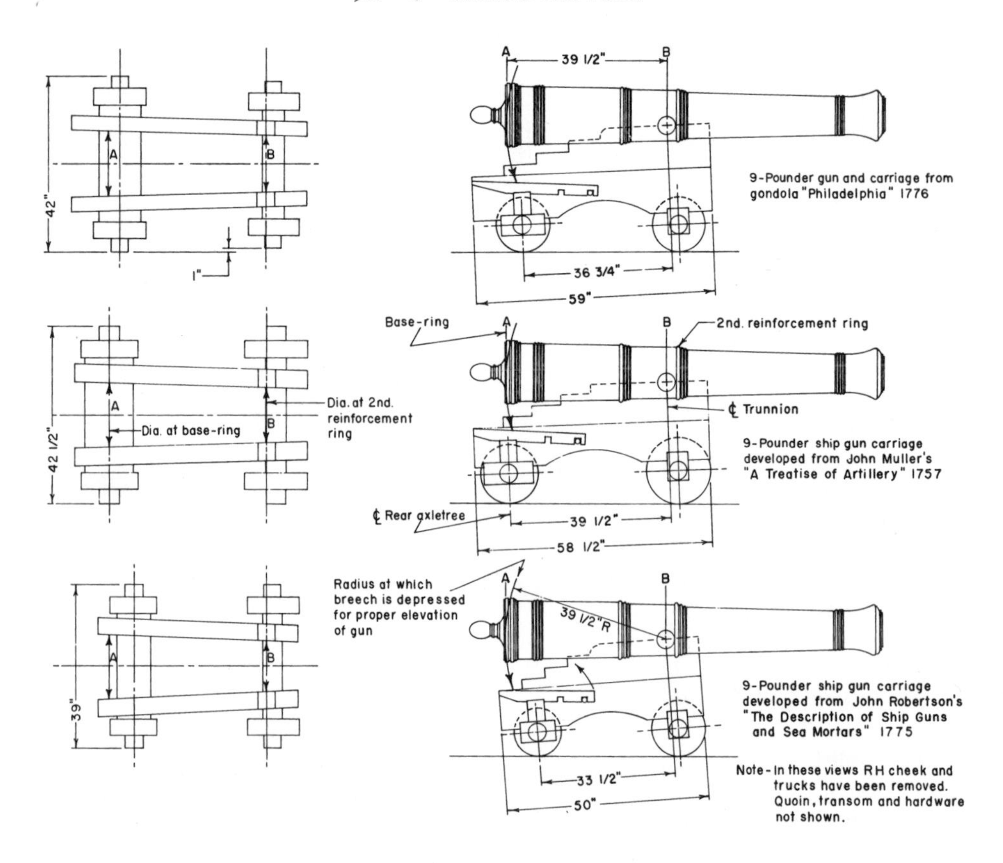

Fig. 37. Truck Carriages by Muller and Robertson, and an American-Made Carriage of the *Philadelphia* during the Revolution. (Drawing by Howard P. Hoffman. Reproduced with the permission of the Smithsonian Institution.)

were made of three-stranded hemp. Side tackles were six times the length of the bore for lower-deck guns and five and a half for others. In 1821, blocks for gun tackles were one and five-sixteenths the diameter of the bore in length for 18- to 42-pounders and one and two-thirds the diameter of the bore for 12-pounders and guns of smaller caliber.

The basic projectile used during the Revolution was solid shot. Shot were cast from soft rather than hard iron, which tended to break up instead of penetrate. Both iron and sand were used for molds in the casting of shot. During the War of 1812 iron molds were specified for shot, but by 1819 a bonus was paid for casting in sand molds and by 1842 the navy specified that shot be cast in sand. Shot cast in sand was more spherical and was free of cavities. Patterns for shot were two hemispheres of polished copper which, by means of a groove in one and a lip on the other, fitted together to form a perfect sphere.

After their casting, and periodically thereafter, shot were inspected. Any cavity exceeding 0.10 inch was grounds for rejection. Shot also had to pass in

TABLE 11

DIMENSIONS OF SHIP AND GARRISON CARRIAGES, 1748*

Nature of the gun	42	32	24	18	12	9	6	3
Width enclosed before	18	18	16.5	15.5	14	13	11.5	9
Width enclosed behind	23.5	23.5	22.5	21.5	19.5	18.5	16.8	12.5
Fore axletree length	57	57	54.5	51.5	45.5	42.5	38.8	32.5
Body length	35.4	36.6	34.9	33.1	29.5	27.5	24.8	19.5
Body height	10.8	10.8	10	10	10	9.5	9	8.5
Body breadth	6.8	6.8	6.8	6	5.5	5.2	5	4
Arms length	10.8	10.2	9.8	9.2	8	7.5	7	6.5
Arms diameter	6.2	6.2	6.2	5.8	5.2	5	4.5	3.5
Hind axletree length	57	57	54	51.5	45.5	42.5	38.8	32.5
Body length	35.4	36.6	34.9	33.1	29.5	27.5	24.8	19.5
Body height	6.8	6.8	6.8	6	5.5	5.2	5	4
Body breadth	12	12	12	12	12	12	12	12
Fore trucks diameter	19	19	18	18	16	16	14	14
Fore trucks breadth	6.5	6	5.5	5	4.5	4	3.5	3
Hind trucks diameter	16	16	16	15	14	14	12	10
Hind trucks breadth	6.5	6	5.5	5	4.5	4	3.5	3
Side pieces height before	26.8	26.2	26	23.6	20	18.8	16	13.6
Side pieces length	78	78	72	69	66	63	60	37.5
Side pieces breadth	6.5	6	5.5	5	4.5	4	3.5	3
Trunnions from the head	8	8	8	8	6.8	6.6	6.6	6

Source: John Muller, *A Treatise of Artillery,* 96.
* All dimensions are given in inches.

all directions through a large gauge ring not less than 4 calibers in length. Less variance was allowed as time went on. In 1845, shot could vary up to 0.060 inch in size, later it was 0.030, and after 1852 it was 0.020. Finally shot was rejected if it was lighter than 1⁄32 of its caliber weight.

Shot were supposed to be lacquered, greased, or painted, and care was taken to ensure that those in the racks (garlands) were always clean. Shot stored below were placed, if possible, where there would be circulating air. Most rust accumulated in shot lockers under the main hatch. When it rained or when the deck was washed down, the shot got wet. It was apparently not unusual to find, on returning from a cruise, shot rusted together. The lack of suitable storage sheds for shot at navy yards was also a problem. Rust damage to shot greatly reduced its accuracy, and large accumulations might actually prevent it from entering the bore of a gun. See figure 38 for an illustration of how just a small accumulation of rust could affect windage.

Shot was supposed to weigh its designated amount, but this was not always the case. During the War of 1812, American shot was lighter than its British counterpart probably because of the density of the iron. In 1856, the average weight of a 32-pounder shot was 32.5 pounds, while that of a 64-pounder was 63.75. (For the dimensions and weight of shot, see table 36.)

Hot shot were also employed at sea, for wooden sailing ships were

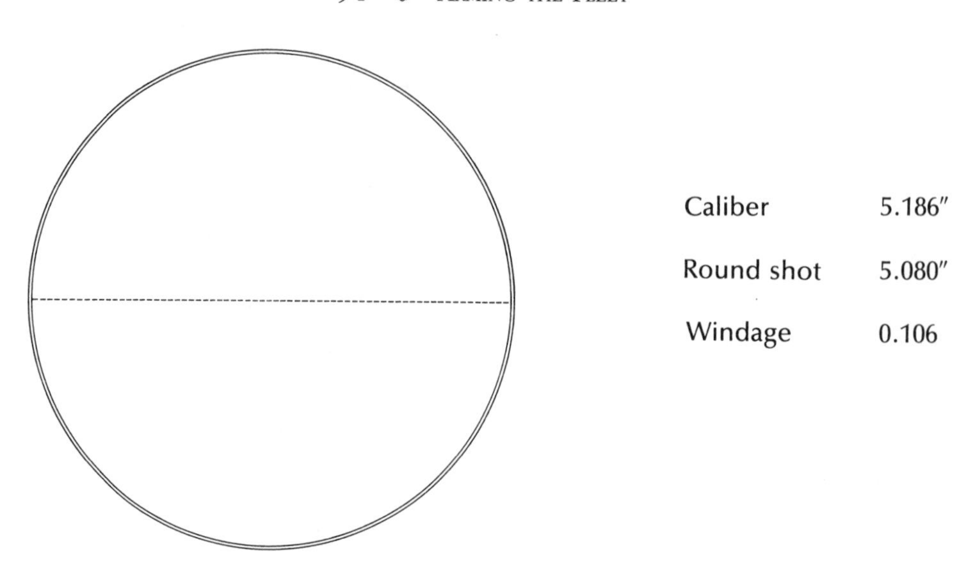

Fig. 38. A Round Shot for an 18-Pdr Carronade. This is half size.

especially vulnerable to it. The shot was heated red-hot (white heat might turn it too brittle). The powder charge, contained in a strong flannel cartridge with no holes, was loaded, and then a tight, dry wad of hay 1 caliber in length was put in. This was followed by a tight clay wad or a wet hay wad with the water squeezed out. The hot shot was then loaded by means of a carrier, and the gun was fired. If it was to be fired depressed, another tight wet wad was rammed in to hold the shot in place. If two wads were used—one dry and the other damp—there was no danger of the shot causing ignition and the gun could be pointed before it was fired.

The gun might also be double-shotted, that is, fired with an ordinary shot followed by a hot shot. Hot shot required a reduced powder charge, usually one-quarter to one-sixth the weight of the ball. This enabled it to penetrate the enemy hull 10 to 12 inches (if it penetrated farther, there would not be sufficient air for burning).

Bar and chain shot, also known as dismantling shot, were used at sea from early times. They were valuable against the rigging of enemy ships, particularly in chase. Such shot were so inaccurate, however, that they were often employed with little or no effect, as in the engagement between the *Constitution* and the *Java* in the War of 1812.

Double-headed shot (bar shot or stang balls) consisted of two solid hemispheres or two round shot connected by a bar from 8 to 14 inches long. Chain shot might be two solid hemispheres or two round shot connected by a chain 8 to 12 inches or more in length. There were many other types of shot, including expanding and star shot. The latter was fired from the *President* when she was being chased by HMS *Endymion* in the War of 1812. One hit

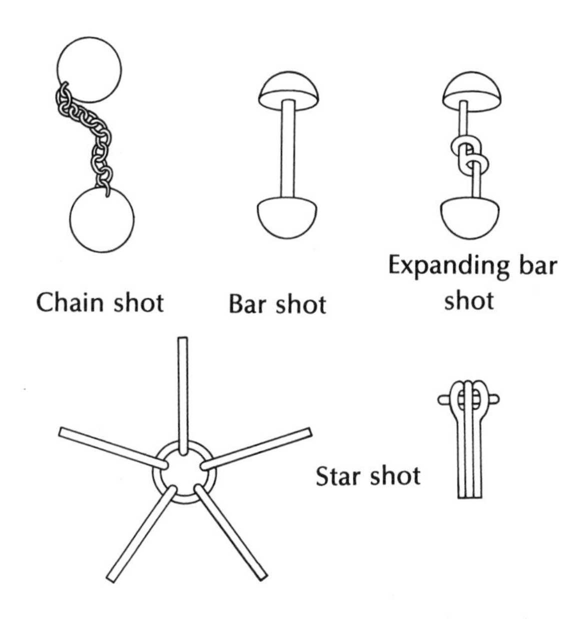

Fig. 39. Chain, Bar, Expanding Bar, and Star Shot.

took away a substantial portion of the foresail of the British vessel. Double-headed shot had about two-thirds the range of round shot fired at the same elevation and charge.

In 1800, bar shot might form 25 percent of the ammunition aboard ship, round shot 50 percent, and grapeshot 25 percent. Bar and chain shot declined in use, however, so that by 1850 they and their offspring were no longer manufactured for the U.S. Navy.

Case shot, known as canister or common case, was an improvement over what was variously called langrel, langridge, and langrage (the U.S. Navy term)—that is, stones, nails, bolts, flints, or bits of scrap fired from cannon. Canister shot consisted of a cylinder or case of iron or tin with tops and bottoms of wood or iron. The cylinder was packed with pieces of small shot, bullets of different sizes, loose iron, or pebbles. William James, a contemporary British writer, complained that in the War of 1812 the *Chesapeake* unfairly employed canister shot made up of jagged pieces of iron, broken gunlocks, and copper nails.[13] The interstices were filled with shavings or sawdust. Canister shot produced a denser pattern than grape; it was intended for use against massed troops on land or in boats and to destroy the rigging of ships. It was effective only at short ranges, not exceeding 300 to 500 yards, owing to the rapid dispersion and lightness of the cylinder's contents. At short range, canister shot was more effective than any other projectile, including grape. Particularly favored for the carronade, it might comprise half of that gun's projectiles (the other half being round shot).

Grapeshot, which appeared as early as the fourteenth century, was also

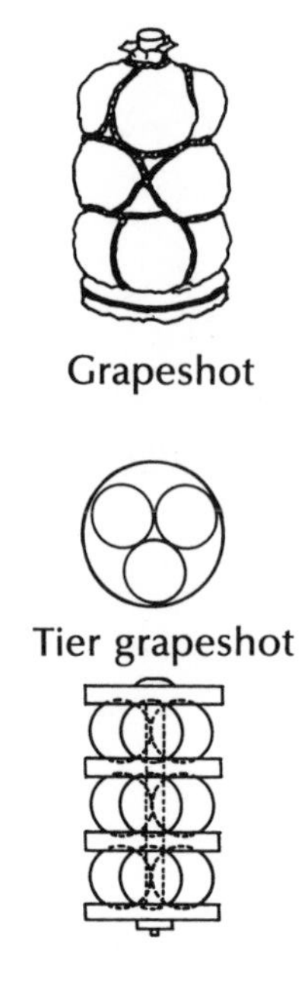

Fig. 40. Grapeshot and Tier Grapeshot.

used at sea during the Revolution. At first it was merely a canvas cartridge, sack, or net containing small balls. Later, it consisted of an iron plate through the center of which passed an iron spindle, the whole being known as a stool. Around the stool were placed nine small round shot enclosed in a canvas bag, which was closed with a strong line. These were later referred to as quilted shot. Individual shot varied according to the size of the gun and might be anything up to 3 or 4 pounds in weight. The whole, however, weighed about the same as a single round shot for the gun. The name grapeshot derived from the finished article, which resembled a bunch of grapes. The shock of the gun's discharge broke the cloth and the balls scattered, much like ammunition from a modern shotgun. Later grapeshot was formed as tier shot.

Grapeshot was not much used at sea except against boats or to sweep exposed decks or beaches, but it could be effective against rigging. Although it carried farther than langridge or canister, grapeshot was employed only at short ranges, not more than 500 yards.

Explosive and incendiary shell were not fired from seaborne long guns during the Revolution.

More than one shot could be fired at the same time, but double-shotting strained the gun and its carriage and breeching and so was not employed without express orders from the captain. If double-shotted, a gun was fired with a reduced charge of powder. A wad might be placed between the two shot to prevent one shot from striking the other and breaking. Later it was

TABLE 12

NUMBER AND TYPE OF SHOT IN THE GRAPE STAND, C. 1815–50

Gun	*Individual Grape Shot (oz)*	*Number*
4-pdr	6	9
6-pdr	8	9
9-pdr	13	9
12-pdr	16	9
18-pdr	24	9
24-pdr	32	9
32-pdr	48	9
42-pdr	64	9

Sources: William Falconer and William Burney, *A New Universal Dictionary of the Marine* (London: T. Cadell and W. Davis, 1815), 168; William Duane, *A Military Dictionary* (Philadelphia: William Duane, 1810), 636; and Atkinson and Clarke, *The Naval Pocket Gunner* (London: Robert Scholey, 1814), 154.

thought that the shot would stay together in flight if there was no wad between them.

Double shot could be used against boats or troops on shore, especially in ricochet, but fired this way it was less accurate than a single shot and had considerably less velocity. While a 32-pounder double shot could penetrate 30 inches of oak from a range of up to 100 yards, at 500 yards the double shot penetrated only 18 inches. Double shot was recommended "only when near, as the shot generally separate so widely after leaving the guns that the chance of their striking the object is small." For carronades, it was to be used only "where the vessels are nearly in contact."[14]

Increased recoil slowed the job of servicing the gun. Whereas a 32-pounder at 2 degrees' elevation with a powder charge of one-third and one shot would recoil, without breeching, 11 feet, one with the same powder charge but two shot would recoil 19 feet 6 inches, nearly double the distance.

Double shot usually consisted of two round shot or round and grapeshot together, the round being loaded first. Triple-shotting a gun was even less efficient than double-shotting. It was recommended for close action and the first broadside only.

The allowances of shot type and number per gun varied greatly, depending on the length of time and purpose for which the vessel was at sea. A general figure in peacetime for the U.S. Navy before the advent of shell was 100 rounds per gun, 75 of them in ordinary round shot. This figure would be about 30 percent higher in wartime, 40 percent if the ship was on an extended cruise far from sources of supply. On 8 August 1798, ordnance supplies ordered for the 18-gun brig *Norfolk* commissioned that year included eighteen 6-pounders, 1,350 round shot (75 per gun), and 450 stands of grape (25 per gun). In April 1799, among the supplies for the frigate *John Adams,* armed with twenty-four 12-pounders, were 1,600 round shot, 400 stands of grape, and 400 double-headed shot.

Fig. 41. A 1-Pdr Swivel Recovered from a British Ship of the Revolutionary War off Yorktown. (Courtesy of the Colonial Historical Park, Yorktown.)

In addition to the larger long pieces, swivel guns were mounted on American vessels. In lighter vessels, these small-bore cannon sat on an oarlock-shaped pivot set in a socket on upright timbers along the rail. In larger vessels, they were mounted in the tops. The trunnions were retained in an iron crotch, the lower end of which terminated in a cylindrical pivot resting in the socket. The socket was bored in a strong piece of oak reinforced by iron hoops to help it sustain recoil. An iron handle attached to the cascabel allowed the gun to be swiveled in any direction.

In the tops of a ship, swivels were frequently loaded with musket balls to fire down on the upper decks of an enemy vessel at close quarters. Being small and primarily employed as "man killers," swivels were never listed as guns in figuring the armament of a ship. Small howitzers were likewise excluded from this designation.

Swivels came in even less standardized form than cannon. They ranged in size from a heavy musket to a small cannon. (An example of the latter is the one surviving from ten said to have been on board the gondola *Philadelphia* in Arnold's Lake Champlain fleet. It is shaped like a cannon and fired a 0.75-pound ball.) In their fixed mounts swivels could not sustain great recoil and so had to be limited in size. Usually they were of the heavier, cannon type, and the loose shot they fired were effective against personnel at close range. Swivels, particularly favored for early colonial merchant ships, were also popular in vessels on the Great Lakes. In general, they varied from 34 to 36 inches in length, from 1.5 to 1.75 inches in bore, and threw shot weighing 0.5 to 0.75 pound.

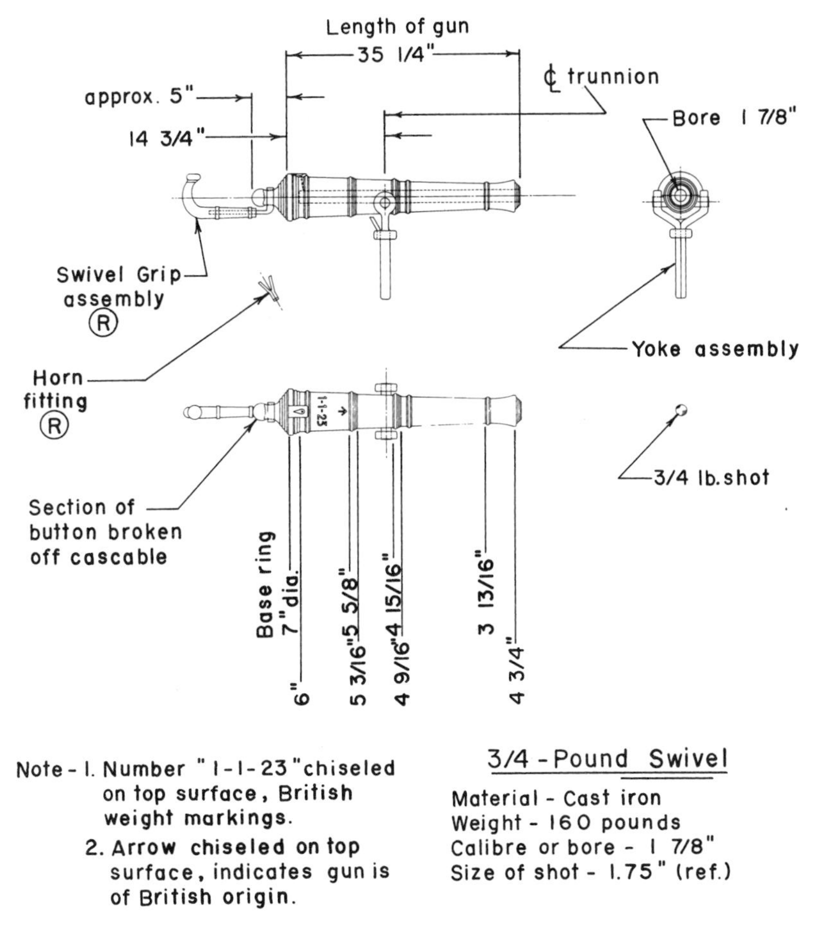

Fig. 42. A ¾-Pdr Swivel from the *Philadelphia*. (Drawing by Howard Hoffman. Reproduced with the permission of the Smithsonian Institution.)

In the American navy, light pieces were usually known as coehorns. The coehorn mortar was named for Dutch artillerist Baron von Coehorne, credited with "inventing" it in 1693. Light enough to be carried by two men, the coehorn had a 4.52-inch bore and fired a 12-pound ball as far as 1,200 yards. There was also at least one 24-pounder model of 1838. *Coehorn* seems to have been a generic term for light howitzers, swivels, and mortars—in short, any ordnance that could be transported by one or two men.[15] Such light pieces were mounted in the tops of larger vessels.

As for hand weapons, crews on board American fighting ships of the Revolution were armed with muskets, pikes, pistols, cutlasses, tomahawks, boarding pikes, and hand grenades.

At the end of the Revolution America's army and navy were disbanded. Naval personnel were dismissed and the few ships remaining were sold. (The

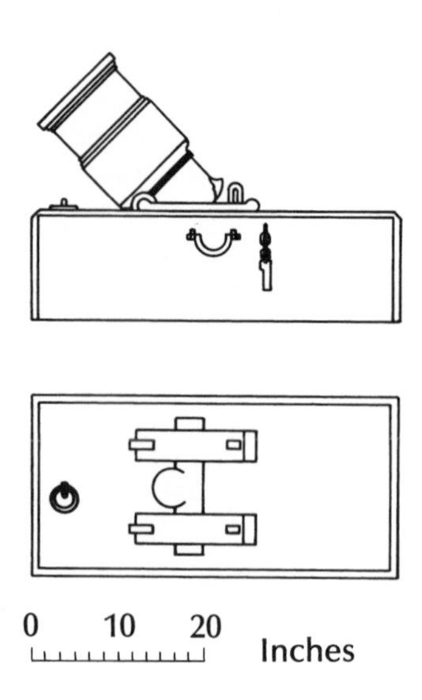

Fig. 43. Coehorn Mortar. (After Muller, *A Treatise of Artillery.*)

last, the *Alliance,* was auctioned off in 1785.) This was owing to several factors, including the public's pacific mood, its distrust of the military and naval establishments, and lack of money. But disbanding the navy did not halt overseas trade. Soon merchantmen sailing under the flag of the United States were carrying substantial cargoes to distant seas, including the Mediterranean, where numbers of them were seized by ships from the Barbary States. Particularly active were vessels belonging to the dey of Algiers, who had declared war on the United States in 1785. Indignation steadily grew in the United States, and pressure, both public and financial, mounted for the creation of a navy to protect American trade. When the federal government was finally established in 1789, the Barbary pirates were a matter of immediate concern.

By late 1793, Algerian corsairs were seizing American merchant vessels in the Atlantic as well as the Mediterranean. Finally, on 27 March 1794, a bill was signed providing for the construction, equipping, and manning of six frigates. In effect, this action created the U.S. Navy. The frigates were the *Constitution, United States, Constellation, Congress, President,* and *Chesapeake.*

Construction of the frigates was so slow that peace was concluded with Algiers (1795) before even one had been launched. Ultimately, all were completed—the *United States, Constitution,* and *Constellation* in 1797, the *Chesapeake* in 1799, and the *Congress* and *President* in 1800.

The six frigates, as constructor Joshua Humphreys put it, "should combine such qualities of strength, durability, and swiftness of sailing, and force, as to render them superior to any frigate belonging to the European Powers."[16] Humphreys took full advantage of the fact that Congress had authorized frigates without giving specifications. As constructed, the new frigates were larger than their British counterparts. After her defeat by the *President,* HMS *Macedonian* was measured and found to be 10 feet shorter (but with 8 inches more in beam) than her American captor. Both ships, however, had the same number of gun ports, fifteen to a side. The *Constitution* was 12 to 15 feet longer than the *Guerriere* and had slightly more beam.

The American frigates also carried a much heavier battery than their British counterparts, which relied principally on the long 18-pounder. The original plan of armament for the forty-fours called for thirty long 32-pounders on the main (gun) deck and from twenty to twenty-two long 12-pounders on the quarterdeck and forecastle. Two long 24-pounders, chase guns, were also to be mounted on the forecastle. The thirty-sixes were to have twenty-eight 24-pounders on their main (gun) decks and eighteen to twenty 12-pounders on the upper decks. On 19 December 1794, the secretary of war stated that gun deck armament was to be thirty 24-pounders for the forty-fours and twenty-eight 24-pounders for the thirty-sixes. He did not specify numbers for the other guns, but the ordnance was to be a mix of 12-pounders and bronze howitzers.

These armaments were not realized, for the growing popularity of the carronade led to its inclusion in place of the long 12-pounders, and individual captains had their own ideas about how to arm their ships. There was, furthermore, no uniformity of cannon type. The guns differed in model, weight, and dimensions. Some were British, some had been intended for land fortifications, and some were of what was intended to be the standard design.

Official armament for the forty-fours finally evolved into thirty long 24-pounders on the main deck and twenty to twenty-two 42-pounder carronades on the upper deck. The thirty-sixes were to carry twenty-eight long 18-pounders on the main deck and twenty 32-pounder carronades on the upper decks.

Again, there was variance and change. The 42-pounder carronades were found too heavy for the *Constitution* and so were replaced with 32-pounders. And the *Constellation* initially carried 12-pounder cannon rather than carronades. This frigate's changes of armament illustrate the regularity with which batteries could alter aboard the frigates. During the Quasi-War with France, when she captured the *Insurgente,* the American frigate had twenty-eight short 24-pounders manufactured by Cecil Furnace on her main deck and twenty 12-pounder carronades on the quarterdeck and forecastle. After this action, her armament was changed to twenty-eight 18-pounders in the main deck battery and twelve 12-pounders and ten 24-pounder carronades on the quarterdeck and forecastle—in all, fifty guns with 888 pounds of shot. The *Insurgente,* meanwhile, became part of the U.S. Navy and continued to use her French-manufactured armament, necessitating the casting, in the summer of 1799, of different-sized round and bar shot for her guns.

In addition to their broadside batteries, the frigates carried long chase guns on their forecastles as well as some howitzers. Both the thirty-sixes and

TABLE 13

Military Stores for Frigates, 1797

On 12 June 1797, the secretary of war wrote to Samuel Hodgdon, intendant of military stores, listing the following as requisite for the frigates *United States, Constitution,* and *Constellation,* all launched that year:

300	muskets with bayonet
100	d° sent to Baltimore May 4
1,797	making 400 stand
250	pair pistols
300	boarding axes
550	cutlasses
44	blunderbusses
300	boarding pikes with staffs
120	battle lanterns
24	signal d° no. 1
24	signal d° no. 2
6	dozen of tin d°
1½	dozen dark d°
670	barrels of cannon powder
10,000	round shot for 24-pounders
1,600	chain and double-headed shot for 24-pounders
2,200	stools for grape and cannister shot for 24-pounders
4,600	round shot for 12-pounders
600	hand grenades
100	rounds of musket and pistol balls
12	speaking trumpets
15	tons of sheet lead
18	howitzers, 8 inch or 4- to 6-pounders
A set of implements for each gun	
30	barrels of powder for muskets and pistols

Source: U.S., Navy Department, *Naval Documents Related to the United States Wars with the Barbary Powers.* Vol. 1, *Naval Operations Including Diplomatic Background from 1785 Through 1801* (Washington, D.C.: U.S. Government Printing Office, 1939), 203.

forty-fours had more ports than guns. The smaller frigates could have mounted fifty-six guns and the larger ones as many as sixty, although there is no evidence this was ever attempted; some of the forty-fours did mount as many as fifty-six guns on occasion.

Armament of the new American frigates was certainly more innovative than that of their British counterparts. While the Americans had 24-pounders on their gun decks, the British had only 18-pounders. Employing 24-pounders as the main armament of frigates was at the time largely experimental. British ship captains had concluded that 24-pounders were too heavy for frigates and in any case could not be worked as easily as 18-pounders. When Captain Stephen Decatur of the *United States* entertained Captain Carden of HMS *Macedonian,* Carden "particularly pointed out the inefficiency of the 24-pounders on the main deck of the *United States,* and said that they could not be handled with ease and rapidity in battle, and that long 18-pounders

... were as heavy as a frigate ought to carry."[17] Later, the *Macedonian* would experience *United States'* power at first hand. In this respect, the British had been misled at least in part by trials conducted at Sutton Heath in 1810 comparing a long 24-pounder of 9 feet 6 inches, a long 18-pounder of the same length, and a short 24-pounder of 6 feet 6 inches. It was found that long 18-pounders had the greatest range, and this influenced the British decision to retain them.

Some British criticism of American frigate batteries was indeed justified. The *United States, Constitution,* and *President* were all overburdened, a fact that became apparent in their first battles. At the beginning of the War of 1812, the *Constitution* carried fifty-five guns with a weight of shot of 1,401 pounds; before the end of the war, her main armament was reduced to fifty-one guns. At the time of her engagement with the *Macedonian,* the *United States* mounted fifty-four guns. When she returned to port six of her guns were landed, but this was not enough to prevent her too from becoming hogged, which may have been why she was overtaken and captured by a British squadron in 1815.

Naval construction continued in fits and starts, augmenting as tensions mounted with both France and Britain. The French had been angered by Jay's Treaty of 1794, which improved trade relations between the United States and Great Britain at their expense, and they vented their displeasure by seizing American merchant vessels. Secretary of State Timothy Pickering reported in June 1797 that the French had taken 316 American vessels in the preceding twelve months.

President John Adams and the Federalists adopted a policy of armed neutrality toward France. The Quasi-War necessitated changes in the navy. In 1798 the Navy Department was made a separate entity, free from War Department control. Under its capable first secretary, Benjamin Stoddert (1798–1801), and with the help of Commodore John Barry, a major building program was carried out and the navy was made into a small but effective fighting force.

All six frigates in the 1794 program were completed by 1800. Five others, all considered very good ships, were built by public subscription: the *New York* (thirty-six guns), *Philadelphia* (thirty-six), *Essex* (thirty-two), *Boston* (twenty-eight), and *John Adams* (twenty-eight). Smaller vessels were also acquired and converted to warships for the navy. The federal government placed great reliance on privateers. A report to Congress from Secretary of State Timothy Pickering on 1 March 1799 listed 365 commissioned privateers with 6,847 men and 2,727 guns.

By the end of 1798 there were fourteen U.S. Navy vessels at sea. In June of that year, the *Delaware* captured the French schooner *Croyable,* a 20-gun ex-merchant ship mounting sixteen 9- and eight 6-pounders. She was the first French vessel ever taken by a U.S. Navy ship. In February 1799, the *Constellation* captured the *Insurgente.* There were many other captures of

TABLE 14

Dimensions for a 9-Pounder, c. 1798

	Inches
Overall length	73.0
Diameter at the breech ring	15.25
Diameter before the trunnions	11.75
Length of the cannon from the back part of the breech ring to the center of the trunnions	30.5
Length from the breech ring to the extremity of the breech ball	8.8
Diameter of the trunnions	4.35

Source: J. Fox Papers, cited in U.S., Navy Department, *Naval Documents Related to the United States Wars with the Barbary Powers.* Vol. 3, *Naval Operations Including Diplomatic Background from September 1803 through March 1804* (Washington, D.C.: U.S. Government Printing Office, 1941), 204. The same dimensions, with the omission of the overall length of the guns, are contained in a Navy Department letter of 22 December 1978 from the secretary of the navy to Robert Gilmore, "Chairman of the Committee, Baltimore," and are noted as being those for the 9-pounder cannon intended for the two ships under his direction. The numbers were supplied so that carriages might be made for the guns. Dimensions of the 6-pounder cannon were to be given later (National Archives, Record Group 45, Letter Book, p. 447).

French vessels by U.S. Navy ships, while the *Retaliation,* a 14-gun schooner, was the only U.S. Navy vessel captured by the French (she was taken by two frigates).

In September 1800 a convention restored peace between the United States and France. The Quasi-War nonetheless provided a strong impetus to expand the U.S. Navy. As early as 1797, Secretary Stoddert had advocated the construction of 74-gun ships. In 1799, he recommended building twelve seventy-fours and maintaining twelve frigates and twenty to thirty smaller vessels.

Congress responded in February 1799 by appropriating $1,000,000 to build six seventy-fours and procure and arm six 18-gun sloops of war. Lumber was gathered for the frames, and by January 1801, $33,000 had been spent on cannon for these vessels. With the exception of the 74-gun *America* constructed during the Revolution, these would have been the largest ships yet built in the United States.

Stoddert decided to build the six ships in as many different places as possible. This led to the creation of the navy yard at Washington in 1800, the first belonging to the Navy Department. One seventy-four was to be built there. Another navy yard was constructed at Gosport, Virginia. The deed for the property that the federal government had rented since 1794 was secured in 1801. A yard at Portsmouth, New Hampshire, was acquired in 1800, and the ones at Philadelphia, Boston, and Brooklyn were acquired in 1801.

The 74-gun ships of the line authorized in 1799 were never built, but their armament was originally to have consisted of twenty-eight 32-pounders on the gun deck, thirty 24-pounders on the upper deck, twelve 9-pounders on the quarterdeck, and four more of the latter on the forecastle. Later, it was decided to make the armament all 32-pounders, and so the plans were changed.

TABLE 15

DIMENSIONS FOR THE ORDNANCE OF SEVENTY-FOURS

Size	*Length (shot-diameters)*	*Length (in)*	*Weight (cwt)*
9-pdr	18	75.00	18
18-pdr	22	116.43	40
32-pdr	18	115.38	60
Changed, as follows:			
9-pdr	18	75.00	18
18-pdr	18	95.26	36
32-pdr	18	115.38	64

Source: Tousard, *American Artillerist's Companion,* vol. 1 (Philadelphia: C. and A. Conrad, 1809), 193.

Draughts for these seventy-fours survive, and if they had been built it probably would have been found that an all-32-gun armament was too heavy. Even with a reduced battery, however, they "would have been among the most powerful ships of their class in the world," and "either in commission or ready for fitting out, their existence might have been sufficient to prevent the events that finally led to the War of 1812."[18]

In 1809, Tousard gave the original dimensions of the guns for the ships. He felt, in view of French practice, that the guns were too light as well as too short.[19]

Despite the fact that the 74-gun ships were not built, Stoddert accomplished a great deal during his tenure as secretary of the navy. Not only were U.S. navy yards established, but by September 1800, the navy had grown from twenty-four to thirty-five ships plus fifteen revenue cutters and galleys. These were manned by 7,600 men and carried 1,044 guns. The force captured eighty-four French ships and recaptured more than twice that number of American ships. Despite such successes, seizures of American merchantmen continued; the U.S. Navy was still not large enough.

Nevertheless, at the end of the Quasi-War in September 1800 the navy was considerably reduced in size. In January 1801, Secretary Stoddert recommended to Congress that the peacetime navy include thirteen frigates and the six seventy-fours that had been authorized in 1799. Instead, Congress authorized thirteen frigates—only six of them were to be kept on active duty—and suspended work on the seventy-fours. Vessels were sold as merchantmen and all naval contractors were discharged. Most of the remaining frigates were dismantled and placed in ordinary, where they soon deteriorated.

It was thus ironic that President Thomas Jefferson, so committed to retrenchment in naval expenditures, would now have to fight a naval war. Depredations by all of the north African states, notably Tripoli, against American merchant shipping continued despite treaties and eventually resulted in the Tripolitan War. The conflict caught the U.S. navy without sufficient vessels for coastal operations. Seven small 14- to 16-gun vessels were

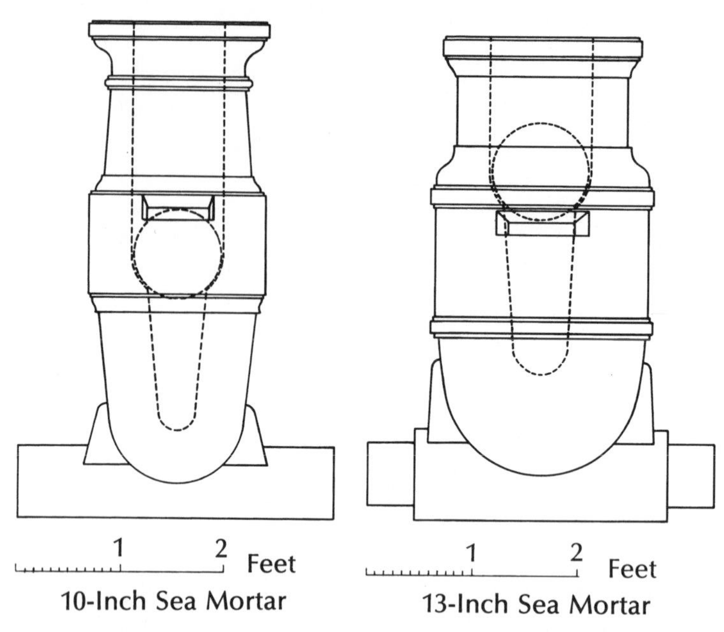

Fig. 44. Ten- and 13-Inch Sea Mortars. (After drawings by William Rudyerd, c. 1793, in Rudyerd, *A Course of Artillery at the Royal Military Academy* [Ottawa, Ontario, 1970].)

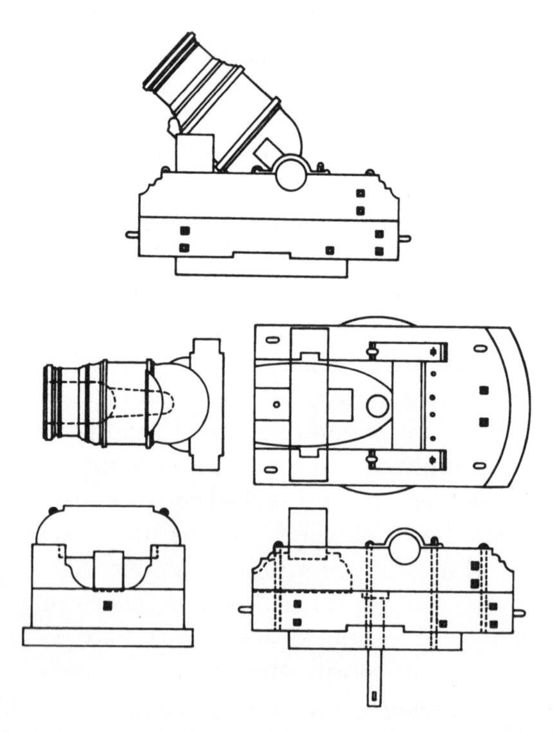

Fig. 45. A 13-Inch Sea Mortar Bed. (After a drawing in National Archives, Record Group 74.)

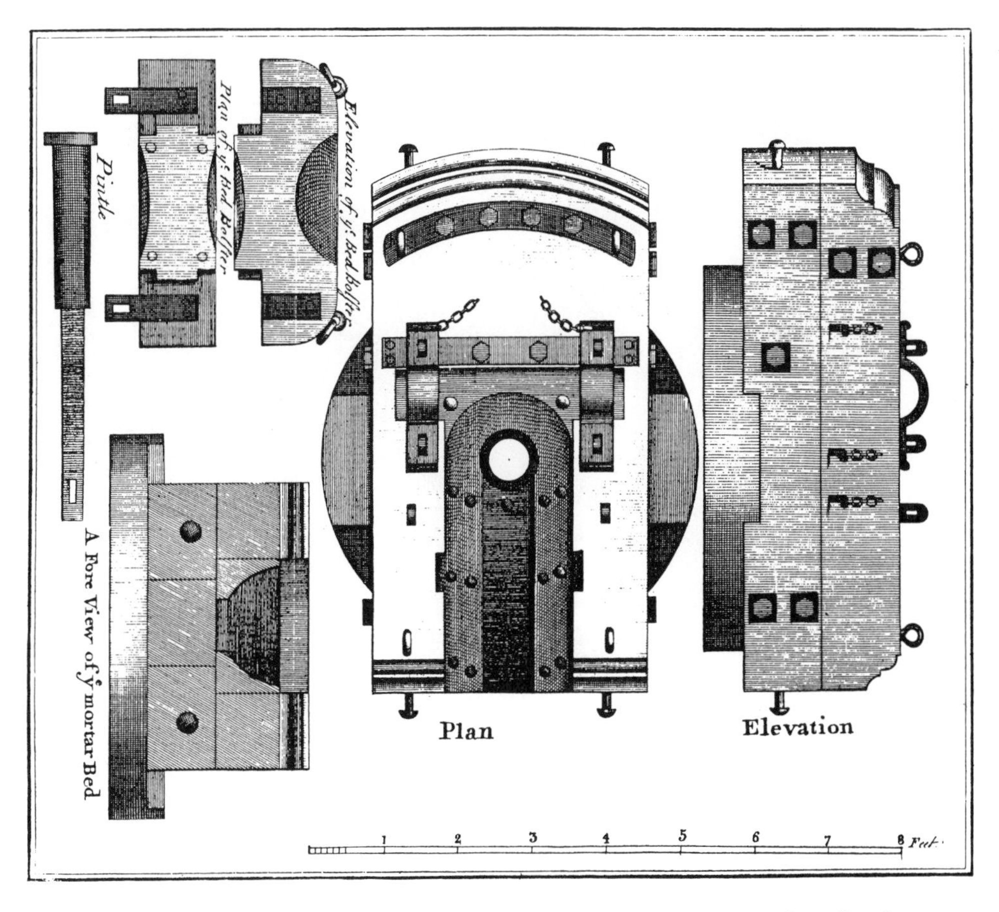

Fig. 46. A 10-Inch Sea Mortar Bed. (From Muller, *A Treatise of Artillery*.)

built or purchased for navy use. Gunboats were also in short supply; the navy borrowed six from Naples for operations against Tripoli, along with two bomb vessels carrying one 13-inch mortar each.

Guns for shore bombardment were also lacking. In the spring of 1805, the navy obtained on loan and purchase from the army one bronze and one iron 13-inch mortar, two bronze 8-inch howitzers, two bronze 5.5-inch howitzers, and a quantity of shells and fuses.

Mortars were short, large-caliber weapons (3 to 4 calibers in length). Sea mortars, usually heavier than those on land, were fixed on a strong wooden bed usually at an elevation of 45 degrees. The bed turned on a vertical axis. The powder charge was considerably less than that for long guns; so too was windage, only 1⁄60 the bore in 1815. Mortar range was most commonly altered by reducing or increasing the charge, since most mortars were fixed in elevation. The shell was loaded by means of hooks with the fuse facing outward toward the muzzle.

The British and U.S. navies employed only two sizes of mortar in their

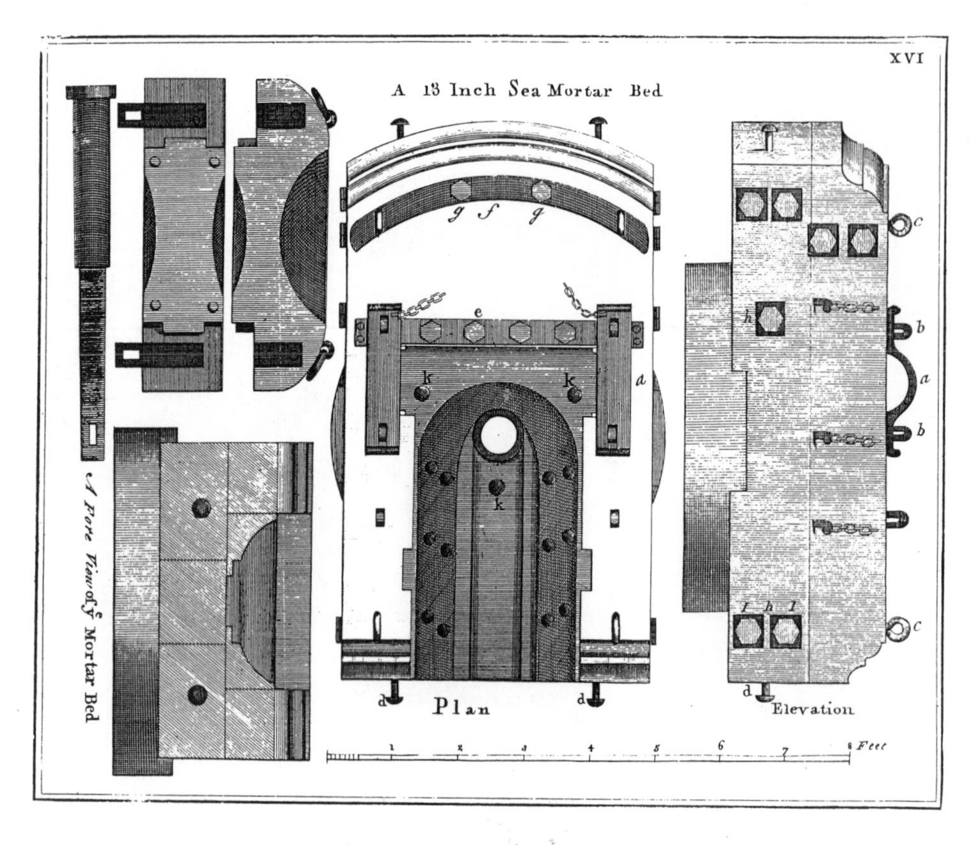

Fig. 47. A 13-Inch Sea Mortar Bed. (From Muller, *A Treatise of Artillery*.)

bomb vessels, 10 and 13 inches, both with chambers. The exact form and caliber of American sea service mortars of the early nineteenth century is unknown, but it is believed they were of British design.

As early as 1803, two 10-inch iron mortars were sent to the Mediterranean as ballast for two brigs. The 10-inch mortar weighed approximately 34 cwt (3,808 pounds) and threw a shell of about 86 pounds. With a charge of 5 pounds 8 ounces, at 21 degrees' elevation, its range was 2,335 to 2,510 yards. Extreme range with a charge of 9 pounds 8 ounces was 4,000 yards.

Two mortars (size unspecified) were also ordered in Britain in November 1805. These arrived at Boston on 6 October 1806, but the bomb ketches for which they were intended, the *Spitfire* and *Vengeance,* had sailed from the port four days before. They were probably armed with the two 13-inch mortars with beds borrowed from the War Department in March 1805. A letter of 16 May 1806 from Preble to the secretary of the navy stated that the bomb vessels *Etna* and *Vesuvius* were each to mount, in addition to their other ordnance, one 13-inch iron English mortar. This was an especially formidable

TABLE 16

DIMENSIONS OF SEA MORTAR BEDS, 1780*

	13-In Mortar	*10-In Mortar*
Diameter of bore	13.0	10.0
Length of bed	94.0	94.0
Breadth of bed	54.0	47.0
Height of bed	27.0	23.0
Pintle hole from fore end	39.0	32.0
Diameter of pintle hole	6.5	6.5
Trunnions from fore end	46.0	42.5
Diameter of trunnion holes	10.0	8.0
Depth of trunnion holes	8.0	5.0
Diameter of circular bed	59.0	59.0
Height of circular bed	8.0	6.0
Distance to bed bolster	15.0	16.0
Depth of cavity	15.0	12.0
Cavity opening above	30.0	21.0
Bed bolster length	53.0	44.0
Length below bed bolster	29.0	2.1
Bed bolster height	16.0	17.0
Bed bolster breadth	14.0	12.0

Source: John Muller, *A Treatise of Artillery* (London: Printed for John Milan, Whitehall, 1780), 123.
* Dimensions given in inches.

weapon. It weighed 5 tons and was capable of throwing a 196-pound shell as far as 4,200 yards with its maximum powder charge of 20 pounds. The flight took 31 seconds.

Howitzers were intermediary weapons, between cannon and mortars. Whereas cannon were at least 12 calibers in length and designed to project shot and later shell the longest possible distance in a relatively flat trajectory, howitzers were short guns of 5 to 10 calibers designed for medium range. Their trunnions rested on the centerline of the bore. Howitzers were usually bronze and had chambers. Their carriages allowed greater elevation than cannon.

Paul Revere may have been the first to cast bronze howitzers for the U.S. Navy. In November 1794, Henry Knox informed Revere that he had asked the Treasury Department to contract with him for six bronze carronades on the pattern of those in the French frigate *Concorde.* If cast, these would not have been carronades but rather what the French called *obusiers de vaisseaux* (ship howitzers), all bronze.

In 1795, Revere cast ten bronze 8-inch howitzers on a War Department contract, as did James Byers of Springfield, Massachusetts. Six of Revere's howitzers were delivered to Samuel Nicholson for use in the frigate *Constitution.* These weighed approximately 1,700 pounds each. Nicholson had trouble mounting them, however, and they may have spent the length of a

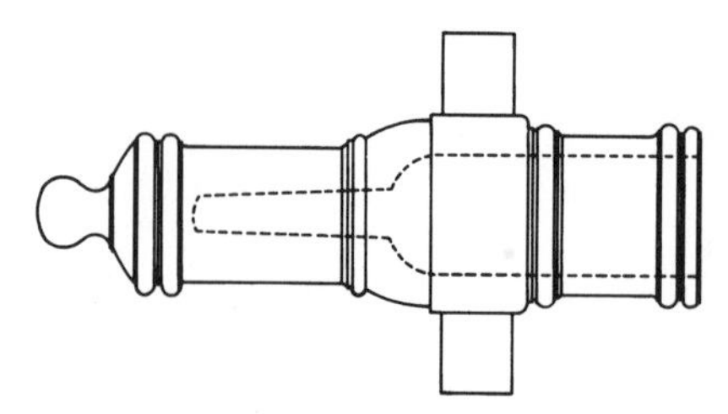

Fig. 48. A 2.85-Inch Bronze Howitzer. This piece was made by Daniel King of Germantown, Pennsylvania, during the American Revolution. The original is at the U.S. Military Academy at West Point.

cruise in the frigate's hold before being offloaded. An 8-inch bronze howitzer at Fort Ticonderoga today, which has an eagle crest but no other marks, is probably a Revere.

The earliest written reference to the use of howitzers in U.S. Navy vessels is dated 1 July 1797. On that day James McHenry ordered John Harris to deliver four iron howitzers for the 14-gun revenue cutter *Virginia.*

A June 1797 list of military stores for three frigates included eighteen 8-inch howitzers (or 4- or 6-pounders, possibly long guns) plus a set of implements for each gun. The *Constellation* probably carried 3-pounder howitzers in 1798. Twenty howitzers were purchased from Daniel King, and by mid-March 1798 ten had been delivered to John Harris, the remaining ten (identified as bronze 3-pounders) to the *Constellation* at Baltimore. A month before, in February, McHenry had ordered Harris to deliver to Captain Truxtun twelve 3-pounder shot to prove howitzers for the *Constellation.* It is reasonable to conclude that the guns in question were the type discussed here—2.85-inch howitzers that would fire a 3-pound shot with a diameter of 2.725 inches. In August 1798, the Navy Department also ordered twelve bronze howitzers shipped to Charleston for two galleys there.

During her engagement with the *Macedonian* in October 1812, the *United States* carried three 6-pounder howitzers in her tops. Small howitzers were also employed in the War of 1812. By 1815, however, carronades had replaced these guns in both the British and U.S. navies, apparently at about the same time.

Still, it was useful to have at least one gun on each side of the quarterdeck and forecastle to fire at enemy rigging. One British authority noted in 1851 that bronze field howitzers, mounted on special carriages to allow greater elevation, were being carried by ships for sea and field service but also to provide dismantling fire. The later Dahlgren boat howitzers filled the need for such weapons in the U.S. Navy.

Both howitzers and mortars fired hollow shells—explosive shells, shrapnel, and carcasses. Explosive shells were hollow concentric spheres of cast iron with a fuse hole. The fuse exploded the charge inside the shell. Shells

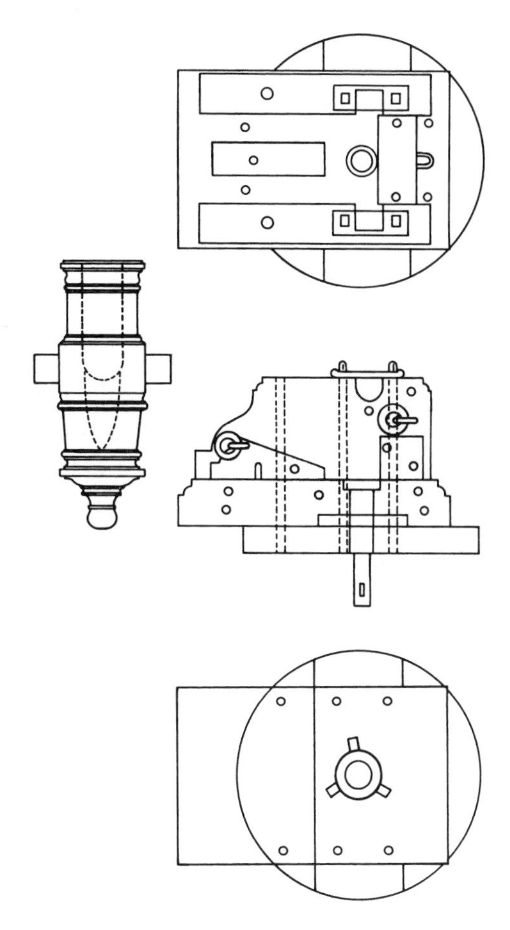

Fig. 49. Howitzer on a Sea Mount. (After a drawing in National Archives, Record Group 74.)

were used at sea to destroy rigging and kill men; in a confined ship space, the smoke from the blast would also greatly inhibit a crew.

Shells probably evolved from the "fire pots" used by the Greeks, which were filled with incendiary compositions and thrown by hand or sling. The Chinese may have used shells as early as the twelfth or thirteenth century. As late as 1815, hand grenades (called grenados—*grenadiers* referred to those doing the throwing) were kept in boxes aboard ship and thrown from the tops in battle. It was noted, however, that hand grenades were "now much less used than formerly."[20]

At first, shells were employed only in mortars and howitzers. It was not until the siege of Gibraltar, in 1779, that they were projected from guns as well. Shells for mortars and long guns were similar except that the former had large fuse holes and no wood bottoms (sabots).

In early practice, the shell was lit and then the gun was fired. This was

TABLE 17

SHELLS IN BRITISH SEA SERVICE, 1815

	Weight (lbs)	*Powder Charge to Fill (lbs-oz)*	*Powder Charge to Break in Most Pieces (lbs-oz)*
13-in	195	9-4.5	7-8
10-in	89	4-14.5	3-4
8-in (for 68-pdr carronades)	46	2-3.5	2-0

Source: Falconer and Burney, *A Universal Dictionary,* 50.

dangerous since fuses were known to be erratic; gunners greatly feared them. While the French continued this practice for some time, the British and Americans placed the shell with its fuse positioned toward the muzzle, along the axis of the bore ("up and out"), so that fire from the discharge of the mortar or gun automatically lit it.

The sabot came to be used with both explosive shell and spherical case (shrapnel). It was a piece of light, close-grained wood turned in a lathe to a diameter slightly less than that of the shell and tapered to fit the slope in chambered guns. It kept the shell properly positioned toward the muzzle. (If the shell turned around in the bore, the gun's discharge might drive the fuse in and explode it before it left the barrel.) Two tin straps held the sabot in place on the shell. The sabot could also be used with round shot to prevent them from rolling on the deck. It took the place of the wad, which sometimes prevented the fuse from being lit. A light wad was used on top of the shell, but only if there was heavy rolling.

Some naval shells had wooden tops rather than bottoms, in either case for better storage and prevention of damage to the fuse during fire. Still, early shells presented so many problems, particularly premature bursting, that crews were reluctant to fire them.

Although this was not common, shells could be fired in combination with other rounds. A double shot might consist of shell and a solid shot, but two shells were never fired together.

Early fuses were paper, wood, and iron. By the mid-eighteenth century the British made them out of beechwood. The fuse, a tapered plug inserted in the shell, had a hole running its length to within a short distance of the small end. It was filled with a composition of gunpowder, sulphur, and saltpeter that would burn for 4 to 5 seconds. Thus the fuse, in addition to igniting the charge, determined the time of explosion. Fuses were ribbed, with each rib representing a fraction of the time it took to burn. A fuse was cut off with a saw at a certain point that determined the duration of burning. The remainder was discarded. (A wooden fuse for a 13-inch mortar was 8 to 9 inches long by 1.5 inch at its widest point.) The cut fuse was then driven into the shell with a wooden mallet. Muller proposed quicker fuses for short range, and by 1779 some British fuses burned an inch in 4, 4.5, and 5 seconds. Wooden fuses

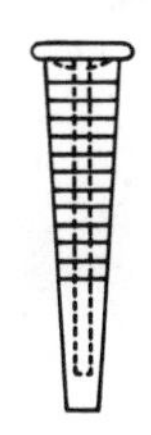

Fig. 50. Wooden Fuse.

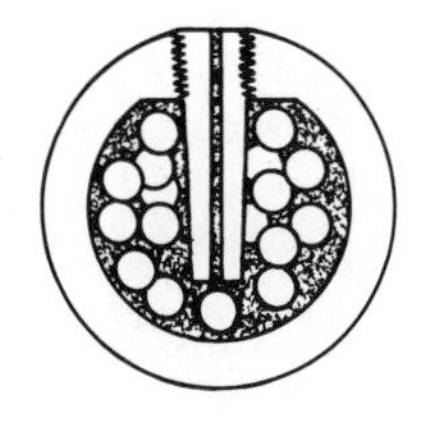

Fig. 51. Shrapnel Shell.

tended to deteriorate in the damp, hot conditions aboard ship. They were also subject to accidental discharge. This led later to experimentation with different types of fuses.

During the Spanish siege of Gibraltar (1779–83), the British successfully employed 5.5-inch mortar shell with 24-pounder long guns. This improvised combination worked well enough, but Lieutenant (later Major General) Henry Shrapnel of the Royal Artillery greatly improved it. In 1784 he invented what he called spherical case, a hollow iron shell with a fuse and a number of spherical lead musket balls surrounding a small charge of powder. The fuse was cut so as to ignite the charge above the target, the charge being just enough to open the shell. The advantage of the small bursting charge was that it did not scatter the shot unduly, and a maximum number would hit the target. Shrapnel's invention was disregarded for twenty years. It was only in 1804, during the Napoleonic wars, that it was given a trial and then adopted by the British Ordnance Committee.

Shrapnel shells were thinner than other shells and had to be carefully cast. Empty, their weight was about half that of solid shot of the same caliber, but when lead balls were added (lead being denser than iron) they weighed nearly as much as comparable solid shot.

Shrapnel was used beginning at the ranges where grape became ineffective. The damage it inflicted was as devastating as that inflicted by grape at short range. It was used against troops on shore or against vessels with many personnel on the upper decks.

The carcass, an incendiary projectile first used in the second half of the seventeenth century, was a shell with three additional vents equally spaced around the middle. The shell was packed with an incendiary mix difficult to extinguish. One composition in the Royal Navy was two parts pitch, four saltpeter, one sulphur, and three corned powder. By the mid-nineteenth century, the U.S. Navy used a mixture of white turpentine, spirits of white turpentine, and portfire composition. Wooden sticks poked holes from the vents through this composition to the center of the shell. Three strands of quick match were inserted in the holes, long enough to allow several inches to be folded over the edge of the hole. Dry portfire was pressed into the vents to keep the quick match in place. Carcass shells burned for 8 to 10 minutes and were designed to set fire to their surroundings.

Fig. 52. The 12-Pdr Bow Gun from the *Philadelphia*, on a Slide Mount. (Courtesy of the Smithsonian Institution.)

In 1815, Captain Thomas Dundas of the Royal Navy described a carcass shell "lately invented": "It spreads a flame in three distinct openings, which is so strong that the fire extends a full yard in length from the ball itself, and is so powerful that any thing under, over, or near, cannot escape its effects."[21]

In addition to creating a need for shore bombardment capability, the Tripolitan War augmented the construction of gunboats. In 1803, the Jefferson administration began a construction program that resulted in as many as 174 gunboats by 1809. They were from 40 to 60 feet in length and mounted up to two long guns. It was hoped they could carry 32-pounders, but most had only 24s. The smallest had one 18-pounder. Some of the guns were mounted on pivots amidships; others were carried at bow and stern. They also mounted small howitzers and swivel guns. For example, gunboats number 11 and 12 (gunboats were known by number only) each had two long 24-pounders and two 5.5-inch howitzers; numbers 13 through 20 each had two 24-pounders.

Slide carriages had been in use since the Revolution. (One of these can be seen in the *Philadelphia* at the Smithsonian.) On firing, the gun slid in its carriage on inclined skids. The incline helped reduce recoil and made it easier to have the gun in battery when it was loaded. On some smaller gunboats the slides were pivoted, but this often meant the bowsprit had to be removed. If it was not capable of traverse, the gun was trained by turning the entire vessel.

In the period before the War of 1812 frequent use was made of pivot mounts for both long guns and carronades. The most common pivot mount consisted of a metal ring known as a circle, 9 to 12 inches in diameter on the deck and brought level by means of a wooden foundation. The circle was

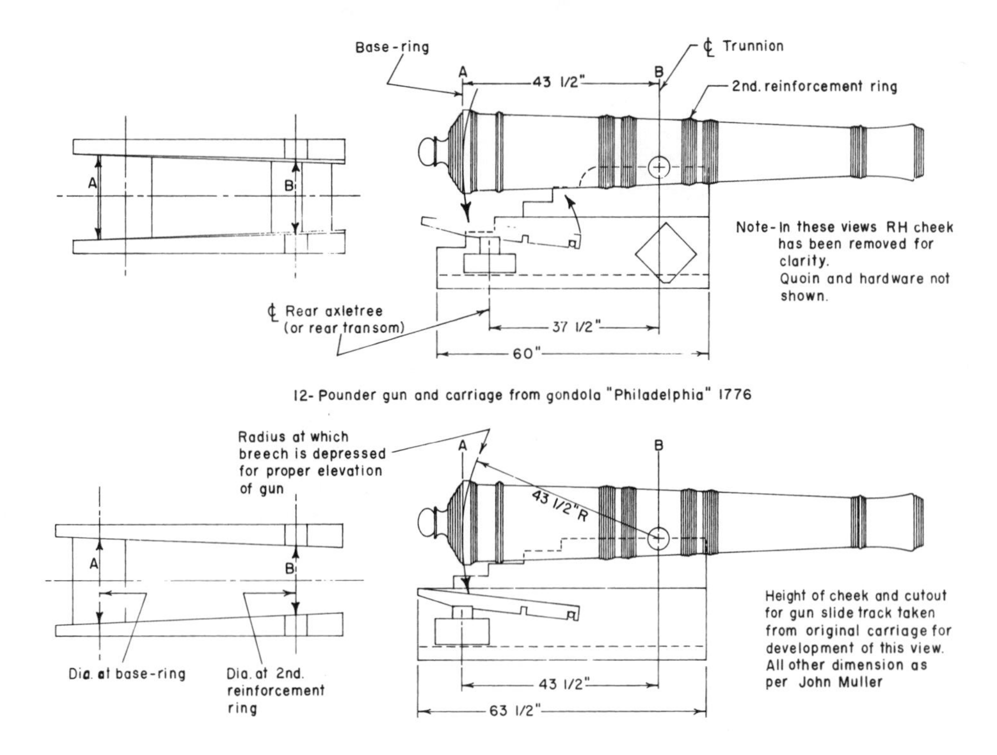

Fig. 53. Twelve-Pdr Slide Carriages. (Drawing by Howard Hoffman. Reproduced with the permission of the Smithsonian Institution.)

shaped like a shallow U to hold rollers attached to the bottom of two long timbers, or skids. Skids supported the carriage as it recoiled. They were fastened together with blocks, or checks, and secured to the deck by means of a bolt or pin passed through the center chock and attached to a heavy timber underneath the deck. This being the point of greatest strain, the pivot bolt had to be supported by a cast-metal socket and plate set in the deck. Handspikes moved the skids. The carriage was simply the old truck carriage with the trucks removed. Brackets rested in rabbets on the upper and inner sides of the skids. The carriage might also have rollers. Breeching running from the breech to bulwark stanchions or ringbolts set in the deck restrained recoil. The breeching of smaller guns was secured to ringbolts in the deck or the rail.

There were a great many variations on the pivot mount. The War of 1812 brought an improved type for use in vessels with high bulwarks. The pivot bolt was located on top of an upright wooden post, and the after end of the skid trucks were fastened to it. The forward end of the trucks were mounted so that the skids were elevated to the level of the pivot. The carriage was the same as before. This was not a strong mount, and as a result it was confined for many years to carronade use. Later, long guns up to 18-pounders were mounted in this manner, chiefly in schooners. The chief advantage was that the gun was

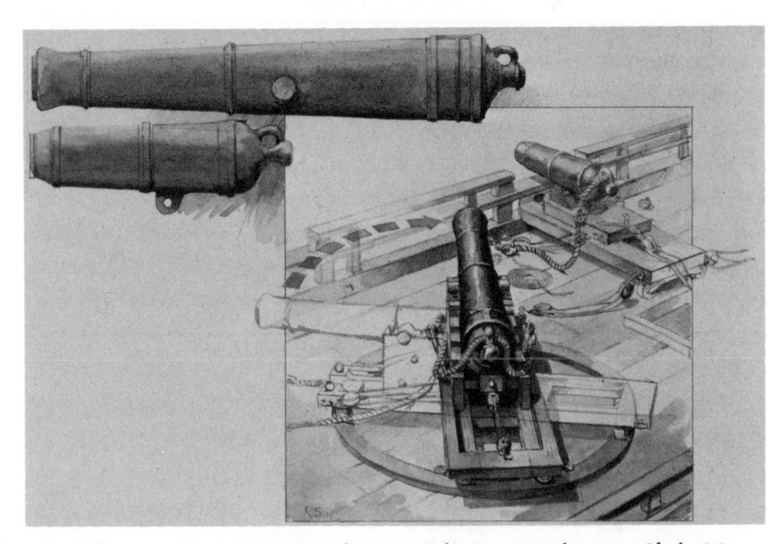

Fig. 54. A 32-Pdr on a Pivot Mount and an 18-Pdr Carronade on a Slide Mount, War of 1812. In August 1813 the schooner *Hamilton*, armed with one 32-pdr long gun and eight 18-pdr carronades, was lost in a sudden storm on Lake Ontario along with the sloop *Scourge*. Plans are under way to raise the two vessels and display them in a museum at Hamilton, Ontario. (Painted by Richard Schlecht for the National Geographic Society.)

now located well outboard, minimizing the danger of damage from the muzzle blast, a particularly vexing problem with carronades. The new pivot was usually located amidships. During the War of 1812, 32-pounders on circle mounts were used in the Lake Ontario squadron. The pivot mount was particularly important in the shift from vessels with as many guns as possible to vessels with only a few heavy guns.

The Jefferson gunboat program was instituted for several reasons. Gunboats were useful in the Barbary wars (they proved effective in the light winds and shoal waters of the Mediterranean); the president favored what was essentially a harbor-defense-oriented navy; gunboat construction could be divided between various concerns, bringing political gain to Jefferson's party; and gunboats were supposedly economical (Jefferson hoped to keep the majority decommissioned unless the United States was actually at war). The program, however, proved to be a disaster when war came in 1812, for gunboats were ineffective and extremely costly per unit compared with larger ships.

Another seagoing vessel built, in 1809, with the gunboat appropriation was the 73-foot cutter *Ferret*. Her name was soon changed to the *Viper* and she was converted to a brig, mounting at least ten 18-pounder carronades.

With the exception of the gunboats, there was little building at this time. Despite the *Chesapeake-Leopard* affair of 22 June 1807, Congress refused to appropriate money for new ship construction and even considered reducing the number of vessels on hand.

The guns of U.S. Navy vessels of this time ranged from 24-pounder long guns and 32-pounder carronades on the large frigates, and 12- and 18-pounder long guns and 18- and 24-pounder carronades on the smaller frigates, to 9-pounders on sloops of war and 6-pounders on the smaller brigs and schooners.

American guns of the period between the Revolution and the War of 1812 were of many patterns and origins. In 1809, Louis Tousard said that he had not included in his book "the artillery of the United States" since "there is as yet no law which fixes them."[22] Since there were no standards established by the army or navy for cannon, no clear records exist of the guns of this period.

Although American founders were producing cannon for the U.S. Navy, they apparently could not handle the number of guns required, at least not in the rapid buildup of the Quasi-War years. As a result, the navy continued borrowing cannon from the army. Examples of this practice abound. When the iron 24-pounders of the *United States* were found unfit for service in March 1798, a request was sent to John Jay for the loan of thirty iron 24-pounder cannon that the state of New York had obtained from Salisbury Furnace. That same spring, when 12-pounders for the upper battery of the *Constitution* failed to arrive, the governor of Massachusetts was asked to loan 18-pounder iron guns from Castle Island in Boston Harbor.

On 6 August 1798, the secretary of the navy borrowed nine 6-pounders from the secretary of war for a brig at Norfolk "nearly ready for sea" (either the *Richmond* or the *Norfolk*). They were to be replaced with others "of equal goodness" within a month.[23] Also, on 8 February 1800, the navy secretary wrote to the war secretary requesting cannon for the *Philadelphia,* noting, "I have loaned to you more than 100 Guns."[24]

Not generally known is the fact that a great many guns were also obtained from Britain, the result of cooperation that developed between the United States and that country over a common enemy in France. The British government wanted the right to recruit seamen in U.S. ports; in return for this concession, it was prepared to loan a squadron of ships and some officers to the United States. President John Adams rejected the idea of a formal treaty with the British, but he did tell Britain's minister to the United States, Robert Liston, that it was "in the interest of this country as well as that of Great Britain to enter into mutual agreements, and to concert plans of operation for the joint conduct of the war against France."[25]

Although British hopes for American seamen were disappointed, the United States did receive approval to purchase a quantity of military and naval stores in Great Britain. As a result, the U.S. Navy obtained a considerable number of guns. In late 1798, arrangements were made with Britain for the return to the United States of twenty-four French 24-pounders. The guns had been taken when the British captured the French ship *Foudroyant;* they were subsequently given to South Carolina during the reign of George II (1727–60). Carried off by the British as they were evacuating Charleston during the Revolution, the guns were transported to Nova Scotia. Destined not for ship use but rather for the defense of Charleston, they were at least forty years old at the time of their return. In the spring of 1799, what had been originally described by the British as a loan became a "transfer of property."

There is also considerable evidence of the importation of guns from England by private contractors, beginning as early as November 1798. A letter of 19 April 1799 from the secretary of the navy to Captain Robert Gill, navy storekeeper, included a bill of lading for cannon that had arrived at Philadelphia aboard the merchant ship *Connecticut* "for account of the United States." Gill was asked to send five of the 12-pounders to New York for the ship *Adams.*[26] In June, five 24-pounders from the same shipment were ordered as replacements for guns in the *United States.* Also in 1799, fifty-nine iron cannon ranging from 4- to 24-pounders arrived from London in the *Galen,* all on the Navy Department account.

Most, if not all, of the importations were handled by private firms that seem to have been acting both for the U.S. government and on a speculative basis. Of the latter activity there is ample documentary evidence. Considerable supplies of guns and shot arrived in both Philadelphia and New York. These were certainly not castoffs, and they included carronades.

The volume of imported pieces must have been considerable. A large number of British guns dating from this period were still in navy yards during the inspection of 1833 and even as late as the 1840s.

A considerable quantity of naval ordnance also circulated in the private sector. In July 1807 George Harrison, perhaps representing the firm of William Davy and Son, offered to sell the secretary of the navy a total of 163 iron guns and shot; most of the guns had been cast at the Carron Foundry in Scotland and were accompanied by certificates showing that they had been proved. These were, however, small guns. In January 1808, James Mosher of Baltimore offered to sell the Navy Department sixteen 18-pounder carronades taken to secure a debt.

English guns purchased during this period for American ships apparently carried the designation P WG 1798 or variations such as 1798 WG. A good number of English guns identified in an inspection of 1833 were so marked. This was probably a release mark of some type allowing the guns to be shipped to the United States.

These were not all surplus pieces; the larger guns seem to have been of the standard Blomefield design with the breeching ring above the cascabel. They were first made in England in 1795. While it appears that all the 24-pounders belonged to this type, some smaller pieces were still cast from patterns of the revolutionary war period. Two 24-pounders at the Maritime College in Fort Schuyler, New York, and four 6-pounders at the U.S. Naval Academy carry the designation described above.

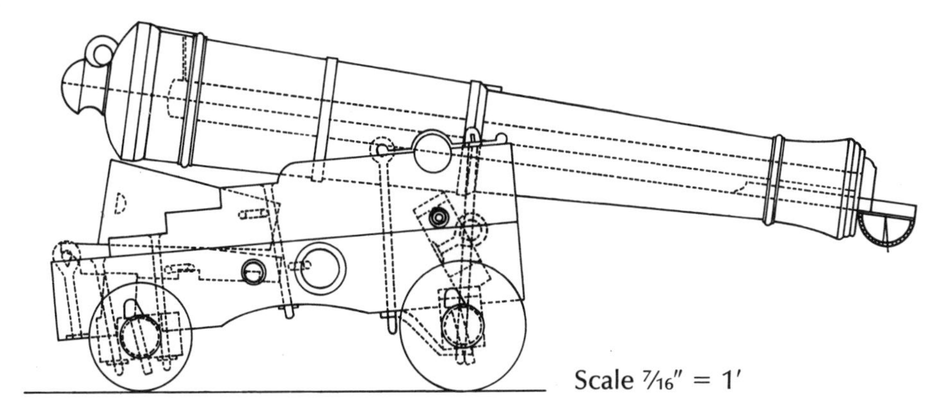

Fig. 55. Blomefield-Pattern Gun on Carriage. (After a drawing in Atkinson and Clarke, *The Naval Pocket Gunner* [London, 1814].)

At least some of the imported 18-pounders for frigates were 8 feet long. Ten were mounted in the *Congress,* even though they differed by a few inches from other guns sent from Philadelphia. It is possible that the latter were part of those listed in an 1846 register of guns as twenty-five 18-pounders, 7 feet 7.5 inches long, weighing 35 to 36 cwt each and described as "rough guns in bad order" with enlarged vents.[27] Another source gives other dimensions for the cannon of the *Congress* (see table 18).

It may well be that naval constructors were responsible for at least some of the gun patterns. In any case, by 1800 the standard length for U.S. Navy guns was 18 shot-diameters; the weight was approximately 200 pounds per pound of shot. This information was given in a letter of 9 November 1799 from Acting Secretary of the Navy Pickering in which he discussed the size of guns importers offered to the navy. He described them as "too heavy and too dear," and also noted that "Mr. Brown of Providence in the American War, cast Ship Guns in length only 16 Diameters of the Shot." His 9-pounders were only 5 feet 4 inches long, measured from the "hind part of the base ring to the muzzle." Following the same rule, a 12-pounder would be 5 feet 10 inches long. Pickering noted that the navy had selected a medium length as its

TABLE 18

Cannon of the *Congress*

	18-Pdrs (in)	*12-Pdrs (in)*
Diameter of the base ring	19.5	16.75
Diameter of the trunnion ring	16.0	13.75
Diameter of the trunnions	5.25	4.81
Length from the hind part of the base ring to the foreside of the trunnions	41.0	36.5
Length of the cascabel	10.75	9.5

Source: National Archives, Record Group 45, entry 464.

standard, and Foxall was casting guns 18 diameters in length. Thus a 9-pounder would be exactly 6 feet long. Foxall's guns weighed 200 pounds per pound of shot, a weight found by experience to be "sufficient." Pickering concluded that if Muller's principles were adopted, lighter guns might be preferable; while he himself was inclined to accept those principles, "universal habit in the American, corresponding with the British, Navy demands high charges, consequently heavy Guns."[28]

American-made guns generally followed the French design, dispensing with the chase astragral. There was a tendency, more obvious as time went on, toward plain functional forms in both land and naval guns.

The most important innovation in naval ordnance of the late nineteenth century was the carronade. This short, light gun of relatively large bore was used extensively over the next half century and marked a transition between the old long gun and the new shell gun. A prototype of the new gun produced by the Carron Company of Scotland appeared in 1776. It was used at first by merchant vessels, in which a gun that could be worked by a small number of men was a considerable asset. By 1779 the Admiralty had been won over and was placing large orders. In 1782, when it replaced the *Rainbow*'s battery of forty-four long guns (two 6-pounders, twenty-two 12s, and twenty 18s) with forty-eight carronades (six 32-pounders, twenty-two 42s, and twenty 68s), her weight of broadside rose from 318 to 1,238 pounds of shot.

The lightness of the carronade allowed it to be mounted where a heavier long gun could not be supported, on the poop or forecastle. The saving in weight and space made the carronade especially popular in the smaller classes of frigates, brigs, and sloops; in fact, it became the principal armament of brigs. Generally speaking, the carronade replaced the small long gun of 4- to 12-pound shot on board navy vessels. But while in smaller ships there was a shift to carronades, in the bigger vessels long guns remained in favor.

The carronade was controversial for the duration of its existence. Thus, while officially sanctioned, it was not recognized in the Royal Navy as part of orthodox ship armament. But despite shortcomings it increased in popularity. By January 1781, 429 ships in the Royal Navy mounted a total of 604 of the new weapons.

The carronade was cast in all calibers, most commonly as 12-, 18-, 24-, and 32-pounders. The true carronade had no trunnions but was mounted on a bed with a bolt running through a loop cast on the underside of the piece. The bed recoiled along a slide, held in place by means of another bolt in a slot. The slide pivoted on a bolt in the ship's side and traversed on small rollers at the rear end of the slide. A wooden quoin or a screw placed through the cascabel (or button or knob) at the end of the gun elevated it. When fired, the carronade recoiled, pushing the bed back along the slide and against the breeching ropes. After reloading, the gun crew used tackle to return the carronade to firing position. In addition to the absence of trunnions, all carronades had chambers and much less windage than contemporary guns—

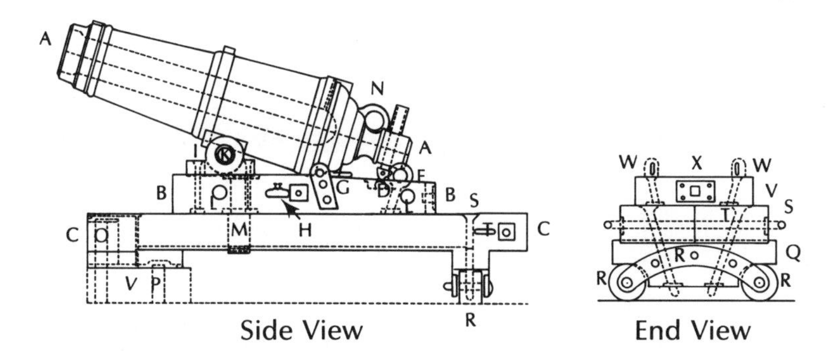

Key:

AA. Length of the carronade
BB. Length of the carriage
CC. Length of the slide
D. Elevating screw
F. Cap of the screw
G. Loop for pointing the carronade
H. Loop for running out the carronade
I. Cast-iron lugs of the carriage
K. Lug bolt
LL. Bolts through the carriage
M. Pintal of the carriage
N. Loop of the carronade for the breeching
O. Fighting bolt
P. Housing bolt
Q. Transom
R. Rollers
S. Transom bolts
T. Loops for trailing the slide
V. Chock fixed to the ship's side
Q. Transom
RRR. Iron rollers with the plates
S. Slide
TT. Transom bolts
V. Carriage
WW. Loops for pointing the carronade
X. Traversing plate

Fig. 56. Nomenclature for Carronade and Mount. (After a drawing in Atkinson and Clarke, *Naval Pocket Gunner*.)

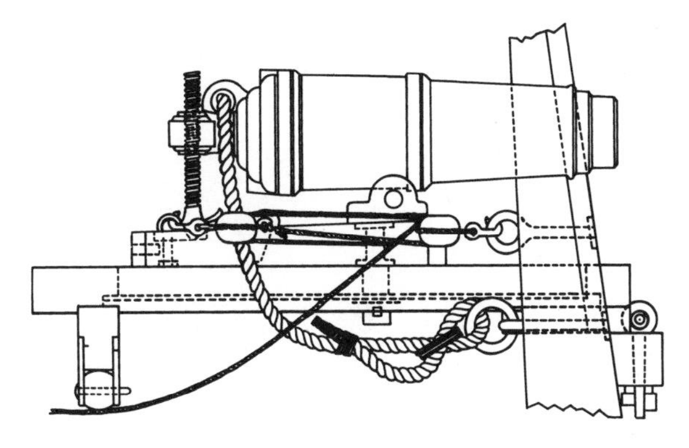

Fig. 57. A 24-Pdr English Carronade., c. 1820. (After Charles Dupin. Redrawn from Clowes, *The Royal Navy*, vol. 5.)

a fact not generally known at the time. There was no muzzle swell on the carronade but rather an enlargement of the bore at the muzzle to facilitate loading. All carronades were short, only about 7 calibers. They weighed 50 to 60 pounds for every pound of shot, in contrast to a proportion of 100 to 1 in

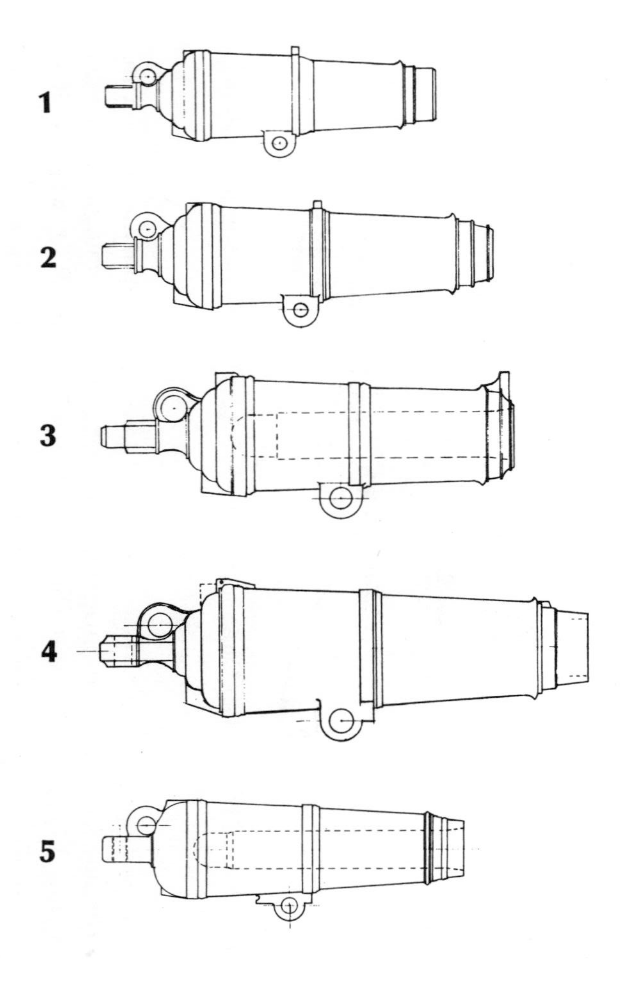
1
2
3
4
5

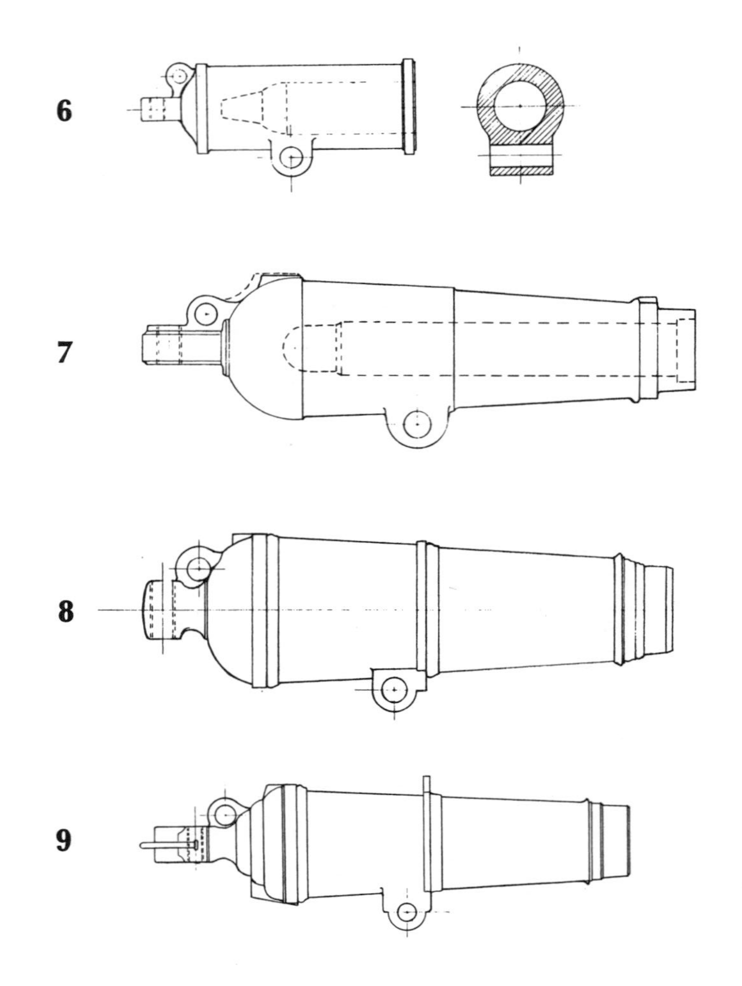
6
7
8
9

Key:

Carronade no. 1: English 12-pdr.

Carronade no. 2: English 18-pdr. This and the no. 1 are almost identical save for size.

Carronade no. 3: English 24-pdr. Carronades that were so short forward and equipped with a high front sight were probably used primarily on land. This piece was described as the carronade of six diameters.

Carronade no. 4: English 32-pdr. Said to have been on the *Cyane* during the War of 1812. Similar to nos. 1 and 2. At the U.S. Naval Academy, Annapolis.

Carronade no. 5: U.S. Navy 32-pdr. This was probably the type carried by sloops (built in the late 1820s) in the 1840s.

Carronade no. 6: French bronze 36-pdr. It may represent the first such weapon used by the French. It is copied from the English, with simplifications. The French experimented with carronades for some time after 1786, before they were formally brought into the establishment in 1790. The first French 24- and 36-pdr (French size) carronades were cast in bronze in 1794 for employment on frigates and smaller vessels. Naval bronze carronades were not cast after 1803 in France.

Carronade no. 7: French 36-pdr, probably the model of 1804. It corresponds to the English and American 42-pdr. The dotted line connecting the rear sight and the breeching loop shows a construction sometimes seen on smaller French carronades. The clean design is typical of French carronades.

Carronade no. 8: U.S. Navy 42-pdr, said to have been used by Confederate forces during the Civil War. Dated 1822, it is possibly of Gradual Increase design. Prior to the War of 1812 all American carronades seem to have been copied from English designs, which the piece here resembles. Apparently the English, unlike the Americans and the French, did not change the design of their carronades during the period they were in use. At West Point.

Carronade no. 9: English 68-pdr carronade similar to the one mounted on the forecastle of *Victory at Trafalgar* in 1805. Only one 68-pdr is known to have been in U.S. Navy service.

Fig. 58. Carronades. (Drawing by C. S. Tucker.)

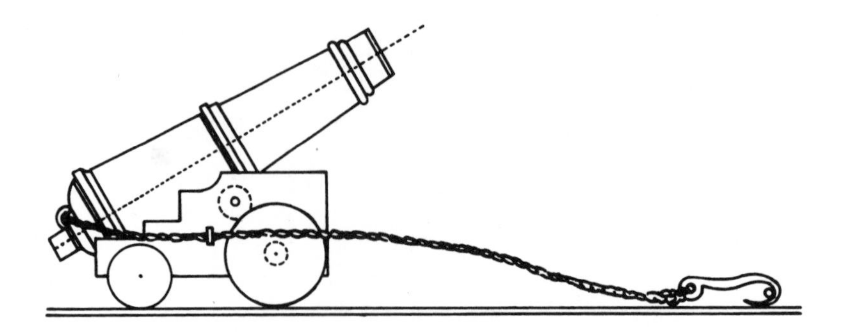

Fig. 59. Carronade Mounted as Launch Armament. Carronades and long guns were used for the armament of launches. Shown here is a carronade intended for service as a launch gun but which had to be ready for other service. It was mounted on a small carriage and was to be fired on the enemy's tops in an engagement. It would be placed either on the poop deck or quarterdeck.

A 6-pdr carronade 2′9.5″ long noted aboard the sloop *Yorktown* was used for her launch. According to records, a 12-pdr of English manufacture was a launch gun for the ship of the line *Columbus* (National Archives, Record Group 74, entry 117). (After a drawing in Robert Simmons, *The Sea Gunner's Vade-Mecum*.)

long guns. In the U.S. Navy, long guns and carronades were both given greater proportional weight (60 to 70 pounds for every pound of carronade shot) than English guns. As a contemporary noted, "Hence our breeching stood better; and we hear less of carronades flying round and 'looking their crews in the face.' "[29]

The advantages of such a weapon, particularly to a merchant vessel, were obvious. The carronade was easily maneuvered and loaded and required half as many gunners as a long gun (in 1815, a crew of four worked a 42-pounder carronade). A 42-pounder carronade, while shorter than a 3-pounder long gun, actually weighed less than a 12-pounder. Carronades were not necessarily small guns, however. Perhaps the most famous were the two mounted on the forecastle of HMS *Victory* that performed so well at Trafalgar; they were 68-pounders. The largest long guns in use at sea at the end of the eighteenth century were 32- and 42-pounders.

The ball fired from a carronade moved toward its target at a relatively slow velocity because of the smaller powder charge, but it produced a large irregular hole and considerable splintering. At its highest initial velocity of 1,500 feet per second, the momentum (weight times velocity) of a 9-pound shot from a long gun was 13,500 pounds; that of a 32-pound shot from a carronade with an initial velocity of 750 feet per second was 24,000 pounds, or nearly double. The carronade used approximately one-third the service powder charge of its counterpart long gun, varying from one-eighth to one-sixteenth the weight of shot. The normal charge was one-twelfth, but this was still proportionately higher for its metal than the charge for a long gun.

TABLE 19

COMPARISON OF IRON LONG GUNS AND CARRONADES, C. 1810*

	Length (ft-in)	*Weight (cwt-qtr-lb)*	*Powder Charge (lb-oz)*	*Bore Diameter (in)*	*Shot Diameter (in)*
68-pdr carronade	5-2.0	36-0-0	6-0	8.05	8.000
42-pdr long gun	10-0.0	67-0-0	14-0	7.018	6.684
42-pdr carronade	4-3.5	22-1-0	4-8	6.85	6.684
32-pdr long gun	10-0.0	58-0-0	10-11	6.41	6.105
32-pdr carronade	4-0.5	17-0-14	4-0	6.25	6.105
24-pdr long gun	10-0.0	52-0-0	8-0	5.824	5.547
24-pdr carronade	3-7.5	13-0-0	3-0	5.67	5.547
18-pdr long gun	9-6.0	42-0-0	6-0	5.292	5.040
18-pdr carronade	3-3.0	9-0-0	2-0	5.14	5.040
12-pdr long gun	9-6.0	34-0-0	4-0	4.623	4.403
12-pdr carronade	2-2.0	5-3-10	1-8	4.50	4.403
9-pdr long gun	9-6.0	30-1-0	3-0	4.200	4.00
6-pdr long gun	9-0.0	24-0-0	2-0	3.668	3.498
4-pdr long gun	6-0.0	12-1-0	1-5	3.204	3.053
3-pdr long gun	4-6.0	7-1-0	1-0	2.913	1.775

Source: Abraham Rees, *The Cyclopaedia; or, Universal Dictionary of Arts, Sciences and Literature* (Philadelphia: Samuel F. Bradford and Murray, Fairman, 1810), vol. 6, n.p., entry Cannon. See also Falconer, *Dictionary*, 77, and Theophilus S. Beauchant, *The Naval Gunner* (London: Hurst, Chance, 1829), 33.
* The cannon are the longest, or chase, pieces. Also, there are discrepancies in bore diameters in different sources at different times.

Owing to low muzzle velocity, the windage on the carronade could be sharply reduced. This quite often produced greater accuracy at shorter ranges of fire. Further, since the carronade used the same-size shot as other guns on board, it did not require special ammunition. (Since windage was so slight for the carronade, however, extreme caution had to be exercised in sizing the shot and protecting it from rust.) A final advantage of the carronade was that, owing to its low powder charge, there were few problems with bursting.

The carronade seemed ideally suited for yard-arm actions. There were, however, disadvantages as well. In theory, because it used less powder, the carronade would have less recoil. But one writer noted in 1812 that the recoil was "almost ungovernable."[30] This was, of course, a consequence of its weight, light compared with its shot. The weapon was known to be particularly bothersome when double-shotted, something that could easily occur by error in the heat of battle. A double-shotted carronade was likely to be dismounted when fired. Double-shotting also greatly reduced the velocity of shot. In the Battle of Lake Erie, fire from the brig *Lawrence* was not as effective as it should have been because a number of carronades were loaded with round, grape, and canister together, and some even with langrage on top of that. Many round shot simply bounced off the *Detroit's* hull, while others stuck in the side of the British vessel without penetrating.

When the breeching stretched, furthermore, the bolt in the slide struck the end of the slide and could break off, putting the carronade out of action. The shortness of the gun was a problem as well as an advantage, for a burning powder charge might damage the ship's side and rigging. The chief weakness, however, which in the end would prove fatal, was lack of range. Carronades were employed at point blank, which meant approximately 450 yards for a 68-pounder and 230 for a 12-pounder. At long range the carronade was at a distinct disadvantage, as was seen in the War of 1812.

Despite the controversy that accompanies most innovations, the carronade grew steadily in popularity. For some time the new weapon remained exclusively British, for the French were slow to accept it. It was not until 1787 that they adopted their first *obusiers de vaisseaux*. In contrast to their English counterparts, French carronades were made of bronze until 1804, when iron pieces patterned after those of the English replaced them.

Just when the Americans adopted the carronade is unknown, although it was after the Revolution. Early carronades were probably imported, but soon they were being manufactured in the United States. Evidence suggests that Henry Foxall was the first American founder to cast the carronade, but probably not until 1799. In any case, carronades manufactured in America were closely patterned after those in English service.

Soon carronades were replacing small long guns—4- to 12-pounders—on the upper decks of American naval vessels. Swivels and howitzers were relegated to the role of boat guns or to the merchant marine. This transition was completed by 1815 in both the English and American navies. It may be that the *Constellation* was the first U.S. Navy vessel to mount carronades. Certainly she carried them in the action fought at close quarters with the French ship *Vengeance* in February 1800, when she mounted twenty-eight 18-pounders on her gun deck and ten 24-pounder carronades on her spar deck.

By 1800 carronades were also placed on the upper decks of smaller frigates. In April of that year, the *Philadelphia* and the *New York* carried carronades in addition to 18-pounder long guns.

During the War of 1812, the *Constitution* mounted twenty 32-pounder carronades, the latter probably ordered from Henry Foxall in 1808. The *President* was the lone American frigate to carry 42-pounder carronades.

There is no evidence that larger 68-pounder carronades were used aboard U.S. warships. Even ships of the line built after the War of 1812 carried only 42-pounders. There is only one record of a 68-pounder carronade in the U.S. Navy; it appeared in the 1821 inventory of cannon and shot at the navy yards.

The carronade's popularity peaked during the French Revolution and Napoleonic wars, when it saw extensive service on land as well as at sea. On land it was used in flank defense for Britain's fixed fortifications. At sea it was particularly well received in the Royal Navy, which preferred close engagement. Americans were more reluctant to employ it, retaining a preference for the long gun used for chase purposes and as the main armament. In the U.S. Navy, carronades performed largely supplementary roles at close range.

But on many American vessels, carronades superseded smaller long guns and comprised virtually the entire armament. During the War of 1812, 32-pounder carronades in the *Wasp* inflicted heavy damage on HMS *Frolic,* also armed largely with carronades, in a battle fought at close quarters. The same was true in the *Hornet*'s victory over HMS *Peacock,* another equal contest between main armaments of carronades.

The Royal Navy, for a time, also used 18- and 68-pounder carronades on its bomb ketches. Six 18-pounders and four 68-pounders replaced one 13-inch mortar. With a 4-pound charge, and at 11.5 degrees' elevation, the 68-pounder carronade could fire a shell weighing 43 pounds 11 ounces a distance of 1,767 yards.

The largest carronade reported aboard a U.S. Navy bomb ketch was the 24-pounder, two of which were aboard the *Vesuvius,* launched in 1806.

The War of 1812 revealed the fatal weakness of the carronade. The British found themselves at a disadvantage when confronted by an enemy who could shoot with reasonable accuracy at long range. This spelled doom for their carronade-armed vessels on Lakes Erie and Ontario. Commodore Sir James Yeo reported on 12 September 1812 that the Americans had been able to bring the British within range of their long 24- and 32-pounders, but since the Americans had the wind it was "impossible to bring them to close action. We remained in this mortifying situation five hours, having only six guns in all the squadron which would reach the enemy: not a carronade was fired."[31] The carronade, while formidable at close range, was no match at longer ranges for long guns even of smaller caliber.

Later in the war the tables turned on the United States. The American frigate *Essex* was armed almost exclusively with carronades. In 1814 she was engaged by the British warships *Phoebe* and *Cherub,* both armed with long guns. The American vessel possessed superior speed, the essential factor for carronade armament, but a storm snapped the main top mast and this reduced the speed and maneuverability of the *Essex.* Much of the subsequent engagement of two and a half hours took place at anchor with the British vessels able to position themselves to rake the *Essex.* Although she severely damaged her attackers, the *Essex* suffered terribly and was on fire and sinking when she struck. This engagement tarnished the reputation of carronades and reinforced the conclusion that vessels should not be armed exclusively with them.

The U.S. Navy continued to use carronades until 1844–48, when they were removed from most ships.

The carronade raised the question of windage and led to windage reduction in all types of guns. It also demonstrated the tremendous advantages of quick firing, and its adoption in ships of the line helped bring about uniformity of caliber. The carronade's relatively smooth lines influenced the

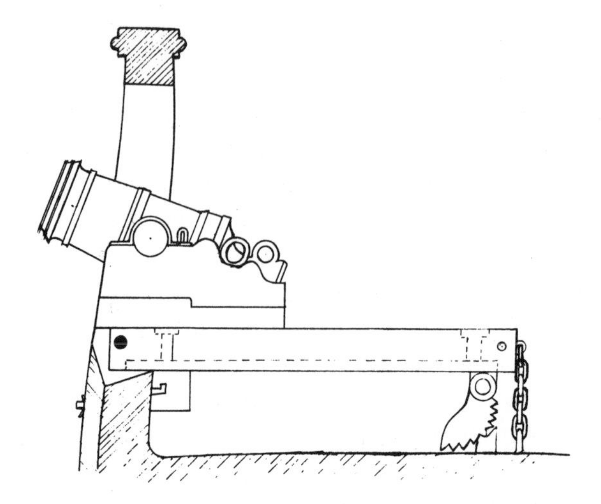

Fig. 60. A Trunnioned Carronade (Gunade). This is the oldest identified illustration of a gunade. It is an enlargement of a rather small cut appearing in Thomas Dodson's *Encyclopedia* (Philadelphia, 1798). Dodson made several references to correspondence with the Carron Company, so it may be that the illustration was either prepared by them or drawn according to their description. No proper scale is shown for the drawing. Most early pieces seem to have come in 12- and 18-pdr sizes.

According to Dodson's description, the slide was pivoted at the forward end to raise or lower it at the rear by the engagement of the "jack's" teeth in the fitting fastened to the deck. The chain held the slide down to keep it from moving as the vessel rocked and perhaps from crashing to the deck if the teeth disengaged. To train the weapon, the piece was pivoted on the slide by means of the large ring above the breech.

Much was made of the fact that only a small crew was needed to work the gun, since it could recoil against the "elastic rope breeching" and more or less bounce back into battery when fired. The port, large in relation to gun diameter, allowed for loading partially outside the hole; if that were not feasible, the piece could be turned on its pivot and loaded. (Redrawn by C. S. Tucker.)

Congreve gun, particularly its muzzle, as well as subsequent gun types. It was also an undoubted influence on the U.S. Navy's columbiad.

The carronade did not lead directly to the shell gun, although its large bore would have made it ideal for the projection of shells. It was not until the experiments of Colonel (later General) Henri Paixhans in France in the 1820s that the potential of shells was recognized. As John Dahlgren noted in 1856, the carronade "included incidently all the elements of a naval shell system." This, if properly developed, "might have anticipated the Paixhans system by half a century. . . . The use of shells was, at best, little more than a vague conception; its formidable powers unrealized, unnoticed, were doomed to lie dormant for nearly half a century after the carronade was invented, despite the evidence of actual trial and service."[32] In spite of this, the carronade was certainly an important transitional weapon in naval gunnery.

All carronades were made with a circular sleeve behind the breech that served as a nut for the elevating screw. At the Mariner's Museum and Fort

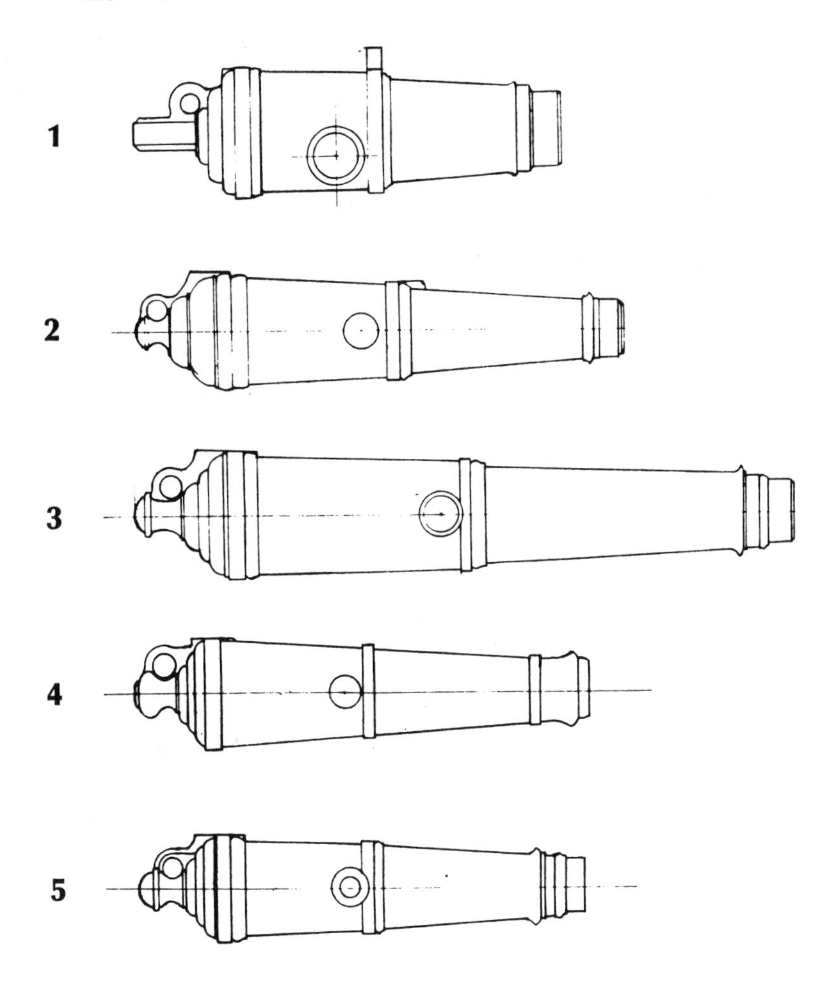

Key:

Gun no. 1: A 12-pdr. More is known about this 12-pdr than about most others. At the end of the right trunnion it is inscribed 1086/Mo.642/6.3.7, and on the end of the left trunnion, Eddington's/12pr. At West Point.

Gun no. 2: A 6-pdr. Taken from a Hudson Bay Company vessel and mounted at Fort Nisqually on Puget Sound about 1833. It carries the marks of a crown and is inscribed 6 PR.

Gun no. 3: This is classified as a gunade, since it is of gun length and carronade form. Mounted on the curtain wall at Fort Ticonderoga.

Guns no. 4 and 5: Both guns are at Fort Ticonderoga (in fact, there are two of each type there). They ornament the historic markers on the approach road. This was probably the only use made of them, as they are not part of the pre-Revolutionary and Revolutionary history of the fort. No. 4 is more a miniature cannon.

Other gunades are to be found in Eastport, Maine, at Fort Leslie J. McNair, and in the East Martello Tower, Key West.

Fig. 61. Gunades. (Drawing by C. S. Tucker.)

Ticonderoga, among other places, there are carronade-like pieces made with trunnions, without the sleeve or nut, and having an oval-shaped button similar to that of the Blomefield guns for the cascabel knob. The position of the trunnions varies; some have their centerline on the bottom of the bore, others on the axis of the bore. Little is known of the history of these guns, but it is safe to assume that they were made to arm merchantmen. In no instance, except in Denmark during the period from 1807 to 1814, were trunnioned carronades used as naval armament. All naval carronades except the Danish have the elevating screw and lug mounting.

The carronade-derivative pieces were known variously as gunades, gunnades, and insurance guns. The term *gunade* is probably an amalgam of gun (long gun) and carronade. The Carron factory, which cast the first carronades, also cast some guns of the same shape as the navy pieces but with trunnions.

The term *gunade* apparently had wide-ranging application. It was used in the inspection report of U.S. Navy ordnance in 1833. Hammersley's *Naval Encyclopedia* describes it as the 32-pounder of 32 cwt—a short, light gun that was cast for the navy in the 1840s. The gunade appeared in other navies as well; Dahlgren noted that in 1835 French trials were conducted between *canon obusiers* and gunades of 30-pounder size (French weight, comparable to the American 32-pounder).[33] In this study, however, gunade applies to those pieces in the U.S. Navy that had the general shape of carronades but were somewhat longer in caliber and had trunnions.

Most gunades differed from the true carronade. The number of actual variations on the basic carronade design must have been considerable, as no more than two or three of the eighty examined by Captain ap Catesby Jones in 1833 seem to have had the same features. The largest of the gunades appear to have been 18-pounders, while the majority were apparently 6-pounders or smaller.

The first extant U.S. Navy reference to a gunade occurs in the 1821 inventory of cannon in the yards. No ordnance dimensions are given in that listing, but there are some in the inventory of 1833. Most of the eighty gunades in the detailed section of that report were identified as being of English manufacture. The only marking that appears, P 1807, is for two 12-pounders. One reason for doubt about the origins of these gunades is that there is also a piece—not inspected by Jones but probably a gunade—that has the mark F on the trunnion. This was the one used by the Finspong foundry in Sweden.

Jones noted that in 1833 the frigate *Java,* in ordinary at Gosport, had twelve 12-pounder and eight 9-pounder gunades for a saluting battery. Two 9-pounder gunades were also mounted as field pieces.

Gunades were phased out of service at the same time as carronades, but as late as 1846 a 9-pounder gunade manufactured in England in 1811 was mo unted on the frigate *Potomac*'s spar deck.

CHAPTER V

U.S. Navy Ordnance and Ship Armament, 1812 to 1846

By the beginning of the War of 1812, the British navy dwarfed its American counterpart. Britain had more than 600 warships, including 124 ships of the line, each carrying 60 or more guns and bigger than any U.S. Navy vessel. The United States had no ships of the line and only three 44-gun frigates, three 38-gun frigates, three sloops of war of 32, 28, and 18 guns, and seven smaller vessels with around 12 guns each—in all, less than 450 guns. In the frigate class alone, the British had 116 vessels. This disparity grew rather than diminished during the war. By June 1813 the British had 723 ships in commission, including 156 liners of 64 to 120 guns, of which 172 were seventy-fours.

The British also had substantial support facilities in the New World: Halifax, Bermuda, and the West Indies. They did have the disadvantage, however, of being at war with France at the same time. As a result, at the outbreak of hostilities with the United States they had only one ship of the line, seven frigates, and a number of smaller vessels operating off American coasts. Faced with vastly superior numbers, the only sound policy for the U.S. Navy was defending the merchant fleet while trying to destroy that of Britain. Fleet actions would be suicidal.

The pride of the U.S. Navy were the frigates *Constitution, United States,* and *President,* which outclassed all other two-deckers and could outrun ships of the line. Crewed by volunteers, they were officered by men who had fought against France in the Quasi-War and against Tripoli. It came as a surprise to the British, overconfident after their successes during the French Revolution and the Napoleonic wars, that early victories went to the Americans: the *Consti-*

tution defeated the *Guerriere* and later the *Java,* the sloop of war *Wasp* defeated the *Frolic,* the sloop *Hornet,* the *Peacock,* and the *United States,* the *Macedonian.* These victories resulted not only from the relatively larger size of American vessels and their heavier batteries but also—as the English themselves later admitted—to superior gunnery and tactics. As one British writer put it, "Our vessels were in general crippled in distant cannonade before close battle commenced. This is fighting skill against skill."[1]

Coming at a time of disappointment after defeats in land battles against Canada, the sea victories were a tonic to Americans and even converted Jeffersonian Republicians to a pro-navy stance. Congress voted an increase of four ships of the line and six heavy frigates, though none of the new vessels got to sea during the war. Soon, however, early success was undone, the euphoria dimmed by HMS *Shannon*'s defeat of the *Chesapeake* in June 1813. The British rushed reinforcements to American waters (albeit six months too late) and imposed a highly effective blockade. As a result, most American ships that put into harbor in the winter of 1812–13 did not return to sea again during the war. As for the enormous flotilla of gunboats constructed by Jefferson and maintained at great expense, it proved to be virtually worthless even under ideal circumstances. In 1813–14, therefore, the situation was much as it had been during the American Revolution before the intervention of France—the British were able to move troops by sea at will.

The U.S. Navy did win victories later, but only on inland waters. In September 1813, Captain Oliver H. Perry led an American squadron to victory over a British squadron on Lake Erie. Captain Thomas Macdonough enjoyed an even more important victory at Plattsburg in September 1814. As a consequence, a 10,000-man invasion force commanded by General Sir George Prevost—the strongest British invasion force ever sent to North America—halted its advance and returned to Canada.

Losses of naval vessels on both sides during the War of 1812 were as follows: the Americans took twenty-three British warships of from ten to thirty-eight guns each, while the British captured seventeen U.S. Navy vessels of from ten to forty-four guns each, not including those burned at the Washington Navy Yard. But of the American captures, eight took place on inland waters (four each by Perry on Lake Erie and Macdonough on Lake Champlain) and four others after the peace treaty was signed. It is a myth that the U.S. Navy at any time during the war inflicted serious injury on the Royal Navy.

During the War of 1812, ships of America's blue-water navy retained their armaments. In November 1812 Secretary of the Navy Paul Hamilton reported them as follows: ships of the line—of which there were none at the time—rated at seventy-six guns were to have four 68-pounder carronades on the poop, thirty long 42-pounders on the lower gun deck, twenty-eight long 24-pounders on the upper gun deck, sixteen 42-pounder carronades on the quarter deck, and eight 42-pounder carronades on the forecastle. This was a total of eighty-six guns in all (forty-three in broadside, with a weight of 1,606 pounds of shot). Frigates rated at forty-four guns had thirty long 24-pounders on the gun deck, sixteen 32-pounder carronades on the quarter deck, and eight 32-pounder carronades on the forecastle. This was fifty-four carriage guns in all—twenty-seven in broadside—for a total of 744 pounds of shot. Corvettes rated at sixteen guns had eighteen 32-pounder carronades and two 9-pounder long guns for a total of twenty carriage guns in all, with ten in broadside and 297 pounds in weight of shot.[2]

The 18-gun sloops built in 1813, such as the *Wasp* (the third of this name) and the *Frolic,* carried two long 12-pounders and twenty 32-pounder carronades.

One area where the Americans could hope to best the British in numbers and ship size was the Great Lakes. Indeed, both sides engaged in a considerable contest there in what has been aptly described as a shipbuilder's war. It was vigorously supported by Secretary of the Navy William Jones. A strong naval force on the lakes could block the traditional British invasion route into the United States.

By the end of the war, both sides were armed to the teeth on the Great Lakes. This was especially true on Lake Ontario. Two American and two British seventy-fours were under construction there, and at Kingston the British were building the *St. Lawrence,* a behemoth of 110 guns.

Of the lake squadrons, the one on Lake Ontario was by far the largest. Of twenty-five American vessels there, the largest were the 74-gun ships *New Orleans* and *Chippewa.* Laid down in January 1815, the two liners were nearly complete by the time peace was proclaimed in March 1815. Each was to have mounted eighty-seven guns—sixty-three 32-pounder long guns and twenty-four 32-pounder carronades. Another contemporary source claimed their armament to be 102 and 100 guns. That would have made their actual armament more than 25 percent above the stated rate.

Neither the *Chippewa,* the *New Orleans,* nor the *Plattsburg* were completed by war's end. The *Superior* was the largest U.S. warship on the lakes. Originally she mounted sixty-two guns, subsequently only fifty-eight—thirty long 32-pounders, two long 24s, and thirty 42-pounder carronades. Later four of the carronades were removed, probably because she was found to be overgunned. The *Superior* was nominally a frigate of forty-four guns.

The squadrons on Lakes Champlain and Erie were smaller. The eighteen vessels on Lake Champlain included ten galleys mounting a total of sixteen guns. In his report of the battle of 11 September 1814, Macdonough listed fourteen U.S. Navy vessels that participated, mounting a total of eighty-six guns. The largest was the frigate *Saratoga* with twenty-six guns. On Lake Erie there were twelve U.S. Navy vessels. The two largest, the *Lawrence* and *Niagara,* were brigs of twenty guns each. The others—eight schooners, one brig, and one sloop—were much smaller. The largest of them mounted four guns, while six had only one each.

TABLE 20

U.S. Navy Active Service Batteries at the Beginning of the War of 1812

Name	Class	Rate	Date	Battery
United States	Frigate	44	1797	54 to 56 guns: 30 long 24-pdrs on main deck, 2 long 24-pdr bow chasers and 20 to 24 carronades (42-pdrs on *President* and *United States*, 32-pdrs on *Constitution*)*
Constitution	Frigate	44	1797	Same as for *United States*
President	Frigate	44	1800	Same as for *United States*
Constellation	Frigate	38	1797	28 long 18-pdrs on main deck; 10 24-pdr carronades on quarterdeck and forecastle
Congress	Frigate	38	1799	Same as *Constellation*?
Chesapeake	Frigate	38	1799	20 long 18-pdrs; 20 32-pdr carronades; 1 long shifting 18-pdr
Essex	Frigate	32	1799	Originally 26 long 12-pdrs on main deck and 16 24-pdr carronades on spar deck; changed to 46 guns: 24 32-pdr carronades and 2 long 18-pdrs on main deck, 16 32-pdr carronades and 4 long 18s on spar deck
Adams	Frigate	28	1799	28 guns: 24 12-pdrs and 4 9-pdrs
Hornet	Ship sloop	18	1805	Originally 18 guns; pierced for 20 when converted to a ship: 18 32-pdr carronades and 2 long 12-pdr bow guns
Wasp	Ship sloop	18	1806	18 guns: 16 32-pdr carronades and 2 long 12-pdr bow chasers
Argus	Brig	16	1803	18 guns: 16 24-pdr carronades and 2 long 12-pdr bow chasers
Syren	Brig	16	1803	18 guns: 16 24-pdr carronades and 2 long 12-pdr bow chasers
Nautilus	Brig	14	1803	16 guns: 16 18-pdr carronades
Vixen	Brig	14	1803	16 guns: 16 18-pdr carronades
Enterprise	Brig	12	1799	16 guns: 14 18-pdr carronades and 2 long 9-pdrs in bridle ports
Viper	Brig	12	1810	14 guns: 12 18-pdr carronades and 2 long 9-pdrs in bridle ports

Sources: Chapelle; Emmons; Roosevelt; Mahan; Maclay; Report of Secretary Paul Hamilton to Cong., 1/27/1812; Capt. Stewart's letter; Peter Padfield; James; American State Papers, Class VI: Naval Affairs, Vol. I.
* Armament varied widely from ship to ship during the course of the war.

In addition to frigates, sloops, and schooners there were gunboats armed with from one to five guns. The smaller of these usually carried one long 18- or 24-pounder pivot gun; the larger usually had two long 32-pounders and several howitzers or swivels. As many as 174 of these gunboats had been constructed by the time the War of 1812 started. There were also galleys, or barges. Thirty-two were equipped and fifty-nine were building in 1814. Galleys had come into use during the Revolution for harbor and river defense. Some were at least 60 feet in length. Many, including those employed on the Chesapeake Bay in 1814, were propelled mainly by oars. In the War of 1812 there were a number of galleys employed on the lakes. Most apparently mounted only one gun, although some carried two, an 18- to 24-pounder long gun and a 32- to 42-pounder carronade.

The four ships of the line authorized by Congress on 9 January 1813—the *Independence, Franklin, Washington,* and *Columbus*—did not take part in the war. The *Independence* was the first of these to be built and the first ship of the line to be commissioned in the navy, but she was not launched until June 1814. The *Independence* was designed to carry thirty long 32-pounders of 55 cwt, thirty long 32-pounders of 50 cwt, and twenty-four 32-pounder carronades. The *Franklin* and *Washington* were of identical design.

All four ships were very heavy rollers and their gun ports sat too close to the water, in large part because they carried the heaviest batteries of any seventy-four at the time. When the *Independence* had been fitted with ordnance, provisions, and a complement, her lower gun ports amidships were only 3 feet 10 inches from the water. As a result, some of her 32-pounders were exchanged for 24-pounders from the *Constitution.* But after trials and prior to her sailing for the Mediterranean in July 1815, a considerable amount of ordnance, food, and equipment had to be offloaded. Although Commodore Bainbridge was opposed to razeeing the ship, ultimately this too was done. The *Independence* lost her spar deck and was cut down to the covered fighting deck with poop and forecastle. In 1837 she was recommissioned as a razee frigate, in which guise she would prove one of the fastest and most powerful large frigates in the world.

The *Washington* was launched at Portsmouth in October 1814, the *Franklin* in August 1815. The *Columbus,* the fourth ship of the *Independence* class, had nearly the same dimensions as the other three liners but was more heavily armed. The British destruction of Washington delayed her launching until 1819.

In addition to the U.S. Navy vessels operating in the War of 1812, there were a large number of privateers that together mounted more guns than the navy. Whereas during the war twenty-three U.S. Navy oceangoing warships with 556 guns captured 254 enemy vessels, 517 privateers with 2,893 guns took an estimated 1,300 prizes.

The guns in the lakes squadrons appear to have been generally heavier than those in the oceangoing navy. The justification for this conclusion is found in lists of cannon returned from the lakes after the war.[3]

American guns cast during the War of 1812 continued to follow those of Britain closely in design. Duane's *Military Dictionary,* published in Philadelphia in 1810, merely repeated the information in British writer Robert Simmons' *Sea Gunner's Vade-Mecum.* Even the ranges for guns were the same. Like Simmons, Duane did not list American-made guns, only British and French.

According to one writer, American ordnance of the War of 1812 had two shortcomings. One was that American shot weighed less than its nominal

Fig. 62. The General Armstrong Gun. The *General Armstrong* was a large and successful brig or schooner fitted out as a privateer in the War of 1812. Originally, she carried eighteen long 9-pdrs and either one long 12-pdr on a pivot or as a Long Tom (a few large privateers had a gun on a pivot; the Long Tom was commonly a shifting gun on a standard carriage to be moved where needed). Twelve of the long 9-pdrs were removed before the ship's last cruise for use in a fort, and the 12-pdr was exchanged for a long 42-pdr (an enormous gun for a vessel the size of the *Armstrong*).

In September 1812 in the Azores, after a hard fight against Britain's 18-gun brig *Carnation*, the *General Armstrong* was scuttled by her crew and set on fire. The 42-pdr, which had been dismounted in the action, sank with the hull. Later salvaged by the Portuguese government and given to the United States, it is now mounted on a reconstructed carriage in the museum at the Washington Navy Yard.

The gun is a French 36-pdr, design of 1786. It measures 116.5″ from the rear of the breech ring to the muzzle, 25″ in diameter over the breech ring, and 18.78″ in diameter at the swell of the muzzle. It has a 7.29″ bore. The gun was originally on board the 74-gun *Hoche*, a French ship captured by the English whose guns were subsequently sold to Americans. The gun was used for a time on a Haitian privateer before being returned to New York, where it was acquired for the *General Armstrong*. (Courtesy of the U.S. Navy.)

weight; the other was that American foundries were compared poorly with those of Britain, producing guns more likely to burst.[4] The latter is an overstatement, although there were several tragic examples of U.S. Navy guns bursting during the war. This happened in the *General Pike* when a starboard bow chaser burst, killing or wounding twenty-two men and damaging the ship. While the *President* was pursuing the 36-gun British frigate *Belvidera,* one of her foremost main deck guns blew up, killing or wounding fifteen men and Commodore Rodgers, who sustained a broken leg. After the war, on 17 June 1815, guns in the frigate *Guerriere* burst during an engagement with an Algerine frigate, the *Mahouda.* There were also reportedly problems with muzzles cracking on American guns.

Generally during this period, windage in British guns exceeded that in U.S. and French pieces. At least one English writer has maintained that this factor influenced the outcome of naval battles during the War of 1812, claiming British windage to have been 0.276 inches, U.S. and French 0.133 inches.[5] In 1815, windage for British long guns was 1/20 the bore; in 1819, windage for American guns was 1/25 the bore (1/50th for carronades.)

Interservice swapping of ordnance continued during the war. In March 1814, the navy requested the army to furnish from military stocks a quantity of cannon and shot for Commodore Chauncey, Captain Macdonough, and the navy agent at New York. Commodore Chauncey was in particular need of 18- and 24-pounders. Lending ordnance stores created problems, however, the chief one being accounting. In the fall of 1814, the navy secretary complained to the war secretary about the loose terms of lending, which had worked much to the advantage of the War Department.[6]

One British gun design, the Congreve, made its debut during the war. Seventeen of these guns sat in the hold of the 4-gun merchant brig HMS *Stranger* when the latter was taken by the *Peacock* in early July 1814. There is no evidence that they were ever used in American service, although all seventeen were still on hand in 1833.

Sir William Congreve designed his gun in 1814. It appeared in only one size, a 24-pounder 7 feet 6 inches in length and weighing 41 cwt. It had a shot-to-gun ratio of 1 to 180. The relatively smooth exterior form and single-curved breech may have inspired the designs of General Millar in England and Lieutenant Dahlgren in the United States. The use of the modified ring cascabel and the earlier "shark's mouth" in American guns may also derive in part from this design. In the U.S. Navy, the muzzle design was variously referred to as the Congreve type, Congreve muzzle, and straight muzzle.

The effectiveness of the British blockade in the War of 1812 clearly demonstrated the need for more capital ships capable of preventing such action in the future. Even during the war, Secretary of the Navy William Jones had pushed capital-ship construction, but in January 1816 the U.S. Navy had only three seventy-fours, the *Independence, Washington,* and *Franklin,* and four forty-fours, the *Guerriere, Java, United States,* and *Constitution.* To remedy this situation, Congress authorized a plan on 29 April 1816—it was amended on 3 March 1821—for the improvement of the navy. Known as the Gradual Increase Act, it authorized the expenditure of one million dollars a year on naval construction for eight years. It was the first real naval construction program in U.S. history.

The plan provided for the construction of nine seventy-fours and twelve

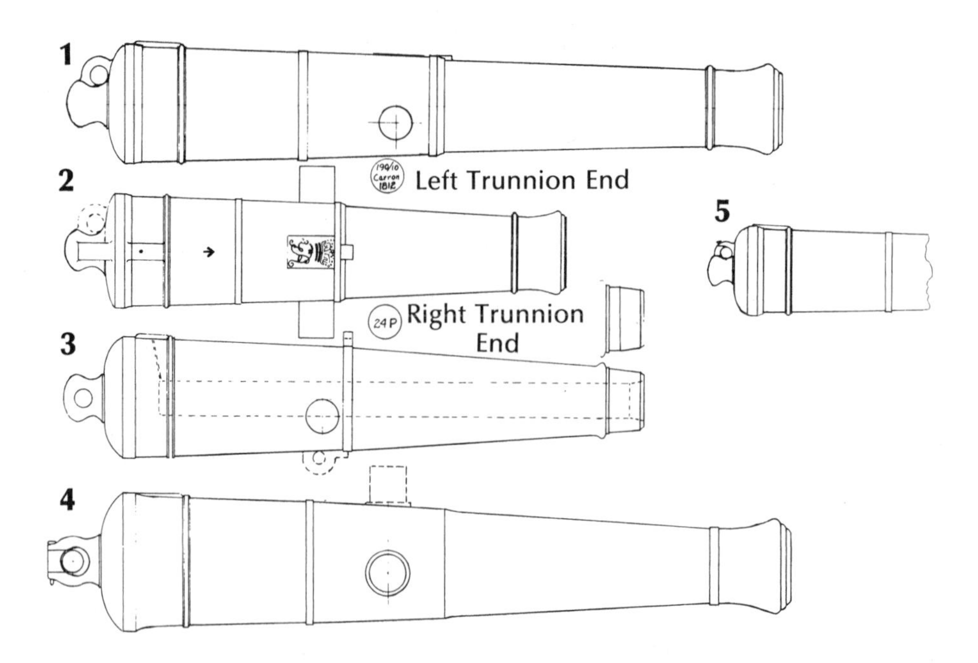

Key:

Gun no. 1: A 24-pdr Blomefield design. Two guns of this type are at the Maritime College in Fort Schuyler, New York. Both bear the marking WG 1798, apparently placed on all cannon Britain sold to the United States at the time. This type is far more likely to have been used aboard the *Constitution* than the design used in her restoration. The two guns at Fort Schuyler were made in 1797 and 1798.

Gun no. 2: A 24-pdr short Blomefield. This gun, aboard HMS *Confiance,* was struck by an American shot during the Battle of Plattsburg in 1814. The impact drove it back, resulting in fatal injuries to Commander Downie. It is 6′6″ long and was cast at Carron in 1812.

Gun no. 3: A 24-pdr Congreve gun. This was designed as an improvement over the short Blomefield and to justify the theory that a piece with a heavy breech and light muzzle would produce higher velocity. It was originally made with a loop or lug mounting (dotted lines), and its likeness to the carronade was increased by the muzzle design (shown separately) used on the first models. The production model had the first ring cascabel, the raised sight on the reinforce ring, and the plain tapered muzzle.

Gun no. 4: A 32-pdr Millar design. Millar was actively designing from about 1820 on, and this piece probably originated in the decade of the 1820s.

Gun no. 5: A 6-pdr. Here the ring was adapted for use with a pin to allow quick changes of the breeching. The piece dates from the 1820s, most likely 1825.

Fig. 63. British Gun Design, 1800–1825. This plate illustrates several gun types in Royal Navy service during the first quarter of the nineteenth century. (Drawing by C. S. Tucker.)

TABLE 21

BATTERIES OF THE U.S. NAVY'S DECATUR SQUADRON DURING THE ALGERINE WAR, 1815

Name	*Class*	*Rate*	*Date*	*Battery*
Guerriere	Frigate	44	1814	53 guns: 33 long 24-pdrs and 20 42-pdr carronades
Macedonian	Frigate	38	1812	49 guns when captured from the British in the War of 1812: 28 long 18-pdrs, 2 long 12-pdrs, 2 long 9-pdrs, 16 32-pdr carronades, 1 18-pdr carronade
Constellation	Frigate	36	1797	50 guns: 28 long 18-pdrs and 12 12-pdrs, 10 24-pdr carronades on quarterdeck and forecastle
Epervier	Sloop of war	18	1814	18 32-pdr carronades
Ontario	Sloop of war	18	1813	20 32-pdr carronades, 2 long 18-pdrs
Firefly	Brig	14	1814	10 18-pdr carronades, 4 long 18-pdrs
Flambeau	Brig	14	1814	10 18-pdr carronades, 4 long 18-pdrs
Spark	Brig	14	1814	10 18-pdr carronades, 2 long 18-pdrs
Spitfire	Schooner	12	1814	8 18-pdr carronades, 2 long 9-pdrs, 1 long 18-pdr
Torch	Schooner	12	1814	8 18-pdr carronades, 2 long 18-pdrs

Sources: Howard I. Chapelle, *The History of the American Sailing Navy* (New York: Bonanza Books, n.d.), and George F. Emmons, *The Navy of the United States* (Washington: Gideon, 1853).

forty-fours (including the one seventy-four and three forty-fours authorized in January 1813) as well as three experimental steam-powered batteries for the defense of ports and harbors. These steam batteries were an innovation at the time, but the president was given authority to suspend construction and little was done on them before 1835. There was some support at the time for a ship of the line of 120 to 130 guns, but it was not until the *Pennsylvania* (120 guns) was built in 1837 that such a ship appeared.

The *Columbus*—the seventy-four authorized by the act of January 1813—was launched in March 1819. Her original armament was 92 guns: 68 long 32-pounders and 24 42-pounder carronades. In 1817, two of the seventy-fours in the new program were laid down, the *Delaware* and *Ohio*. The former, the design for the five subsequent seventy-fours, was launched in October 1820.[7] The latter was laid down in 1817 and launched in 1820. The first ship of the line named for a state, the *Ohio* was one of the finest vessels of her rate in the world and certainly the best in the American navy. She handled almost like a frigate, carried her ordnance with ease, and remained in service (though as a stationary hulk in later years) until 1883. Her first armament consisted of 32-pounder guns and carronades, with long 32s on the lower deck. Later, the lower deck was armed with long 42-pounders and the carronades were upgraded to 42s.[8] It should be noted that the guns carried by the *Ohio* and other 74-gun ships varied from 86 to as many as 102, even though the ships all continued to be classed as seventy-fours.

The *North Carolina,* also authorized under the 1816 act, was launched in 1821. She was pierced for 102 guns and is said to have originally mounted 94 (32- and 42-pounders).[9] The *Vermont* was completed about 1825 but remained on the stocks until her launching in 1848. She was not commissioned until 1862, when as a station ship she was armed with 4 8-inch shell guns and 20 32-pounders. The *Alabama,* authorized in 1816, was ready for launching by 1825 but remained on the stocks until the Civil War, at which time she was renamed the *New Hampshire.* Launched in 1864, she was armed as a station ship with 4 100-pounder Patriot rifled guns and 6 IX-inch Dahlgren smoothbores. The *New York* and *Virginia* were both ready for launching around 1825 but remained on the stocks. The former, built at Norfolk, was burned in 1861 to prevent her from falling into Confederate hands. The *Virginia* was built at Boston and remained on the stocks until she was broken up in 1884.

The largest sailing warship ever built for the U.S. Navy was the liner *Pennsylvania,* laid down in 1822 but not launched until 1837. For a time she was the largest warship in the world. She had four complete gun decks, three covered, and was pierced for 136 guns. Her original armament was 16 8-inch shell guns and 104 32-pounders.[10]

Interest in the expansion of the navy waned as the lessons of the War of 1812 were forgotten. Transformation of the postwar economic boom into a recession reinforced this attitude. Appropriations for the navy were cut in half, heavier ships that had already been constructed were laid up, and available funds went into storing timber for the day construction resumed. Essentially, the navy was reduced to a patrol force without the ability to conduct offensive operations against the fleets of major naval powers.

At the end of 1822, the U.S. Navy had twelve 74-gun ships and nine first-class 44-gun frigates. Of the liners only one, the *Franklin,* was in commission; five were in ordinary and five were listed as building. Of the 44-gun frigates only one, the *Constitution,* was in commission; four were in ordinary and four were listed as building. In addition to the two larger ships, there were in actual service one 36-gun frigate—the *Constellation*—two corvettes with twenty-four guns, three sloops of war with eighteen guns, two brigs with twelve guns, six schooners with twelve guns each, and one gunboat with one gun.

In 1824, Secretary of the Navy Samuel Southard requested approval from Congress for the construction of ten additional sloops. The Gradual Increase Act had provided for additional ships of the line and frigates but not sloops of war, and in 1824 there were only three of this class in service. With American overseas interests growing, the need for these vessels was pronounced, particularly off the Pacific coast of South America and off the coast of the Oregon Territory. The new sloops were designed to be more powerful than their predecessors of 1813. Authorization for the construction of 18-gun sloops came in March 1825, and ultimately nine were launched in the period from 1825 to 1828: the *Boston* and *Lexington* (1825), the *Vincennes* and

TABLE 22

ARMAMENT FOR THE SCHOONERS OF 1831

10	18-pdr carronades @ $150	$1,500
2	9-pdr long guns @ $180	360
14	barrels of powder @ $20	280
900	18-pdr shot	810
200	9-pdr shot	90
		$3,040
50	muskets @ $12	$600
50	pistols @ $6	300
50	swords @ $2.70	135
50	boarding pikes @ $2	100
30	boarding hatchets @ $1.50	45
		$1,180

Source: American State Papers, class 6, *Naval Affairs,* vol. 3, 789.

Warren (1826), and the *Fairfield, Vandalia, Falmouth, St. Louis,* and *Concord* (1828).

The War of 1812 had shown that sloops were most effective when armed with a battery of long guns, which were more useful than carronades in battles against merchantmen. Although sloops were better suited to an armament of twenty to twenty-two guns, the Board of Navy Commissioners directed that they carry twenty-four 24-pounders on a flush deck. Their armament was subsequently reduced to twenty guns—two medium 32-pounders and eighteen 32-pounder carronades. They were then rated as 18-gun sloops.

Augmenting batteries involved much more than just the added weight of ordnance. Two extra 32-pounder broadside guns alone necessitated fifteen more crew members, including one powder boy, to service either the port or starboard piece, depending on which side the vessel was engaged. The extra men would consume 20,000 pounds of supplies on a hundred-day cruise. Moreover, they would weigh 2,500 pounds, their clothing and bedding 1,000 pounds, and the two guns with their carriages 16,000 pounds. All of this amounted to an additional 39,500 pounds.

It is not known exactly when the change to carronade armament was made in the new sloops, but the sailing capabilities of some of them in later years can probably be attributed to the lighter armament they carried in the 1840s. The armament of each of the six sloops still in service in 1850 was four 8-inch shell guns and sixteen 32-pounders, the latter long guns of 27 cwt.

A shortage of small vessels led to the construction of three additional schooners, all launched in 1831. The *Boxer, Enterprise,* and *Experiment* were to be armed with ten 18-pounder carronades and two 9-pounder long guns. The request for their construction included a detailed list of armament as well as projected costs (see table 22).

By 1832, as a result of Jacksonian economy and interest in the problems of

TABLE 23

Warships in Commission, 1836

	Royal Navy	*French Navy*	*U.S. Navy**
Ships of the line	23	15	2
Frigates	15	13	7
Sloops and corvettes	51	{65}	14
Brigs and schooners	25		7
Steamships	21	23	0

Source: *The Naval Magazine* 2 (January 1837), 11.
* Figures for the U.S. Navy include new construction authorized by Congress in 1836 and not yet in commission.

settling the West, the U.S. Navy had in active service only twenty-one vessels: three frigates, eleven sloops, and seven schooners. Five years later, Captain Matthew Perry noted that the navy had fallen to eighth place in world rank, just behind Egypt. This was particularly significant when considering the navies of Britain and France (see table 23).

In 1839, the U.S. Navy had forty-three sailing vessels and one steam warship, the *Fulton II.* In 1840, under Secretary of the Navy James Paulding, sixteen more ships were built. Although not even a majority were in active commission, by 1841 there were eleven ships of the line (all seventy-fours, with the exception of the 120-gun *Pennsylvania*), fifteen first-class frigates (forty-fours), two second-class frigates (thirty-sixes), eighteen sloops (sixteen to twenty guns), two brigs and four schooners (ten guns), and four steamers. This new ship construction was a reaction in part to rising anti-British sentiment, itself resulting from Anglo-American disputes that included the burning of the American ship *Caroline* by Canadians in 1837. The Anglo-American war scare continued under Paulding's successor at the Navy Department, George Badger. Congress authorized a home squadron of two steam warships, the frigates *Mississippi* and *Missouri,* both launched in 1841.

Continuing tensions with Britain, burgeoning American foreign trade, and a new Whig administration led to a substantial naval building program under Secretary of the Navy Abel Upshur. Upshur favored razeeing some ships of the line and turning them into large frigates to meet comparable classes in foreign navies. He also wanted construction of smaller sloops of war, brigs, and schooners.

Upshur ordered six large sloops of war in 1843, the *Portsmouth* (1843), *Plymouth* (1843), *St. Mary's* (1844), *Jamestown* (1844), *Albany* (1846), and *Germantown* (1846). Except for the *St. Mary's,* which had six 8-inch and sixteen 32-pounder guns, they carried twenty-two guns—four 8-inch cannon and eighteen 32-pounders.

By December 1846, there were forty-six vessels operating in the U.S. Navy. Secretary of the Navy John Mason recommended the addition of four steamers. Authorized the next year by Congress, they were the *Saranac* (1848), *Powhatan, Susquehanna,* and *San Jacinto,* all launched in 1850.

In 1853 there were about seventy vessels in the U.S. Navy, but only about forty of them could be made ready for duty within three months. Secretary of the Navy James Dobbin was determined to improve this situation and proposed a number of steps. He wanted six new first-class propeller steam frigates built; the frigates *Santee* and *Sabine,* which had been on the stocks since 1820 and 1822 respectively, altered and launched; and the ship of the line *Franklin* made into a first-class steam frigate, which meant breaking her up and rebuilding her. This would give the navy seven new steam frigates and two first-class sailing frigates, each capable of carrying fifty guns. Congress approved the plan, but still the active navy numbered less than fifty ships.

Dobbin continued to press for new construction, and in early 1857 Congress authorized five new screw-propelled steam sloops of war, all launched the next year. In June 1858, seven additional screw-propelled sloops and one side-wheel steamer were authorized. By this time technology was clearly moving in the direction of steam. Although U.S. Navy vessels of the Civil War were still mostly wind powered (even steamers had sail rigs, steam being regarded as auxiliary power), few saw constant active service. Most served as store and station ships and in other auxiliary roles.

The period between the War of 1812 and the Civil War saw great change in naval armament throughout the world; the trend was toward fewer but larger cannon in ship batteries and from batteries composed exclusively of shot guns to batteries with increasing numbers of shell guns. These changes were late in coming to the United States. Indeed, for many years the old long and medium cannon as well as carronades were standard issue in the U.S. Navy. Long guns were mostly of 4-, 6-, 9-, 12-, 18-, 24-, 32-, and 42-pounder sizes. Marshall did not list the 42-pounder in his book of 1822, but the inventory for that year included only sixteen 42-pounders cast since 1816. These were undoubtedly the guns for the lower-deck armament of the 74-gun ships of the line authorized in 1816. Carronades were 12-, 18-, 24-, 32-, 42-, and 68-pounders (the latter were not installed in ships).

Virtually all U.S. Navy guns of the period were iron, except for the smaller bronze guns in boats or revenue cutters and large bronze mortars for the bomb brigs.

On hand in various navy yards in 1822 were the following G.I. guns, which referred to all those cast for vessels authorized under the Gradual Increase Act:

Iron cannon	*Carronades*
16 42-pdrs	122 42-pdrs
219 32-pdrs	1 32-pdr
1 18-pdr	1 24-pdr
	1 gunade 24-pdr
	9 howitzers

Listed as "procured under former appropriations, fit for service, and applicable to general purposes" were 1,109 long guns of iron and 613 carronades.

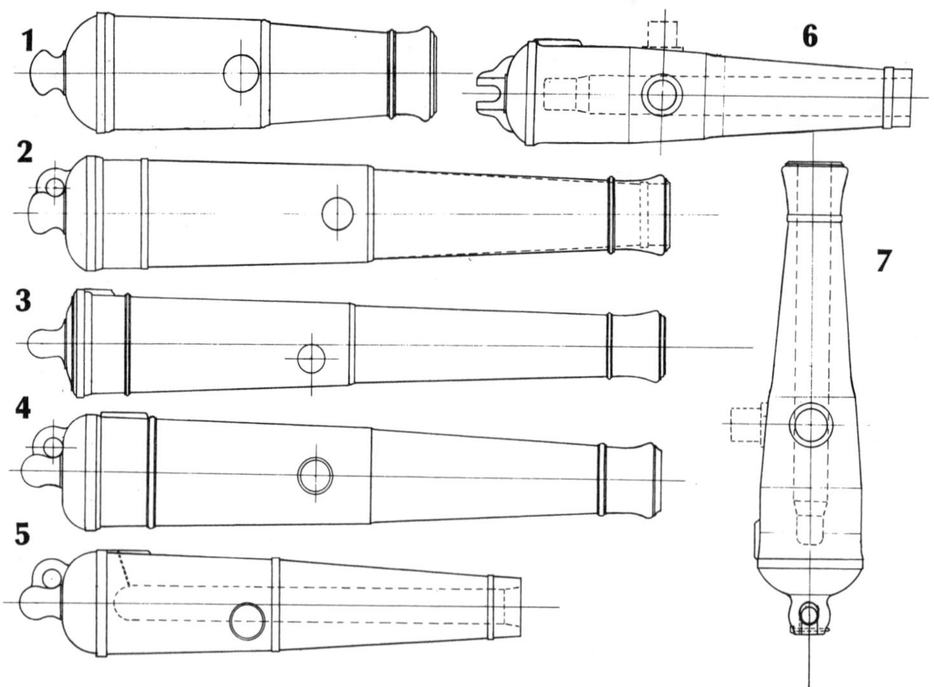

Fig. 64. U.S. Navy Guns, 1800–1850. These drawings show the main changes in the design of U.S. Navy guns from 1800 to 1850. Most are taken from pattern drawings in the National Archives. Unfortunately, there are no drawings in the archives preceding 1826. The burning of Washington in 1814 is usually given as the reason for the scarcity of earlier material, but it is possible that other drawings exist and have not surfaced. (Drawing by C. S. Tucker.)

The same list included 10 bronze cannon from 1.5- to 6-pounders, 21 howitzers, 6 mediums, 42 gunades, 5 mortars, 18 eprouvettes, 22 swivels, and 72 repeating swivels.[11]

The War of 1812 created a more effective administrative system for the navy. In February 1815 Congress created the Board of Navy Commissioners, which remained in existence until 1842. It consisted of three senior captains who, under the "superintendence" of the secretary of the navy, directed the procurement of naval stores and materials as well as the construction, armament, equipment, and employment of vessels of war. In 1820, the board established armament for frigates and ships of the line as follows:

	Lower deck	*Gun deck*	*Spar deck*
Frigates	—	32-pdrs	42-pdr carronades
Ships of the line	42-pdrs	32-pdrs	42-pdr carronades

Although this was not the battery in all ships, it was a simple and powerful one, in Dahlgren's view the best of its day.[12] Because the War of 1812 had demonstrated the superiority of long-gun armament over carronades, at least in commerce raiding, the board decreed that the nine new sloops of 1825–28 were to be armed with twenty-four 24-pounders. These, 240 of them, were

Key to fig. 64.

Gun no. 1: A 50-pdr columbiad of 1811, the only existing columbiad of the early period. At this time columbiads were 18-, 24-, 50-, and 100-pdrs. Apparently all had the same profile. At West Point.

Gun no. 2: A 24-pdr bored up to a 32-pdr. A notation on the National Archives drawing reads, "In 1842 55 or 60 of these were bored up to 32's and the chase turned down as shown." This work was apparently carried out by Cyrus Alger in 1842. The drawing probably represents pieces made in imitation of the English Blomefield design (1800) or of the Gradual Increase type (1816–35). Note the location of the trunnions on the centerline.

Gun no. 3: A medium 24-pdr. This type of cannon was made for the army in the period 1800–1815, but the navy made some use of it. A photostat of the original drawing (now lost) is at Fort McHenry, and specimens of the gun type can be found in Lewes, Delaware, and at Gun Square in Stonington, Connecticut, where a half battery tangled with three English ships in 1814 and thwarted a landing attempt. This cannon, the type Louis Tousard advocated for U.S. Navy use, is copied from the French design of 1786. It is sometimes called the Tousard design, although he made no claims to its invention.

Gun no. 4: A long 24-pdr of 1832. This possibly represents a pattern adopted after the War of 1812; the piece might have been one of the Gradual Increase guns case in the 1820s.

Gun no. 5: A medium 24-pdr for the sloops of 1825–28. In 1833 lightweight guns like this were condemned by Captain Thomas Ap Catesby Jones, navy ordnance inspector, who was an advocate of the long gun.

Gun no. 6: The so-called Paixhans or shell gun design modified for a lightweight 32-pdr. The bore (dotted lines) illustrates the use of a chamber for the powder. This gun was known as the 32 of 25 cwt.

Gun no. 7: The 32-pdr of 27 cwt. Probably copied from the English General Millar design, which it closely resembles. The gun is 72" long. The diameter of the bore is 6.4", that of the chamber 5.3". The *Yorktown,* a third-class sloop that was wrecked in the Cape Verde islands in 1850, was probably carrying sixteen of these short 32-pdrs.

ordered in 1826. There are two drawings of the 24-pounder medium gun in the National Archives. One, marked "10 sloops' gun," is dated April 1826; the other is marked "old sloops' gun" and is dated 1827. The gun shown is 6 feet 7 inches in length. Its design was based largely on the suggestions of Commodore Charles Morris. It was soon discovered that they were too heavy, and the sloops' batteries were reduced to two medium 32-pounders and eighteen 32-pounder carronades.

In the 1830s, Inspector of Ordnance Captain Thomas ap Catesby Jones was sharply critical of these guns and all others that did not have 200 pounds of metal for each pound of shot. In 1837, a board was convened for the purpose of conducting experiments with the 24-pounder guns of 1826. Members were Jones, Captain Kearney, another critic of the light guns, Commodore Charles Morris, and Commodore Patterson and Captain Shubrick, both uncommitted. The lighter guns were vindicated in a vote of three to two. As Morris, who had

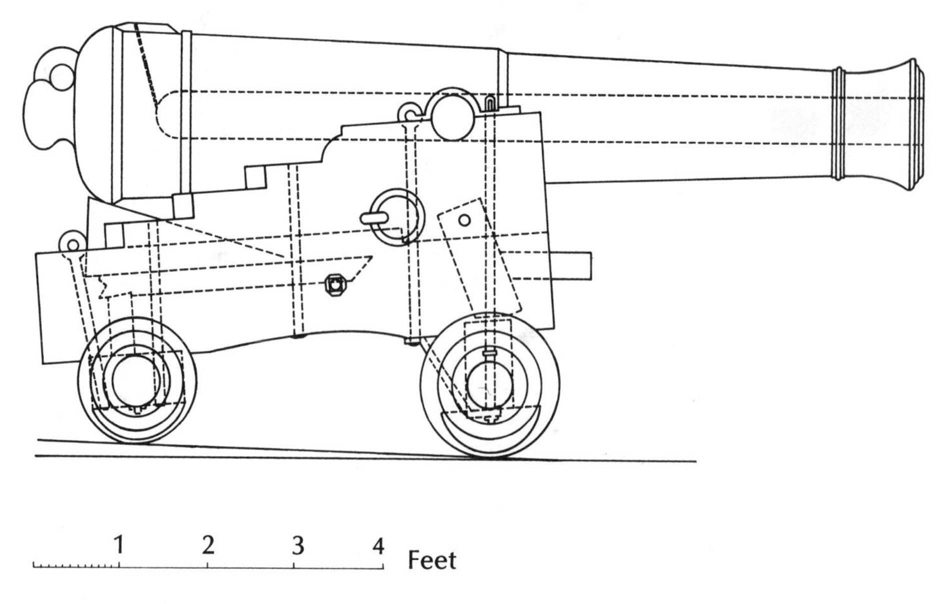

Fig. 65. U.S. Navy Long 32-Pdr on Its Carriage, 1819. (After a drawing in National Archives, Record Group 74.)

a vested interest in the success of the trial, noted later, "The result of the experiments fully established the safety of the guns. Their relative efficiency, compared with carronades of greater caliber, or long guns of less caliber and equal weight, was decided favorably by a majority, Jones and Kearney dissenting."[13]

The worldwide trend in the 1830s toward fewer and larger guns of new types was prompted in part by the American policy of utilizing the largest and most powerful batteries in the War of 1812. But both the French and British had already shown interest in improving their guns; in Britain at least this was motivated by the belief that the early American victories at sea had resulted from superior guns and gunnery. In 1832, the Royal Navy set up HMS *Excellent* at Portsmouth as an experimental and training gunnery ship.

The experiments of 1837 with the 24-pounder sloop guns were important for other reasons as well. As Morris noted, "The opportunity was improved to test some other guns, of new patterns, and the use of shells in guns instead of shot. Though these experiments were very rude, from the want of necessary instruments, and conveniences, the approximations that were obtained were useful by dispelling some unfounded prejudices and fears, and turning attention to subjects which had been too much neglected, and by laying a foundation for further and better investigations."[14]

In 1839 and 1840, on orders from Secretary of the Navy James Paulding, Commodore Matthew Perry conducted gunnery experiments at the proving ground that had been established at Sandy Hook. He set up targets at 800 and

TABLE 24

LONG GUNS OF THE U.S. NAVY IN THE EARLY 1820S

		WEIGHT					
*Type**	*Length (ft-in)*	*CWT*	*Qtrs*	*Lbs*	*Total*	*Bore Diameter (in)*	*Shot Diameter (in)*
4-pounder	6-0	12	2	10	1,410		
6-pounder	6-6	16	0	12	1,804	3.65	3.45
6-pounder	7-0	17	1	14	1,946	3.65	3.45
9-pounder	8-0	22	0	12	2,476	4.2	4.1
9-pounder	8-6	23	2	4	2,636	4.2	4.1
12-pounder	8-7	31	2	8	3,536	4.6	4.5
12-pounder	9-0	32	3	0	3,668	4.6	4.5
18-pounder	9-0	41	1	8	4,628	5.35	5.2
24-pounder	9-4	48	0	0	5,376	5.8	5.7
32-pounder	9-6	53	3	20	6,040	6.4	6.3

Source: George Marshall, *Marshall's Practical Marine Gunnery: Containing a View of the Magnitude, Weight, Description & Use, of Every Article Used in the Sea Gunner's Department, of the Navy of the United States* (Norfolk: C. Hall, 1822), 80. Total weight is calculated by the author. The book lives up to its title, but unfortunately Marshall gives only the sizes and not the other dimensions or weights of carronades. His information, based on twelve years of service in the U.S. Navy, is helpful in determining the size of breechings, tackle blocks, length of rammers, handspikes, and so forth.
* Carronades were 12-, 18-, 24-, 32-, 42-, and 68-pounders.

1,200 yards' range for testing both conventional and Paixhans guns as well as hollow and solid shot and explosive shell. He also had gunnery practice carried out aboard the steamer *Fulton II*. About the same time, target practice commenced aboard U.S. Navy ships.

In 1840, as a result of the Sandy Hook trials, windage in U.S. Navy guns was reduced and fixed at from 0.10 to 0.20 inch for all calibers. Windage was reduced in navies around the world during the 1840s and 1850s, a development made possible in part by better casting and machining techniques and more perfectly spherical shot.

In 1845, a captain's board established U.S. Navy bore diameters (expressed in inches) as follows:

10-in gun	10.00
8-in gun	8.00
42-pdr gun	7.00
32-pdr gun	6.40
24-pdr gun	5.82
18-pdr gun	5.30
12-pdr gun	4.62
9-pdr gun	4.20

Reduced windage greatly increased the strain on the gun carriage, however, which meant sacrificing practice with hot shot. The shot of an 8-inch gun was 7.9 inches; at white heat, it was 8.013 inches or greater than the diameter of the bore.

In addition to the need to reduce windage, the Sandy Hook tests revealed the superiority of shell guns and shortcomings in the way solid shot was maintained. Perry proposed that cannon balls be dipped in some rust-resistant substance when they came from the foundry.

The Navy Department was reorganized not long after the Sandy Hook trials. In 1842 the old Board of Navy Commissioners was replaced by five bureaus, including the Bureau of Ordnance and Hydrography. Not until 1862, in the course of another reorganization that led to creation of eight bureaus, did the Bureau of Ordnance become entirely separate.

It has been suggested that the trend toward a few heavy guns on new carriages was an innovation of the 1830s. Actually, it started much earlier. Shipbuilders had long been drawn to the possibility of utilizing a few guns of great range on one ship. As early as 1760, Chapman of Sweden had designed galley-type vessels armed with a battery of heavy guns on pivot mounts along the centerline. In 1798 the Royal Navy purchased a former merchant ship, the *Rattler,* which had been fitted with guns on this plan. Renamed *Wolverine,* the bark-rigged vessel could employ her eight main-deck guns to either side using tracks, or skids, and pivot mounts.

The gunboat navy of the Jefferson administration reflected this trend in the United States. Gunboats had been armed with a few heavy pivot guns, as some lake vessels would be in the War of 1812. The *Sylph* and *Ariel,* with batteries of pivoted long guns, were examples.

The success of the sloop in the War of 1812 produced advocates for this type of vessel (as opposed to the frigate). They supported the construction of large corvettes armed with a few more powerful guns rather than the traditional armament of numerous smaller guns.

For the U.S. Navy, the War of 1812 demonstrated the superiority of ships armed with long-range, heavier guns. It also made apparent that heaviest guns, usually chase guns, effected the most damage. With the advent of explosive shell, it was thought that large corvettes might profitably be armed with a few large shell guns and a supporting battery of heavy, long-range shot guns.

The next step was the arming of large ships with several heavy guns and omitting numerous but ineffective smaller pieces. This was a long, hard struggle, even if the arguments for change were impressive. One obstacle was that for centuries ships had been classed by the number of guns they carried, which in turn established the rank and pay of commanding officers, a process begun in the American navy in November 1776. It was not until the arrival of large steamers with their few guns that the navy finally accepted the idea that the value of a ship rested in the effectiveness of its armament and that her captain's rank should be determined accordingly.

Another trend of the 1830s was toward fewer types of guns, that is, standardization of caliber. The French took the lead in this. In 1820, they

TABLE 25

CHANGES IN U.S. NAVY GUN BATTERIES, 1820–53

				32-PDR GUNS			
Type		*No. of Guns*	*8-In Shell Guns*	*Long*	*Medium*	*Light*	*Other*
Changes in Battery							
Line-of-battle ships	1820	88	0	32 42-pdrs, 34 32-pdrs	0	0	22 42-pdr carronades
Line-of-battle ships	1841	88	8	28 42-pdrs, 30 32-pdrs	0	22	
Line-of-battle ships	1845	84	12	60	12	0	
Line-of-battle ships	1853	84	20	48	16	0	
Frigates, first class	1841	54	4	28	0	0	22 42-pdr carronades
Frigates, first class	1845	50	8	30	0	12	
Frigates, first class	1853	50	10	24	0	16	

				32-PDR GUNS		
Type		*No. of Guns*	*Weight of 8-In Shell Guns*	*Long*	*Medium or Light*	*Total*
Changes in Weight of Broadside (lbs)						
Line-of-battle ships	1820	88	0	1,248	462	1,710
Line-of-battle ships	1841	88	204	1,068	462	1,734
Line-of-battle ships	1845	84	306	960	192	1,458
Line-of-battle ships	1853	84	510	768	256	1,534
Frigates, first class	1841	54	102	448	462	1,012
Frigates, first class	1845	50	204	480	192	876
Frigates, first class	1853	50	255	384	256	895

Source: John A. Dahlgren, *Shells and Shell Guns* (Philadelphia: King and Baird, 1856), 284–85.

dropped 12-, 18-, 24-, and 36-pounder long guns and carronades in favor of the single 30-pounder for all batteries. Different-sized 30-pounders were used, depending on the type of ship and the height of a gun above water. This change was not introduced without opposition. Dispensing with the heaviest gun, the 36-pounder, meant reducing broadside power. But the 1837 French regulations specified only one caliber of gun, the 30-pounder, with the exception of a small number of 22-centimeter (80-pounder) shell guns.

In the British navy, up to the time of the War of 1812, the long 32-pounder was the principal gun for heavier ships, the long 18-pounder for frigates. In 1825, Colonel Munro of the Royal Artillery proposed to the Admiralty that the Royal Navy take its heaviest gun, the 32-pounder, as the standard for all batteries with 25 cwt, 42 cwt, and 56 cwt weights for different decks and ships. In 1829 a number of 25-cwt and 48-cwt pieces were cast, and beginning in 1830, substantial numbers of 18-pounders and 24-pounders of the Congreve

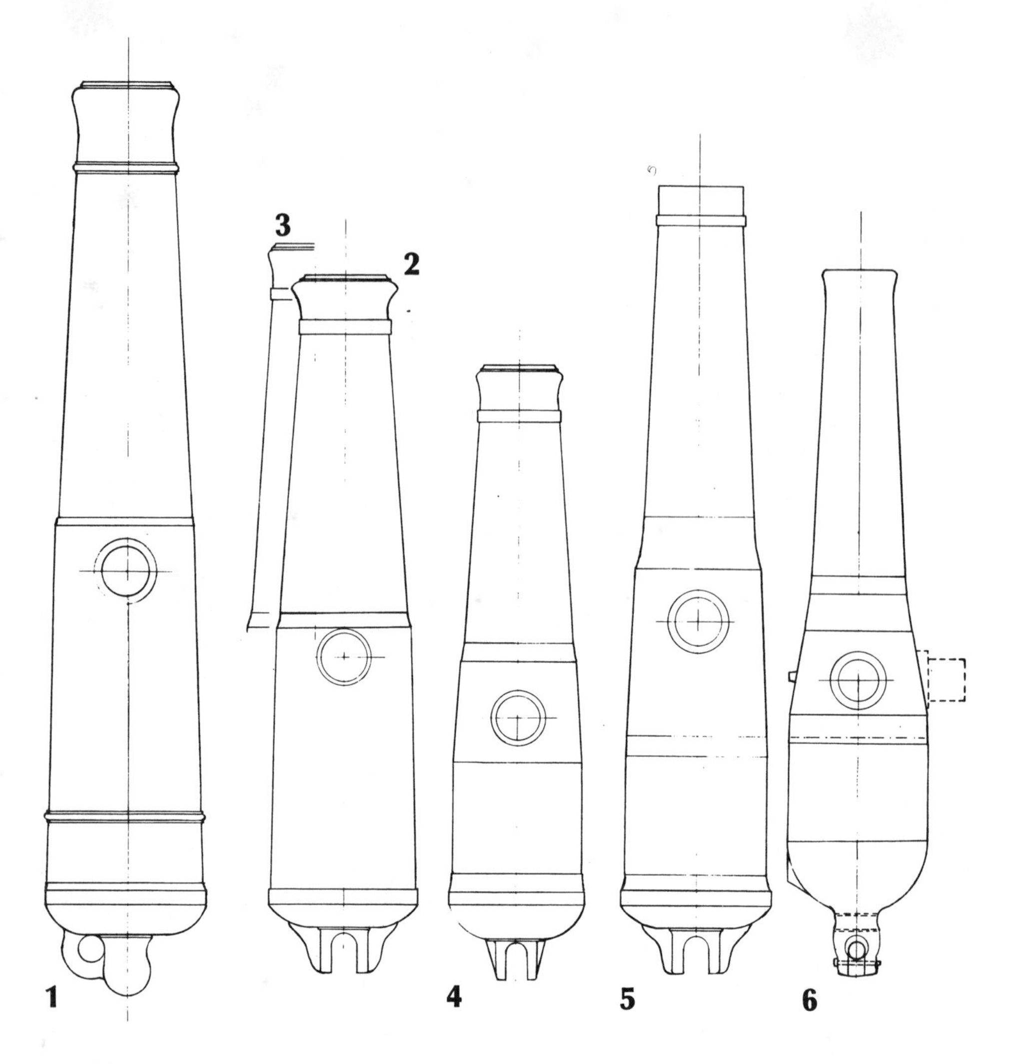

Fig. 66. U.S. Navy 32-Pdr Cannon, 1823–65. These cannon reflect the lines of ordnance development during the period. (Redrawn by C. S. Tucker after drawings in National Archives, Record Group 74.)

and Blomefield patterns, weighing 33 cwt, 40 cwt, and 41 cwt, were reamed to make 32-pounders.

Because of its superior striking power, the 42-pounder found advocates in both Britain and later the United States, but in 1839 the British, following the French regulations of 1837, officially adopted the 32-pounder as the standard gun size for the fleet. There were six classes of gun: 25, 32, 42, 45, 50, and 56 cwt. The 1839 regulations also included General Millar's 8-inch shell guns of 53 and 65 cwt.

In the U.S. Navy, frigates and ships of the line built after the War of 1812

Key to fig. 66.

Gun no. 1: A navy 32-pdr of 1823, probably a Gradual Increase gun. Length was 110″, weight 60.75 cwt, and bore 102.72 × 6.4″.

Gun no. 2: A light 32-pdr of 4,500 pounds. Length was 7′. Twenty-four of these were cast by Cyrus Alger in 1842 for the *Saratoga*. The tulip was afterwards turned off to make a straight muzzle. This appears to have been the first of the shark's mouth guns, as the original drawing is dated 1837 and carries the notation, "Altered at breech and cascabel, approved by the commissioners, 1841."

Gun no. 3: This might be called the production model of gun no. 2. A total of 213 of this type were cast in 1843 and 1844. The gun is 4″ longer and estimated to weigh about 150 pounds more than gun no. 2. Otherwise it is the same design.

Gun no. 4: A 32-pdr of 27 cwt. The gun was 6′ long. Note narrower flanges of the shark's mouth. A total of 150 guns were made of this design. Between 1837 and 1845 contracts were let for 190 32-pdrs of 27 cwt.

Gun no. 5: A navy short 32-pdr, 8′ long. Alger and Fort Pitt cast 136 of this model in 1842. The straight muzzle was not used on guns cast after this. A vertical pin running through the flanges usually held the breeching in the shark's mouth.

Gun no. 6: A 32-pdr designed by Dahlgren in 1855 for the screw steamer *Antelope*. This gun was designed to weigh 3,300 pounds and fire a shell weighing 25, with a charge of 3.5 pounds of powder. The bore was 69.92 × 6.4″. The elaborate breech aside, the form of the piece was not so revolutionary as it was said to be. The breech is deeper and the neck has a threaded hole for the elevating screw. This design was repeated in 1864 with a longer cylinder (dot-dash line). The number cast is unknown but was probably small.

were armed with 32- and 42-pounders, but in 1841 a few 8-inch shell guns of 63 cwt were added, usually four on each gun deck.

In June 1844, on the suggestion of Commodore William M. Crane, Secretary of the Navy John Mason sent two officers to Europe to study the standardization of naval armament carried out in Britain and France. The next year a captain's board adopted the 32-pounder as the basic gun for the U.S. Navy and introduced 55-cwt 8-inch shell guns on spar decks in addition to those already authorized for gun decks in 1841. In the American navy there were six classes of 32-pounders: 27, 32, 42, 46, 51, and 57 cwt. Over the next several years batteries were converted to this new system and, although not always immediately, carronades were replaced by 32-pounders of 27 or 32 cwt.

The change to standard caliber was beneficial in that it greatly simplified the types of shot and charges and eliminated possible costly error in battle. But gun weights continued to vary. For the three weights of 32-pounder on board a first-class frigate built in 1820 (the *Raritan* and her class), there were seven different powder charges, from four to nine pounds. While confusion in the shot locker may have ended, it still existed in the powder magazine.

There was another effect of standardizing caliber: the weight of broadside

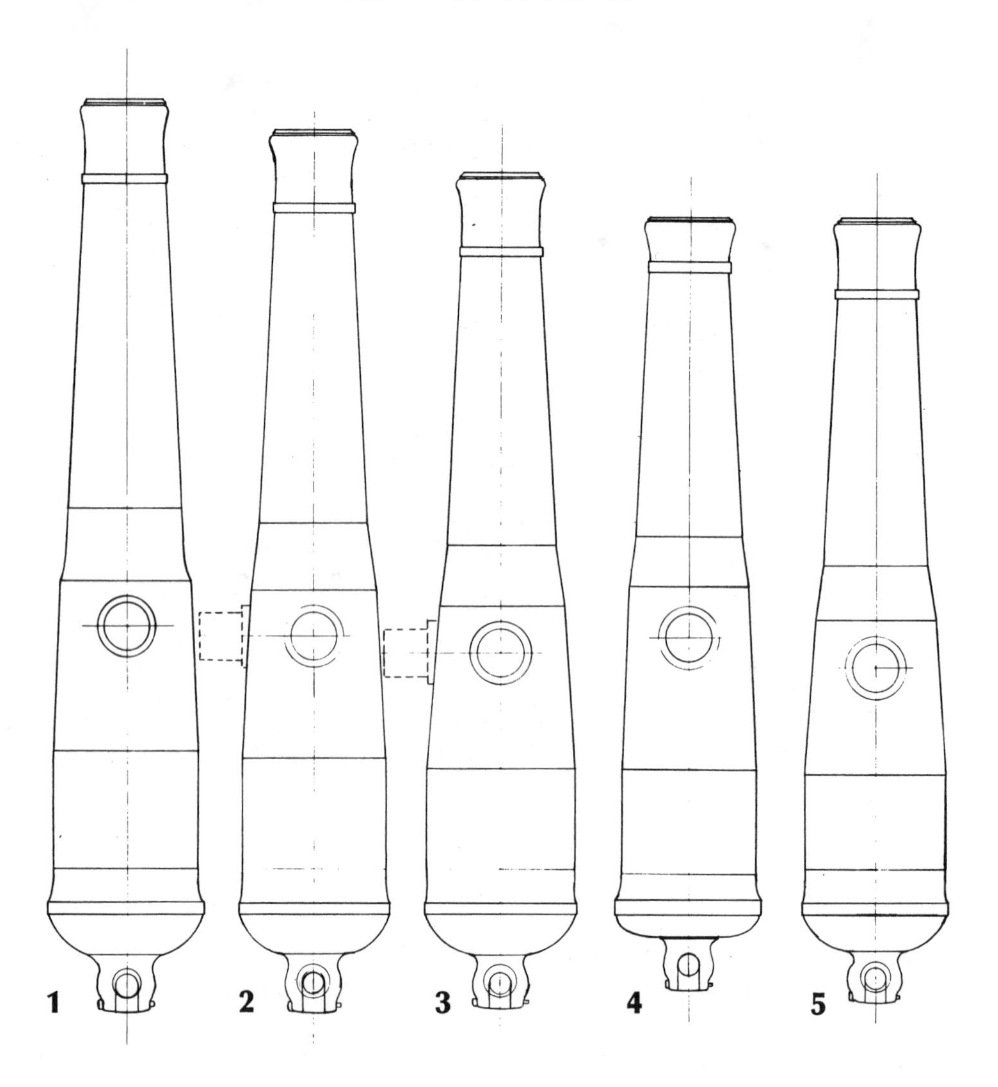

Fig. 67. U.S. Navy 32-Pdrs of the 1840s. A number of these guns should be shown with lock lugs and sight masses; in order that the proportions might be more clearly appreciated, these details have been omitted. (Redrawn by Cary S. Tucker after drawings in National Archives, Record Group 74.)

was effectively reduced (see table 25), at least in the American navy. The Royal Navy actually increased the weight of broadside in its ships of the line and frigates.

The change to one standard caliber was not as complete as it seems. Despite regulations, in the French navy the 36-pounder gun remained in service and indeed new ones were cast. In 1851, under a decree of May 1838, a total of 1,868 36-pounders were cast for the lower decks of ships of the line built before 1834. And in the U.S. Navy, 24-pounders were still in active service

Key to fig. 67.

Gun no. 1: The long 32-pdr of 57 cwt. The favored gun of the period, it was 112″ long and had a bore of 107 × 6.4″ and a preponderance of 450 pounds. A total of 850 were let on contracts between 1846 and 1851.

Gun no. 2: The 32-pdr of 51 cwt. Length was 108″, bore 104″, and preponderance 400 pounds. It was first cast in September 1846. Between 1846 and 1851, 103 guns of this type were let on contracts; 102 were cast.

Gun no. 3: The 32-pdr of 46 cwt. Length was 102″, bore 90.02″, and preponderance 400 pounds. Sixty guns of this type were let on contract in 1846.

Gun no. 4: The 32-pdr of 42 cwt. Length was 96″, bore 80.5″, and weight 4,650 pounds. The chamber was 5.88 × 7.25″ long. The comparatively flat breech marks this as an early design of the general type. Between 1842 and 1847, 312 32-pdrs of 42 cwt were let on contracts.

Gun no. 5: Another 32-pdr of 42 cwt, but slimmer toward the muzzle than the preceding one. It had the same length, 96″. The more rounded breech, not counted in the length, allowed for a longer bore, 92.05″. Preponderance was 350 pounds. Cannon contracts for the period 1837–60 show 312 32-pdrs of 42 cwt cast.

in 1841, as were 42-pounders of 9 feet and 70 cwt on the lower decks of ships of the line.

In form, the guns of the period became more functional. In new U.S. Navy guns based on patterns proposed by Commodore Wadsworth in 1845, all rings except those at the base and muzzle were eliminated. Gun profile in fact approached that of the later Dahlgren pieces with its unbroken, curved lines.

In the 1840s, both the army and navy carried out extensive experiments with new guns. One was designed by Professor Daniel Treadwell of Harvard University, who sought to take advantage of the fact that wrought-iron had about twice the tenacity of cast iron. The Treadwell gun was an important innovation based on the buildup principle of early breechloaders. The body of the gun—bore and breech—were cast iron whose thickness only amounted to about half the diameter of the bore. On top of this were placed successive rings or hollow cylinders of wrought-iron welded together. Each ring was made up of bars wound spirally and then welded and shaped in dies. A hydrostatic press capable of 1,000 tons of pressure forced the rings together. The rings, made slightly smaller than the final fit, were then heated so the expanded iron could be put on the gun before cooling and contracting.

The softness of wrought-iron subsequently induced Treadwell to change the process, beginning with a steel band about a third the thickness of the whole. Wrought-iron bars were then wound over the steel ring. The object was to arrange the metal so that the fiber ran in a direction opposite to that of tangential rupture—in other words, to produce a gun of equal strength in all directions.

Between 1841 and 1845, upwards of twenty Treadwell guns were manufactured. A 6-pounder made with the steel ring sustained 1,560 firings, beginning with service charges and ending with ten charges of 6 pounds of

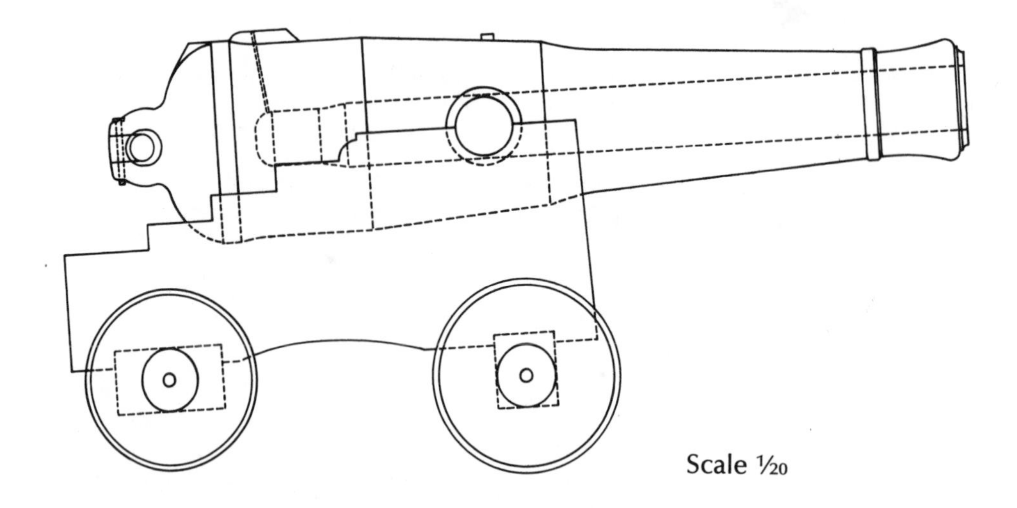

Fig. 68. The 32-Pdr of 32 CWT. (After a drawing by John Dahlgren in National Archives, Record Group 74, "Report on 32 Pdr of 32 Cwt.")

powder and seven shot. To rupture a 32-pounder Treadwell, it had to be fired with 14 pounds of powder and five shot. Surprisingly, the guns were quite light. The 32-pounder weighed only sixty times its shot, about the same as a carronade.

Both the army and navy tested Treadwells and found the smaller guns to be satisfactory. In 1846, the army's Ordnance Board recommended the establishment of batteries of 6- and 12-pounders and 12- and 24-pounder howitzers, which the secretary of war approved in 1847. Four 32-pounders the navy contracted for in 1843 had a bore length of 70 inches, a tulip muzzle, and a weight of between 1,700 and 1,900 pounds; they were delivered but did not prove successful.

Factors leading to the gun's rejection by the navy may have been its high cost, its recoil, and doubts about its reliability. While wrought-iron guns had greater tensile strength, their welds tended to be weak. As the chief of the Bureau of Naval Ordnance, Captain Henry A. Wise, noted in 1864, "You may make one gun that will stand ten thousand rounds, and the next gun may not stand ten rounds. You cannot get the uniformity desirable."[15]

No Treadwell guns of the army pattern survive, though there is a pair of identical 32-pounder Treadwells at the Washington Navy Yard. The name Daniel Treadwell is inscribed just behind the trunnion band of each. The base ring of one is marked No. 1, that of the other, No. 2. It is believed these are from the navy contract of 1843.

Despite the failure of the Treadwell in this country, Britain's successful Armstrong breech-loading gun was built on its principle. In both guns, requisite strength was obtained by coiling wrought-iron and welding it in place.

Treadwell also experimented with shot in the 1840s. He placed it in a bag made of felt or hard woolen cloth, which proved to minimize balloting and hence damage to the bore during fire.

Certainly the most infamous ordnance experiment of this period involved the Peacemaker gun on the screw-steamer *Princeton*. The sloop was specifically designed to carry new heavy ordnance. In 1844, her armament consisted of two 12-inch wrought-iron guns and twelve 42-pounder carronades. One of the 12-inchers, designed by the brilliant Swedish-born engineer John Ericsson, arrived in the United States in 1841. Named the Orator, it had been manufactured at the Mersey Iron Works near Liverpool. In proof firing at Sandy Hook the gun developed cracks behind the trunnions. (Ericsson claimed this resulted from its breech being buried in sand, where it could not recoil, and the use of powder charges of up to 56 pounds.) To reinforce the gun, 3.5-inch bands of the best American iron were shrunk on the breech. The gun itself had a 13-foot unchambered bore and fired shot capable of penetrating 4.5 inches of wrought-iron. Accounts of the number of firings after original proof differ. Captain Robert Stockton subsequently maintained it was 180, at which point the gun was still in perfect condition.

The new wrought-iron piece attracted considerable attention, and shortly after its arrival Stockton had another one built on the same principle. In 1837 and 1839 he had been in England, where he met with Ericsson and, without authorization, ordered the first 12-inch gun. The second one was rather hastily made, of hot-blast iron, forged by Ward and Company of New York and then bored and finished at the Phoenix Foundry under Ericsson's direction. This second gun, described as a better piece of workmanship, had the same-size bore and chamber as the first but was a foot greater in diameter at the breech to compensate for the bands on the first gun, making them the same size overall. In the winter of 1843–44, it was given a cursory proof, fired only five times, once with a charge of 49.6 pounds of powder and one ball. At the time it was manufactured the gun was the largest mass of wrought-iron ever forged, weighing 27,390 pounds before it was bored.

The two guns, the one built in the United States and misnamed Peacemaker and the one from England which, because of tension between the two countries over the Northwest boundary, was renamed Oregon, were installed in the *Princeton*.

In 1845 the Mersey Iron Works forged a third wrought-iron gun to replace the Peacemaker. Its dimensions are given as follows: total length, 14 feet 1 inch; diameter at the chamber, 28 inches; length of bore, 12 feet; and weight, 16,700 pounds. This gun, fired only once with a charge of 45 pounds of powder and two 224-pound shot, was never mounted for service. It has no chamber. The shot was enveloped in felt to prevent damage to the bore. It became known as the Brooklyn Navy Yard Gun because it was housed at the Sands Street entrance to that yard for many years.

The Oregon is at the U.S. Naval Academy, Annapolis, the replacement

Fig. 69. The Oregon Gun. (Photograph by Malcolm Muir, Jr.)

piece cast in Liverpool at the Washington Navy Yard. The latter, however, is marked as weighing 7 tons 10 cwt, or 16,800 pounds. It is mounted on a 13-inch mortar carriage.

In any case, in January 1844 both the Oregon and Peacemaker were put in the *Princeton,* the Peacemaker accorded the place of honor at the bow. Ericsson also designed a new wrought-iron carriage that did away with breeching and was the forerunner of his Civil War monitor carriage. The Peacemaker was said to be so accurate "that it could hit an object 'the size of a hogshead' 9 out of 10 times half a mile away. The gun had a range finder and the elevation was set by means of an invention enabling the firing to be just the right point in the ship's motion. A tackle fixed to the breech allowed the gun to be elevated precisely."[16]

The *Princeton* made several trial runs during which the guns were fired. There was considerable interest in them and in the sloop itself. On 28 February 1844 approximately four hundred people, including President John Tyler, his department heads, and their families, were taken on board the *Princeton* at Alexandria. On the way down the Potomac to a point below Fort Washington, the Peacemaker was fired several times. As the vessel made her way back up river, Stockton agreed to fire the gun another time. But this time it burst, killing Secretary of State and former Secretary of the Navy Abel Upshur, Secretary of the Navy Thomas Gilmer, and six others. A number of people, including Senator Thomas Hart Benton and Stockton, were injured. President Tyler was below decks and therefore escaped injury. A belated casualty was the chief of the Bureau of Ordnance and Hydrography, Commodore William M. Crane; despondent over the tragedy and his inability to bring Stockton under control, in 1846 he resigned his post and committed suicide.

An inquiry was ordered into the tragedy, and in August 1844 a committee of the Franklin Institute issued a report. It concluded that, given manufacturing techniques of the day, the attempt to use large wrought-iron guns like the Peacemaker should be abandoned. The problem was the difficulty, if not impossibility, of securing satisfactory welds and the weakness of iron after long exposure to intense heat during manufacture.

Stockton defended the wrought-iron gun, contending that it was bad metal as well as poor welds that had caused the tragedy. But he maintained that the Oregon was safe. In addition to its original proof, the gun had been fired 180 times, 28 with 30 pounds of powder, 102 with 25 pounds, 21 with 20 pounds, and 29 with 14 pounds. It was, he said, "perfect and as safe now, as when the experiments commenced. Every precaution has been taken, with the most delicate gauges and instruments, to detect the slightest change in the gun, inside and outside, but none can be detected." Stockton believed that if the Peacemaker had been made of sound materials, it would not have burst.[17] Nonetheless, after the tragedy the Oregon was removed and never fired again. Apparently it was offloaded at Philadelphia and taken to Annapolis. The *Princeton* received a new propeller in 1845. During the Mexican War, her armament consisted of one 8-inch pivot gun and eight 42-pounder carronades.

Ericsson's refusal to accept any responsibility for the Peacemaker explosion led to a break with Stockton, and the inventor did not receive full compensation for his work on the *Princeton.* Stockton demanded an official inquiry into his own conduct and was subsequently vindicated. Many remained critical, however. Although he retained the confidence of President Tyler, the House Committee on Naval Affairs censured the navy for allowing Stockton to carry out his own particular views and cautioned against allowing individuals to order armament without proper approval.

The bursting of the Peacemaker may well have given Congress an excuse to hold up construction of more steam or iron warships; it may also have delayed the introduction of heavy ordnance aboard U.S. Navy ships, though it seems not to have retarded ordnance development. Indeed, as has been noted, the tragedy resulted in a series of government-ordered experiments into metal casting techniques and quality control that produced higher-quality guns. Rodman, for one, was motivated by the Peacemaker event to patent his new process for casting safer guns. Another effect the explosion had was to reduce powder charges for guns aboard ship. By the time of the Civil War the maximum was 15 pounds, and this was for the XI-inch Dahlgren gun.

Meanwhile, the casting of heavy guns continued. In July 1846, a 12-inch (225-pounder) piece was cast at Alger's foundry in South Boston for the army. Known as the Bomford gun after its designer, Colonel Bomford, head of the Army Ordnance Office, it was at the time the largest in the world, weighing

Fig. 70. The Stockton (Mersey) Gun. (Photograph by Malcolm Muir, Jr.)

25,510 pounds and firing a shell of 181 pounds. Propelled by a powder charge of 28 pounds, its shell had a range of 5,800 yards or 3.5 miles.

Although ordnance was changing in these years, gun carriages were not. Despite attempts to replace it with new types, the ordinary truck carriage was still standard for broadside guns of ships of war. There had been slight modifications. An extension to the breastplate, adopted from the French navy and apparently not much used on contemporary English ship carriages, had appeared sometime before the War of 1812. Initially it was a solid and later a hinged shelf. When the hinged part was up, the carriage could be run out so that the fore trucks rested against the waterways, with the breast of the brackets against the side timbers. Thus the weight of the gun and carriage was not concentrated on any one point of the ship's side; this was especially important in bad weather with the gun secured. When the outer piece of the breast piece was down, the fore trucks were brought back clear of the waterways and the arc of the breastplate touched the side of the ship, which allowed lateral training of the gun for oblique fire. Dumb trucks had also been added, by 1850 chocking quoins furnished. Two of the latter were placed before the front trucks to prevent the gun from returning to the side after firing. Chocking quoins were also used when the gun was housed.

A gun was elevated in its carriage by means of a wooden quoin sliding on the bed. The quoin's side was marked in degrees of elevation and depression. Later, these marks were made on the flat part of the quoin. To depress the gun the quoin was turned on its side, and the greatest depression was made with the quoin run home. Because of the violent movement of the carriage after firing, the quoin frequently flew out, endangering the crew. David Porter rectified this when he invented an iron projection on the bottom of the quoin

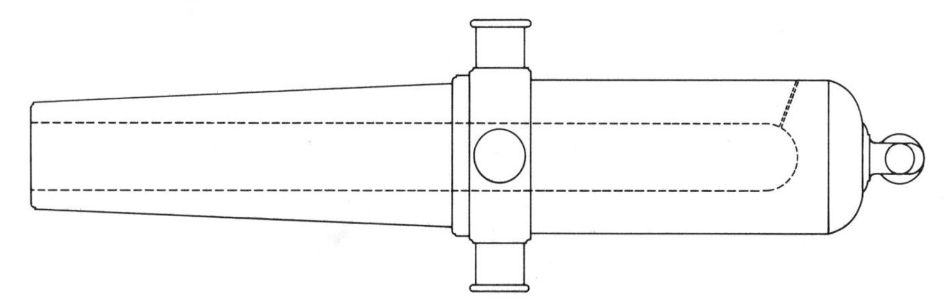

Fig. 71. The 12-Inch Wrought-Iron Cannon (Mersey Gun). (After a drawing in National Archives, Record Group 74, marked "12-inch wrought-iron cannon made in England to order to Captain Stockton. Weight, 7 tons 10 cwt. November 1845.")

that caught in a ratchet secured to the bed. Of other modifications, the most effective was the horizontal screw quoin first suggested by Lieutenant (later Commander) J. H. Ward and later improved on (see figure 75). While it performed well in tests, it seems not to have been adopted by the navy at the start of the Civil War. Apparently the horizontal screw quoin was first used in the French navy.

A vertical, metal elevating screw for field carriages was first employed at sea on the carronade. The French used it for their long-gun carriages. The British retained the quoin, as did the U.S. Navy, which, however, also experimented with screws designed by Dahlgren and Hart. The vertical elevating screw was easily bent or damaged and slow to operate—not a serious disadvantage since great change in elevation was seldom required. While not precise in determining elevation, the old quoin allowed the greatest extremes of elevation and could be rapidly operated.

Wood deteriorated under constant exposure to the elements, particularly in the high humidity of the tropics, and so a number of experiments were conducted in the first half of the nineteenth century with cast- and wrought-iron carriages. The latter were judged more successful, but neither proved satisfactory. The shock of the gun's discharge often broke these carriages (they could not be used safely with charges greater than one-fourth the weight of the shot), and if struck by shot they were prone to shatter, producing the same effect as grapeshot. In addition, iron carriages were difficult to repair.

It was hard to improve on the standard truck carriage, which combined strength, stability, simplicity, and ease of transport on board ship. It could also be brought back into battery again (in case of a break in the breeching) more easily than any other carriage.

The principal defects of the wooden truck carriage remained the expense of its construction, the violent and unequal recoil of the gun on its breeching, the difficulty of training it, and its great and cumbersome weight. In 1861 a wooden carriage for a heavy 32-pounder gun weighed 1,200 pounds, while the lightest truck carriage for a 32-pounder, of 33 cwt, was 1,000 pounds.

Paint protected carriages from the elements. A dull red color was often

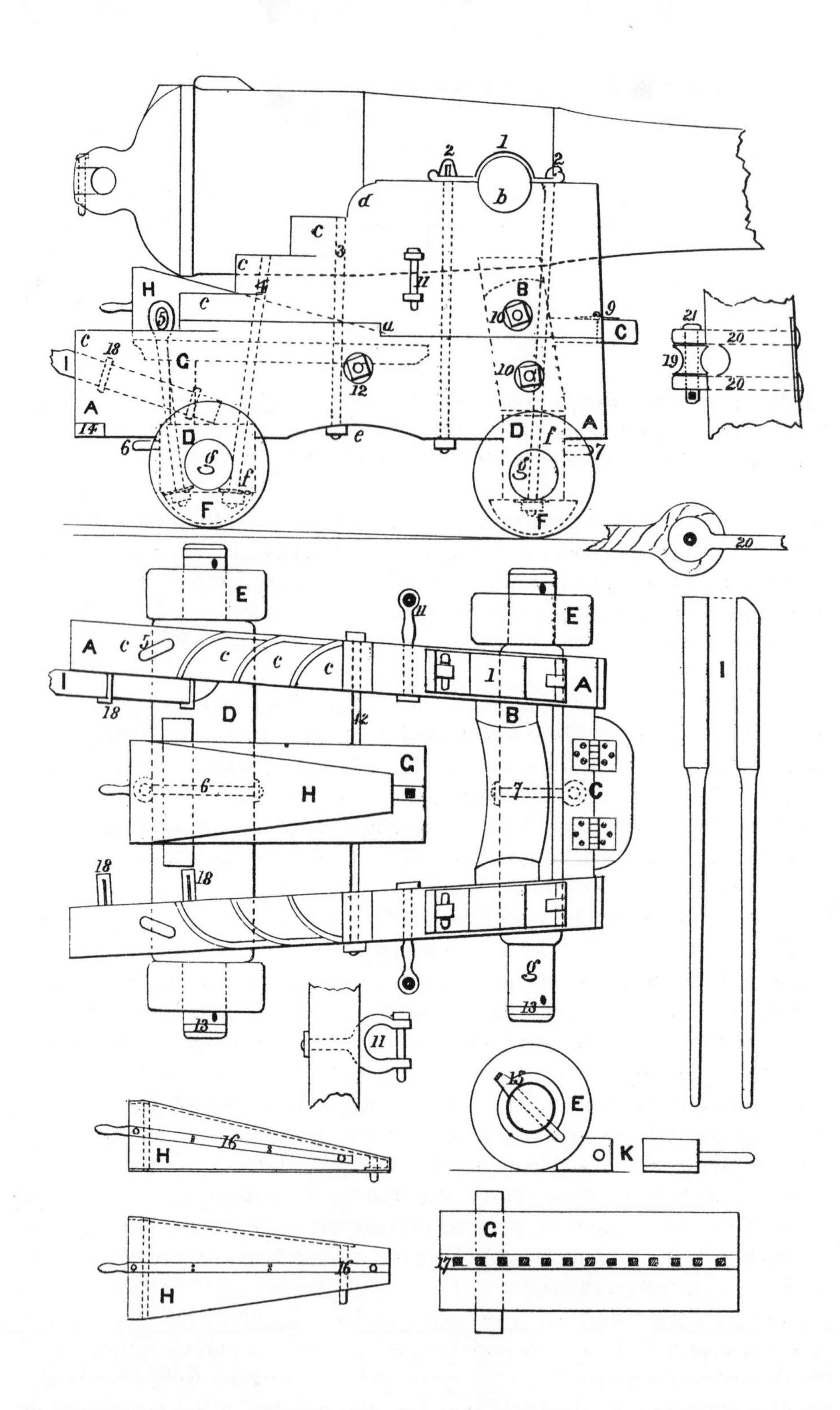

Fig. 72. Naval Truck Carriage and Nomenclature, 1852. (Bureau of Ordnance, Navy Department, *Instructions in Relation to the Preparation of Vessels of War for Battle* [Washington, 1852].)

Key to fig. 72.

WOODEN PARTS

Carriage

A. Brackets of large carriages are each made of two pieces joined by a jog *a* and doweled. The remaining parts are the trunnion holes *b*, steps *c*, quarter rounds *d*, and arch *e*.
B. Transom
C. Breast piece in two parts, the inner part fixed, the outer part moveable, connected by hinges.
D. Front and rear axletrees each consisting of the square body *f* and arms *g*
E. Front and rear trucks
F. Dumb trucks
G. Bed and stool
H. Quoin

Implements

I. Handspikes
K. Chocking quoin

METAL PARTS

Carriage

1. Two cap squares
2. Four cap square bolts and two keys
3. Two bracket bolts
4. Two rear axletree bolts
5. Two side tackle eye bolts
6. One train tackle eye bolt
7. One transporting eye bolt
8. Breast bolts
9. Two hinges of breast pieces
10. Two transom bolts (upper and lower)
11. Two breeching shackles and pins
12. Bed bolt
13. Four axletree bands
14. Two chafing plates
15. Four linchpins and washers
16. Quoin plate and stop
17. Ratchet for quoin stop
18. Four training loops
19. Breeching thimble (cast iron)
20. Side shackle bolts for breechings
21. Shackle pin, plates, and keys

TABLE 26

CARRIAGE FOR A 32-POUNDER CWT, 1848*

Height of cheek	21.5
Length of cheek	57.0
Width of cheek in front	20.25 (clear)
Width of cheek in rear	22.0 (clear)
Fore trucks in diameter	20.0
Hind trucks in diameter	18.0
Arms of axles in diameter	5.5
Weight	1,040
Breeching	7.75

Source: National Archives, Record Group 74, Records of the Bureau of Ordnance, section I, "Report on Firing of 32-pounder Gun," p. 22
* All dimensions are given in inches except weight, which is given in pounds.

favored since it hid the blood that might be splattered about in an engagement. This color was extended to other ship fittings for the same reason. By 1860 the U.S. Navy commonly painted its carriages black.

For maintenance, linchpins, shackle bolts, and other parts were removed twice a week and cleaned and rubbed with black lead inside. All the ironwork of the carriages along with the guns themselves was kept free of rust. Tallow protected the elevating screws, pivot bolts, and so forth. Cap squares were removed frequently, the guns lifted out and the trunnions cleaned.

Commander James Ward of the U.S. Navy proposed an improvement on the common truck carriage. In the Ward carriage, dumb trucks were removed and fore and aft pieces bolted between the axletrees. A handspike with fixed rollers 9 inches in diameter was added just beneath the trunnions. The carriage was placed on a slide high enough to lift the trucks clear of the deck. The ends of the breeching were spliced together and shackled to a bolt beneath the center of the sill. The advantages of the new carriage included ease of running out, recoil, and transport, and equal strain on both legs of the breeching. The gun was always in the center of the port and the tackles did not have to be dropped before firing. The disadvantages of the Ward carriage included the space needed for its operation; the damage done to the vessel by the slide, which, moreover, was heavy and expensive; and the fact that it could not use the vertical screw. Advantages seemed to outweigh defects. The damage the Ward carriage did to the deck of the vessel was judged to be less than that inflicted by the old truck or new Marsilly carriages, while the slide was lighter and at the same time stronger.

In trials on board the receiving ship *North Carolina* the Ward carriage was compared to a conventional truck carriage, both mounting a 32-pounder of 61 cwt. The Ward was judged easier for training. Despite this, it appears to have been little used.

Prior to the Civil War, various carriages were developed that applied

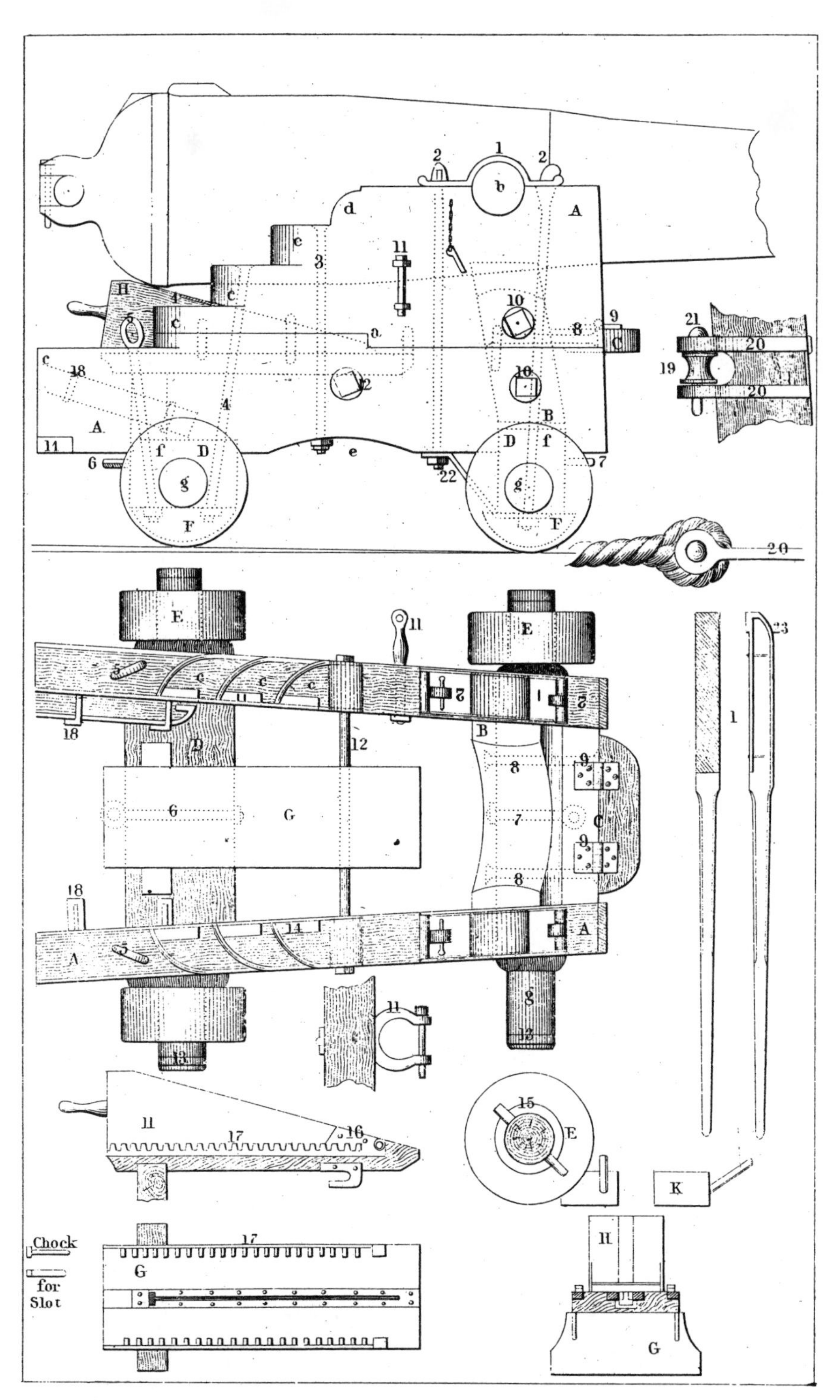

Fig. 73. Naval Truck Carriage, 1866. (Bureau of Ordnance, *Ordnance Instructions,* 1866.) Additions to the 1852 carriage illustration consist of *22*, two axle stays; and *23*, handspike shoe.

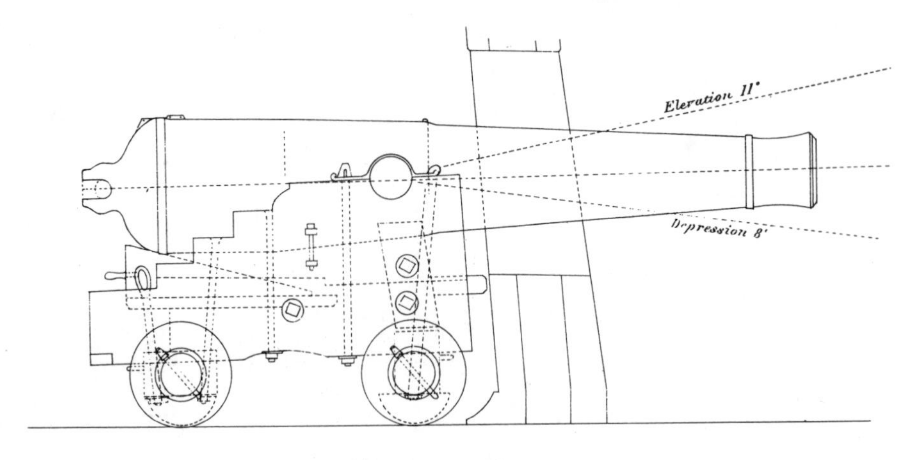

51-CWT Gun

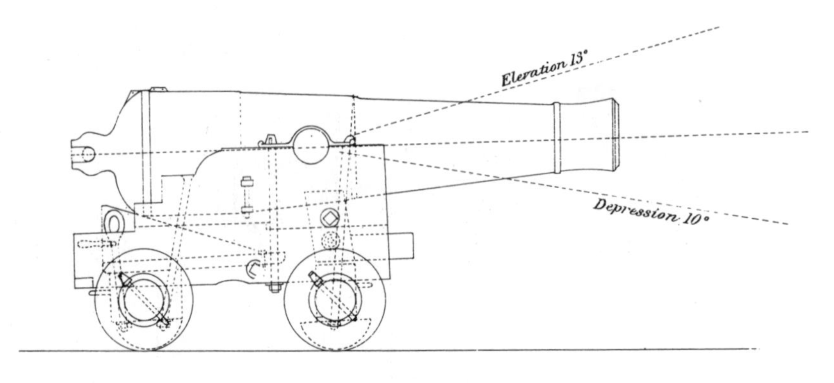

32-CWT Gun

Fig. 74. New-Pattern 32-Pdrs of 51 and 32 CWT and Their Carriages. (Jeffers, *A Concise Treatise.*)

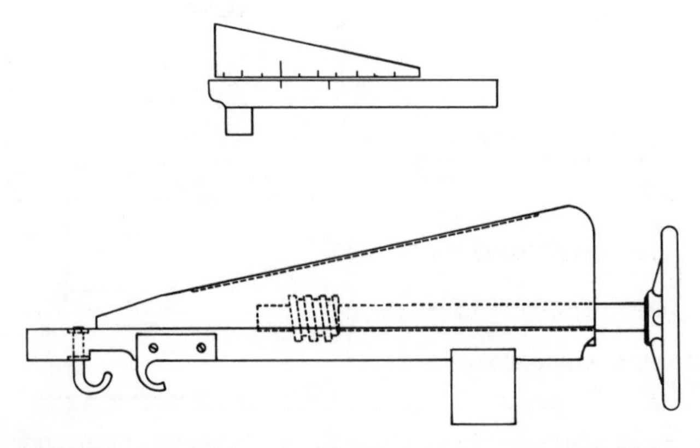

Fig 75. A Screw Quoin, Shown beneath an Old Quoin.

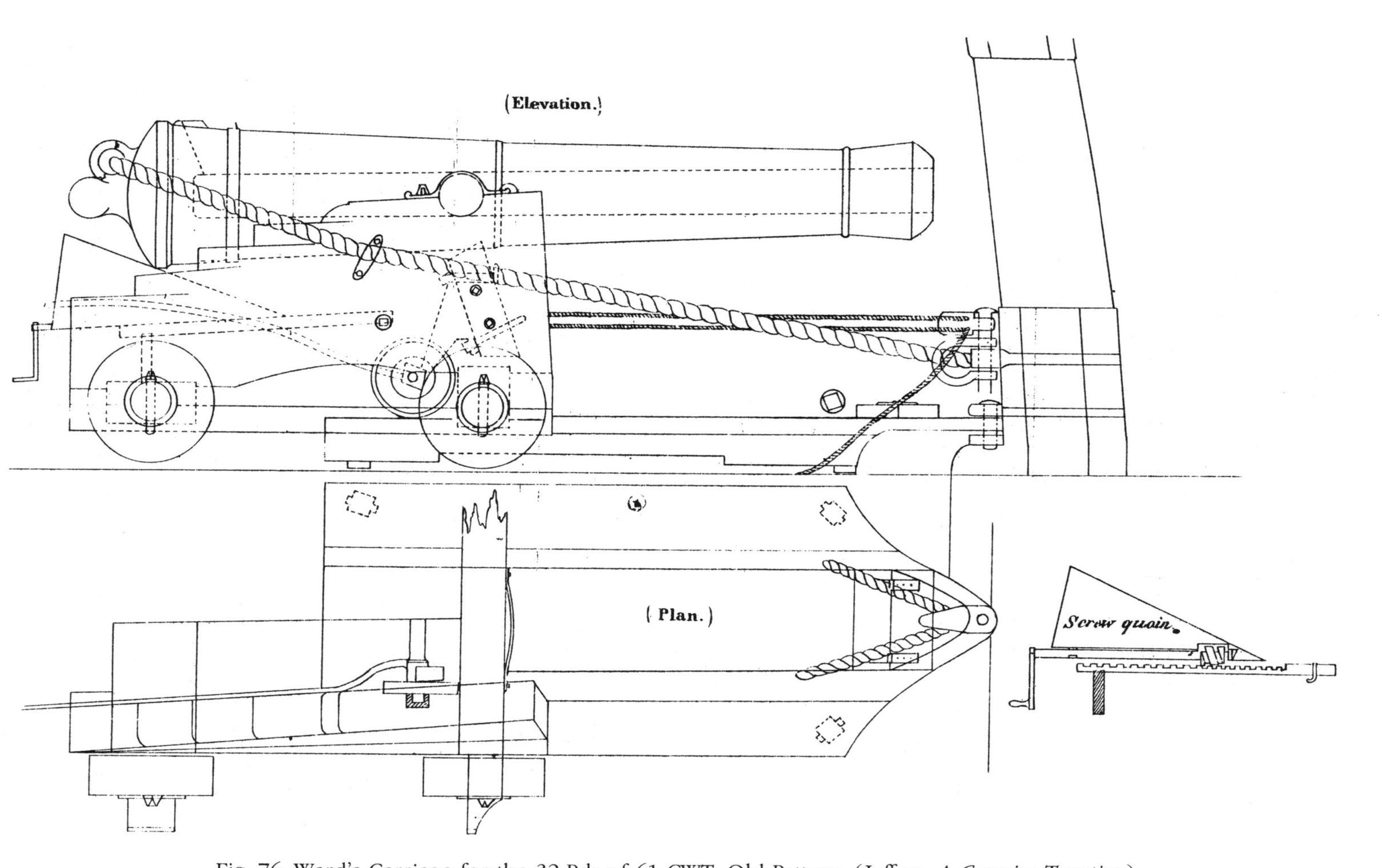

Fig. 76. Ward's Carriage for the 32-Pdr of 61 CWT, Old Pattern. (Jeffers, *A Concise Treatise*.)

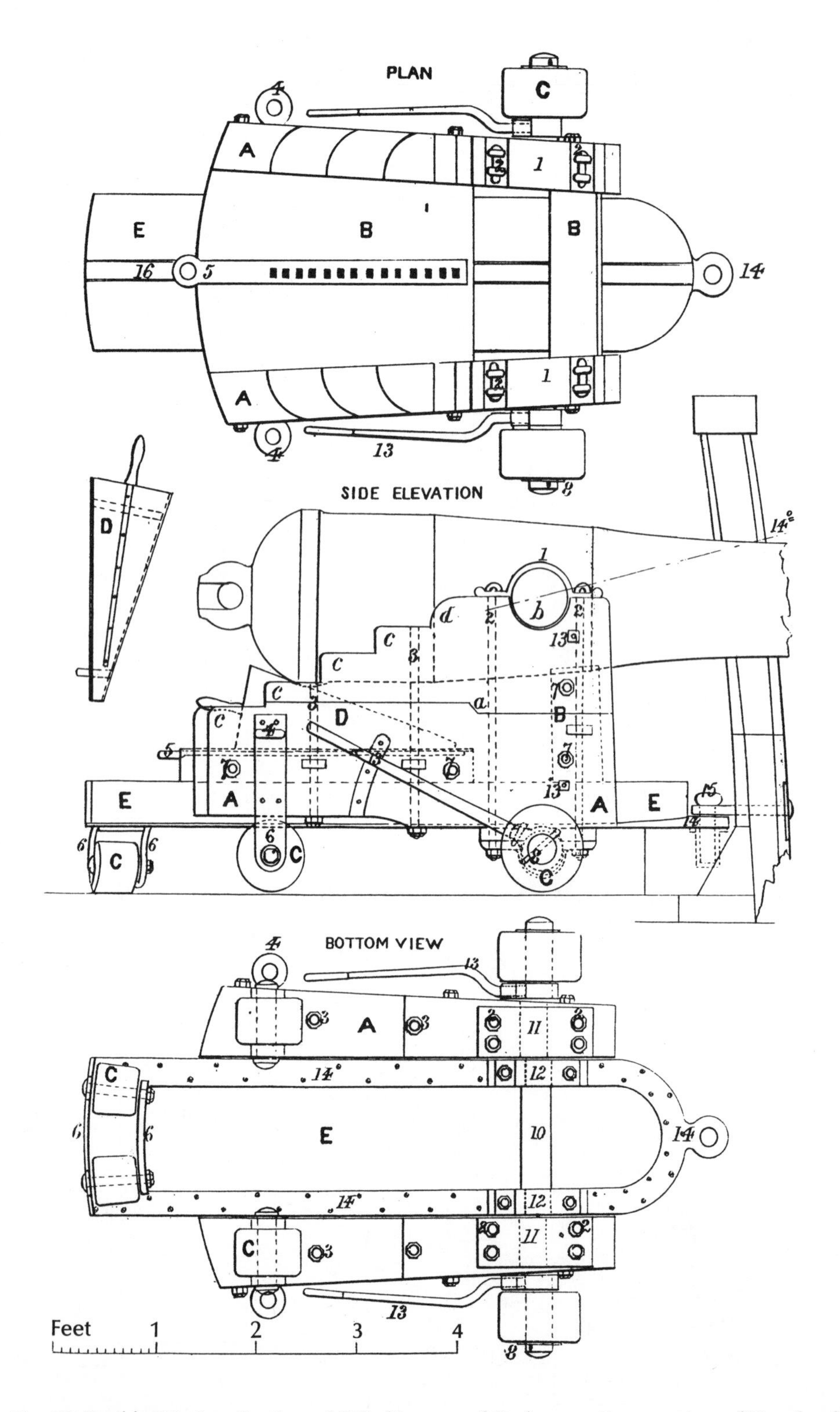

Fig. 77. Pook's Friction Carriage, 1852. (Bureau of Ordnance, *Preparation of Vessels of War for Battle*.)

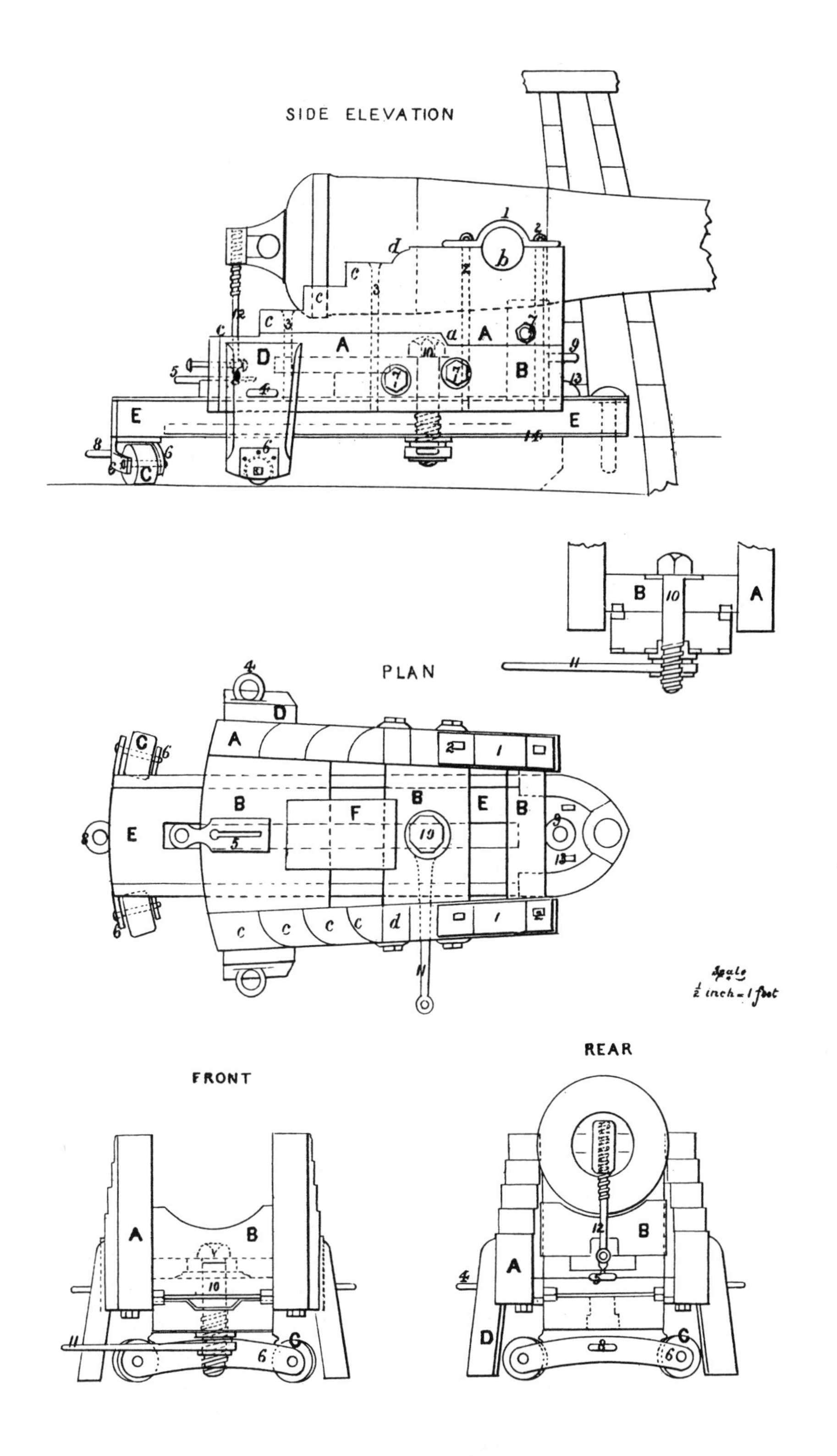

Fig. 78. Van Brunt's Friction Carriage, 1852. (Bureau of Ordnance, *Preparation of Vessels of War for Battle.*)

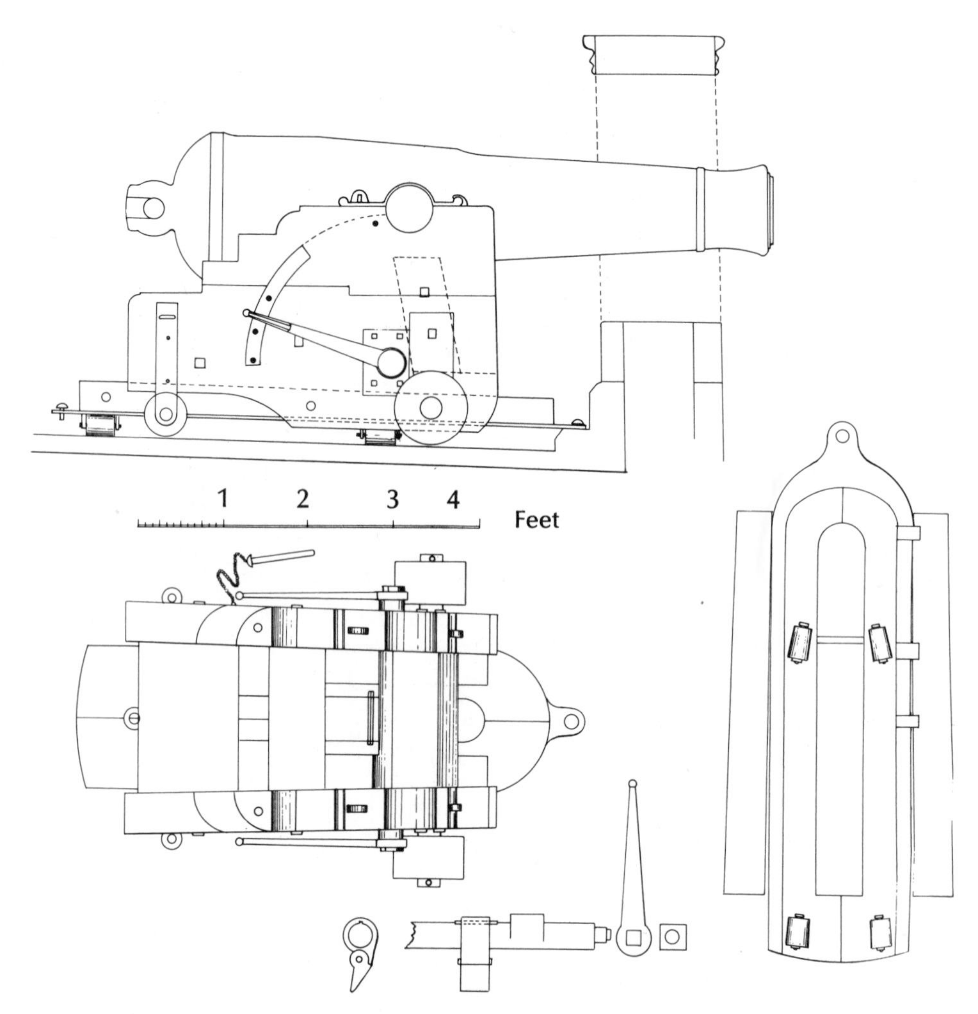

Fig. 79. The Improved Van Brunt Carriage, 1853. (From National Archives, Record Group 74.)

friction to lessen recoil. The top carriage of one was mounted on a slide. A clamp and compressor increased friction on the slide. Another, the Pook friction carriage, was tried out in smaller vessels carrying light 32-pounders of 27 and 33 cwt. By 1852 it was still experimental. Objections to the carriage were expressed because in action the crew might forget to compress it on the slide and thereby endanger it and themselves when the gun was fired. The carriage was also vulnerable; a shot hitting it anywhere might disable it.

In competition with the Pook friction carriage for light 32-pounders on smaller ships was a carriage designed by Hardy. By 1852 it had been adopted for the light guns of third-class sloops. The initial carriage was judged too heavy, inconvenient to work, complex, large, and hard to transport aboard ship. Compared with the common truck carriage, it was deficient in every area except recoil. By 1852 Hardy's invention had been fitted with a compressor designed by Captain Van Brunt of the U.S. Navy. The carriage itself was also, at some point, redesigned and improved so that it could be effective with broadside guns, particularly light ones. It came to be known as the Van Brunt carriage. Ordnance instructions for 1860 show a Van Brunt carriage combining features of the Pook and Hardy carriages. In the Van Brunt, transoms were substituted for axletrees. The carriage rested on a slide, but four trucks secured to the brackets by bronze boxes and axles rested on the deck at the sides of the slide, supported the weight of the carriage, and kept the transoms up from the slide. This enabled the carriage to run out more easily.

Friction produced by an eccentric shaft running across the carriage arrested its recoil. The shaft had levers attached to its ends; when these were hove down they pressed two compressor blocks onto the upper surface of the slide; at the same time, pressure on the underside of the slide was produced by clamps that projected a short distance under the slide. Trucks attached by a bronze box to the rear underside of the slide made training easier.

CHAPTER VI

The Revolution in Naval Ordnance: Steam, Ironclads, and Shell Guns

IN THE HALF century after the War of 1812, steam propulsion replaced sails and wooden hulls gave way to ironclad construction. These two developments were closely related to changes in naval ordnance.

In 1813, Robert Fulton submitted to President James Madison plans for a steam warship. Secretary of the Navy William Jones and Captains Decatur, Jones, and Perry supported the idea. Congress authorized the vessel in March 1814, and Fulton was placed in charge of the construction. The new vessel, named the *Demologos* ("voice of the people"), was launched at the end of October. She was renamed the *Fulton* after her designer's death in February 1815 and was subsequently called the *Fulton I*.

At the time of her commissioning in June 1815, the *Fulton* was the first steam frigate in any navy in the world. Intended for harbor defense at New York City, she was not a true frigate. Fulton saw her as a floating battery using steam power simply to move from place to place. With a length of 156 feet, a width of 45, and a depth of 20, she was the largest steamer in the world. She displaced 2,475 tons. Her outer bulwarks, of wood 58 inches thick, were considered shot-proof. As a ship-rigged catamaran the *Fulton* could make 5.5 mph under steam alone. Fulton had planned propulsion solely by steam, but Captain David Porter, given command of the vessel while it was being built, insisted that sails be added. This required building up sides originally flush with the spar deck in order to create bulwarks protecting the men working the sails. All of this added greatly to the *Fulton*'s weight without improving her fighting qualities.

The *Fulton* was rated at thirty guns. There were plans to arm her with at least some large columbiads, but she carried long 32-pounders on her trial run. Discussion of her armament is academic since she was never fully completed for service. She became a receiving ship at the Brooklyn Navy Yard and in 1829 was destroyed there in an accidental explosion of her magazine.

Secretary of the Navy Jones planned for at least two similar vessels to be built at Baltimore and Philadelphia. The Philadelphia vessel was never begun and Jones's successor, Benjamin Crowninshield, halted work on the steam warship at Baltimore. Thus by the late 1820s, none of the three steam batteries for coastal defense authorized in the Gradual Increase Act of 1816 existed. Meanwhile, as the United States fell behind, experimentation moved forward in Europe. The first steam vessels in the British navy were towing vessels for men-of-war: the *Comet,* built in 1819, and the *Lightning* and *Meteor,* a year later.

Proponents of steam vessels, including the man regarded by many as the father of the steam navy in the United States, Captain Matthew Perry, continued to push for seagoing steam warships. It was not until 1835, however, that Secretary of the Navy Mahlon Dickerson, a friend of Perry, was able to proceed with such a vessel. The next year the *Fulton II,* designed by Samuel Humphries, was laid down. Launched in 1837, this 700-ton side-wheeler was the second steam warship to be carried on the U.S. Navy list. She was 180 feet in length, had a beam of 35 feet, and was powered by two engines totaling 625 horsepower. Under steam she could make about 12 knots. She also had a schooner rig on three masts. The *Fulton II* carried only nine guns: eight long 42-pounders and one long 24-pounder. Initially under the command of Perry, she proved to be slow, mechanically inefficient, and poorly armed. In 1851, the *Fulton II* was razeed and her armament reduced to one long 68-pounder (8-inch) and four medium 32s.[1]

Many in the navy opposed the new steam-powered vessels. Among them was James K. Paulding, secretary of the navy from 1838 to 1841, who is reported to have said that he "never would consent to see our grand old ships supplanted by these new and ugly sea-monsters."[2] In fairness, however, it should be pointed out that the opposition to steam resulted not only from obscurantism but also from the fact that the early steamships had serious shortcomings. They could maneuver easily in calm or light winds, but slow speed and a high rate of fuel consumption reduced their cruising range. Side-wheels, moreover, were an inefficient means of propulsion, and the drag of the paddles inhibited these ships when they sailed. Paddle wheels were large and vulnerable targets for enemy fire and took up so much room on the sides of a vessel that little remained for standard broadside batteries. Accommodation of the engines, boilers, fuel, and boiler water forced reductions in other areas, including crew and hence the number of men available to work guns.

Steam frigates did not have the tiered broadside batteries common to sailing men-of-war. Side-wheelers carried only a few guns, but these were so much more powerful than their predecessors that steamers could initiate fire before the more numerous broadside guns of a sailing warship were able to reply effectively. As a result, heavy guns soon appeared on pivot mounts in steamships. In the British navy, the 56-pounder Monk gun and the 68-pounder Dundas were adopted in the 1840s and early 1850s. By the early 1850s, steamers in the U.S. Navy were generally armed with a few 8-inch (or 64-pounder shot guns) or 10-inch shell guns on pivot mounts to permit a wide arc of fire and considerable elevation. In addition to pivot guns on the spar deck, the largest steamers had broadside pieces on their gun decks. Even so, these guns were not sufficient in number to match those of sailing ships of the same tonnage.

Though batteries varied from ship to ship in the U.S. Navy, by 1850 first-class steam frigates generally carried ten guns—eight 8-inchers in broadside and two 10-inchers in pivot. Second-class steam frigates were armed with six guns, all 8-inchers, while third-class steamers carried only two 8-inch guns.

Only in 1837, after the steam warship program had been revived, was the 120-gun *Pennsylvania*—the largest American sail battleship ever built—launched. Two years later, in 1839, Congress authorized three additional steam warships. Two of these, the twin first-class steam frigates *Mississippi* and *Missouri,* were laid down the same year. Both 1,700-ton side-wheelers were completed in 1842. While handsome vessels, their machinery was above the waterline, leaving them vulnerable to one well-placed shot and making guns difficult to work. The earlier *Fulton*s had been little more than floating steam batteries; the two new ships, despite their shortcomings, marked the true beginning of the steam navy of the United States. Both were armed with ten guns, two 10-inch pivots and eight 8-inchers. The *Missouri* was destroyed by fire at Gibraltar in 1843; the *Mississippi* had a longer service record but was lost in the Civil War while trying to pass the guns of Port Hudson in 1863.

Three other steamers, all with submerged paddle wheels in their hulls—the *Union* and *Allegheny* (965 and 1,000 tons) and the *Water Witch* (190 tons)—were experimented with in the period 1842–48 but did not prove successful. The *Union* and *Allegheny* each mounted four 8-inch guns.

Early steamers were wood, but in 1842 an iron vessel was laid down on the orders of Secretary of the Navy Abel Upshur. The new vessel, the *Michigan,* was launched in 1844.

A small but vocal minority including Matthew Perry, Robert Stockton, Franklin Buchanan, and Secretary Upshur continued to push for modernization of the navy. Funds were made available for a prototype vessel to combine the innovations of a new heavy armament and screw propeller. This was the 672-ton steam sloop *Princeton,* launched in 1843. The vessel, named for his hometown, was Stockton's pride. He oversaw her construction and was responsible for the sail rig and hull design. John Ericsson, co-inventor with Francis Smith of the screw propeller, designed the engines and six-blade screw propeller. The *Princeton* was the first screw propeller warship in any navy; the first steamship with machinery entirely below the waterline; and the first to burn anthracite coal and use fan blowers for furnace fires. Her capabilities silenced the objections to steam warships.[3]

The success of the *Princeton* and other steam vessels during the war with Mexico encouraged the development of steam construction. While they did not engage in battles at sea, the steamers *Mississippi* and *Princeton* along with small steam gunboats performed well in the blockade of the Mexican Gulf Coast. The Crimean War gave further impetus to steamer construction, not only in Britain and France but also in the United States. Steamers proved their value during Perry's expedition to Japan in 1853–54, in the laying of the first transatlantic cable in 1858, in the expedition against Paraguay in 1859, and in the reduction of the fort guarding the mouth of China's Pei-ho (Hai) River in 1859.

At the end of 1846, Secretary of the Navy John Mason recommended the addition of four steamers. Next year Congress authorized the construction of the steam frigates *Saranac* (launched in 1848), *Powhatan* (1850), *Susquehanna* (1850), and *San Jacinto* (1850). All were side-wheelers save the *San Jacinto,* which was given a screw propeller for purposes of comparison. The *Saranac* and *San Jacinto* had two 8-inch and four medium 32-pounder guns; the *Powhatan* and *Susquehanna* had three 8-inchers and six medium 32-pounders.

The screw propeller combined with improvements in steam engines again made it possible to employ broadside guns along the entire length of a vessel. The screw propeller also offered the great advantage of not being vulnerable to shot; in this respect, it improved not only on the paddle wheel but also on sails, masts, and yards. Steam was still regarded as auxiliary power. Propeller-driven steam warships retained the heavy pivot guns but in reduced numbers, so that they remained subordinate to broadside armament.

Secretary of the Navy James Dobbin asked for the construction of six new first-class screw frigates; the *Niagara, Roanoke, Colorado, Merrimack, Minnesota,* and *Wabash* were authorized by Congress in 1854 and constructed over the next two years. The *Niagara,* the largest, was 4,500 tons; the others displaced something over 3,000 tons each. These large frigates were to form the backbone of the U.S. Navy. They were all ship rigged, their steam power being intended for auxiliary use only.

Of more use during the Civil War were the twelve large sloops of war authorized in 1857 and 1858. In early 1857 Congress approved Dobbin's request for five shallow-draft, screw-propelled steam sloops. These were launched in 1858, and in June of that year Congress authorized the construction of seven additional ones as well as a side-wheel steamer. By 1860 six were in service and one was under construction. The side-wheeler *Saginaw* also entered active service in 1860.

The best known of the five first-class sloops came to be the *Hartford, Brooklyn,* and *Richmond.* The *Iroquois, Pacotah,* and *Pawnee* (the first U.S.

Navy vessels with twin screws) were the largest and most typical of the second-class sloops. In 1860, the latter were known as third-class screw steamers and were armed with two XI-inch Dahlgren guns and four 32-pounders of 57 cwt. By comparison, the *Lancaster,* a second-class screw steamer, was armed with two XI-inch and twenty IX-inch Dahlgrens in 1860.

Older sailing ships were not worth repairing, so Secretary of the Navy Toucey advocated not only a larger navy but also its conversion entirely to steam. By the time of the Civil War some ninety ships comprised the U.S. Navy list. That the transition from sail to steam was only partially complete is shown by the fact that fifty of these, including line-of-battle ships, frigates, sloops, and brigs, were sailing vessels.

While steam power was being adapted to warships, experiments were being conducted with iron-hulled vessels. The first iron warships in the world were actually two steam frigates, the *Guadalupe* and *Montezuma,* built in Britain for Mexico in 1842. Two years later the British navy had added six iron steamers of 334 to 378 tons and five steam frigates of 1,391 to 1,953 tons. But a series of experiments showed that iron tended to fracture under the impact of shot, whereas wood merely absorbed it. As a result, there was a temporary swing away from iron hulls.

The Crimean War changed that thinking, spurring the development of steam-powered ironclads. On 30 November 1853, in the Battle of Sinope, a Russian squadron destroyed a Turkish fleet at anchor. The Russians fired both shot and shell, but it was the latter, fired against Turkey's vessels, that accounted for the devastating victory. Wood could absorb iron shot, but shell tore large holes in it.

The introduction of shell guns at sea thus led to the use of iron armor for warships. First France and then Britain employed floating batteries armored with sheets of forged iron. The *Devastation, Lave,* and *Tonnante* took part in an attack on Russia's Kinburn forts in an estuary at the mouth of the Dnieper and Bug rivers in October 1855. The forts housed eighty-one guns and mortars. The French vessels were protected by 4-inch armor plate backed up by 17 inches of wood, and each carried twelve 50-pounder guns. These fired more than 3,177 shot and shell, reducing the forts to rubble. The vessels themselves remained largely impervious to Russian fire, though they were hulled repeatedly. The *Devastation* sustained sixty-seven hits but received only a dent of not more than one and a half inches.

The success of these vessels during the Crimean War induced France and Britain to add ironclads to their navies. Britain built three self-propelled 1,973-ton *Erebus*-class ships armed with sixteen 68-pounders each. They had iron hulls supported by 6 inches of oak. In addition, 4 inches of iron armor extended from the gunwale 2 feet below the waterline.

At the end of 1859 the French launched the revolutionary and highly successful steamship *Gloire,* a wooden screw frigate of 5,675 tons that was the first seagoing ironclad. She was protected by a 4.5-inch belt of iron running from 6 feet below the waterline to the upper deck and along the whole length of the ship. The belt was backed by 17 inches of wood.

The British response was the *Warrior,* 6,109 tons, launched in 1860. In all respects, she was more advanced than the *Gloire.* The first large seagoing, iron-hulled warship, the *Warrior* was protected by a 4.5-inch band of iron bolted to 0.625-inch plating and 18 inches of teak running from 6 feet below to 6 feet above the waterline. Both the *Warrior* and the *Gloire* retained sail rigs.

Ironically, the United States had been in the forefront of these developments. Robert Livingston Stevens of Hoboken, New Jersey, is credited with the idea of attaching iron plates to a vessel to protect it from enemy fire. In 1843, during the war scare with Britain and with the active support of Secretary Upshur, Stevens and his brother experimented with laminated iron plate 4.5 inches thick and discovered that it could, at 30 yards, withstand shot from a 64-pounder gun. They used riveted iron plates rather than rolled iron, which at the time was not available in the United States.

In April 1842, Congress authorized the secretary of the navy to enter into a contract with Stevens for a war steamer that would be shot- and shell-proof and not cost more than the average amount expended on the steamers *Missouri* and *Mississippi.* The ship was intended for harbor defense. Upshur and Stevens signed the contract in February 1843, and thus the decision to construct an ironclad vessel utilizing plates in fact preceded by fifteen years the launching of the *Gloire* in France. But the Stevens battery, as the project vessel came to be called, was never completed. Problems abounded; even before construction John Ericsson arrived in the United States with his heavy wrought-iron 12-inch gun. The demonstrated success of this gun in smashing 4.5 inches of wrought iron forced the Stevens brothers to increase the thickness of the armor to 6.75. The ship had to be enlarged to take the extra weight, one reason it was never finished. Ultimately, more than $700,000 was expended on the Stevens battery, $500,000 by congressional appropriation. In October 1854 five hundred men were at work on it; in 1856 work ceased altogether. In 1861 it was decided not to finish the vessel (one estimate was that it would take an additional $812,000), and in the 1870s the battery was sold for scrap.

The first iron-hulled warship actually built in the United States was the 582-ton side-wheeler steamer *Michigan,* launched in 1844. Parts of the new bark-rigged ship were built in Pittsburgh and assembled at Erie. Her original armament was to be two long 42-pounders of about 73 cwt each and two 8-inch shell guns of 66 cwt each, which along with the shot were to be made at Pittsburgh. Despite the plan, when commissioned she was armed with two 8-inch and four 32-pounder guns. This violated the Rush-Bagot agreement providing for mutual disarmament on the Great Lakes and led to a reduction to only one gun, an 8-incher, in 1845. The *Michigan,* a first-class steamer, was the first iron vessel on the Great Lakes and remained in service until 1923.

Little more ironclad construction was done after the *Michigan.* It was not until the Civil War, six years after the shelling of the Kinburn forts, that action was taken, although as early as September 1854 John Ericsson had submitted plans for an ironclad that was in its essential features the *Monitor.* On 4 July 1861 Secretary of the Navy Gideon Welles—goaded into action by the knowledge that the Confederates had raised the *Merrimack* and were iron-plating her—recommended to Congress the establishment of a board to investigate the subject of "iron-clad steamers or floating batteries." Welles took no stand on the issue himself, leaving it up to Congress to decide. On August 3 Congress authorized the board and appropriated $1.5 million to pay for three experimental ironclads. This was the origin of the *Monitor* and her successor vessels.

As has been seen, it was the shell gun that helped bring a shift to ironclads. Shells were not new in warfare, of course. The first ones were used in mortars by the Venetians as early as 1376. The Turks used bombs or hand grenades in the siege of Rhodes in 1522. The howitzer, which was increasingly popular after the mid-eighteenth century, also fired shell but in a flatter trajectory than a mortar. Explosive shells, however, were not very common at sea. Heavy mortars were fired in shore bombardment, and special bomb ketches were built to carry them, but mortars were never intended for use against other vessels.

Still, the idea of firing shells at other ships in a flat trajectory similar to that of shot persisted. As early as 1756 the British conducted a trial at Gibraltar. The great French artillerist Gribeauval suggested the idea in a memoir on coastal defense. The French made a trial on a timber target at Toulon in 1795, using 18-, 24-, and 36-pound shells, and in 1797 24-pound shells were fired experimentally at a small ship at Cherbourg. Other trials were held during the period from 1798 to 1803, when 24- and 36-pound shells were fired at a target representing a line-of-battle ship. Napoleon was impressed with the results and ordered 36-pound shells for all coastal defense guns of that caliber; he also ordered some 48-pounder guns cast to fire shell.

Meanwhile, enterprising English Brigadier General Sir Samuel Bentham, then a colonel in Russian service, fitted out a flotilla of small galleys armed with 32- and 48-pounder cannon and 8- and 13-inch howitzers firing both shot and shell. A number of these pieces were arranged in a way that eliminated recoil; others received new carriages designed by Bentham. In 1788, at the mouth of the Liman River in the Sea of Azov, Bentham won a great victory over a superior Turkish force largely as a result of the use of explosive and combustible shells at close range. The significance of this event, however, and of Captain Mercier's innovation of utilizing shell in long guns during the siege of Gibraltar in 1779, seemed lost on European naval experts.

The English did conduct trials with shell in 1798 and actually fired 8-inch shell from 68-pounders aboard the *Tigre,* a seventy-four, against French troops attempting to storm Acre in 1799. Shells did not come into general use at this time, although a marine dictionary of 1815 included a range table for 5.5-inch shell fired from 24-pounders.

Meanwhile, the carronade had made its appearance. General Robert Melville suggested that it fire shells and hollow shot as well as solid shot, though in demonstrating its performance he had fired only hollow or cored shot. It should be pointed out that the carronade was indeed used on occasion with shells. The application of shell to the *Tigre*'s 68-pounders has already been mentioned, as has the Royal Navy's use of 68-pounder carronades and 18-pounders to fire shell from bomb ketches in lieu of 13-inch mortars.

The idea of a pure shell system was first taken up systematically in France by Colonel Henri Joseph Paixhans, who is generally credited with developing the shell gun. Paixhans advanced his ideas in two books, *Nouvelle force maritime et artillerie* (1822) and *Experiences faites sur une arme nouvelle* (1825). Paixhans called for the abandonment of solid shot in favor of exploding shell and concentration on large-caliber guns. He also advocated a change to uniform caliber for 36-pounders aboard French ships, with different-weight guns on different decks. The lighter 36-pounders would be reamed-up 24-pounders. All would fire charged shell. Paixhans did not develop anything new, but he brought scattered technological elements together.

Why shell? For centuries shot had been the mainstay, used to hole an enemy vessel near the waterline, destroy spars and masts, and kill the enemy. But wooden ships had hulls of stout oak and could sustain a tremendous amount of punishment. Even if shot penetrated them, it might leave only a small hole on the outside, since wooden fibers tended to close back again once shot had passed through. A hole had to be made at the waterline to cause fatal damage to a wooden vessel. Generally, a good plug could contain the damage, and it took a tremendous number of shots to hole a vessel sufficiently to sink it. Moreover, shot striking the water lost much of its force, and the sloping surfaces of a vessel further deflected that force. Iron hulls were nearly impervious to shot.

Indeed, it was rare for large frigates or ships of the line to sink in battle; they could take a tremendous battering even by large-caliber guns in lengthy engagements. In 1800 a British seventy-four, the *Foudroyant,* fired 2,758 shot at close range at a French line-of-battle ship, the *Guillaume Tell,* before the latter struck; two other British ships were firing at the French vessel at the same time. She survived and was soon afterward incorporated into the Royal Navy.

Most vessels were not sunk by shot but rather were disabled by damage to masts and spars or by casualties. If a vessel sank, it was often from an explosion caused by hot shot igniting powder magazines.

The anti-personnel effects of shot occurred during its egress from wood. It was recognized that splintering and damage were greatest when the force of the shot was only slightly more than that required to pass through wood. (The carronade had been introduced to take advantage of that principle.) But far too frequently, shot failed to pass through wood and hence injured neither material nor men.

The purpose of shell was to lodge and explode in its target. The structure of a ship could be much more effectively damaged by shell than shot, and the explosion of one large shell in the side of the vessel could produce a hole sufficiently large to sink it. During a trial in September 1852, shell was fired from a IX-inch Dahlgren against a target of white oak 30 feet thick at 1,300 yards' range; the explosion of one shell displaced 27 cubic feet of wood. Shot might have greater accuracy and range, but shell was infinitely more destructive.

The French took the lead in moving to shell because they had less to lose than the English and more to gain from the introduction of a new system. Inferiority in numbers of ships could be offset by superior ordnance, a point also stressed by Lieutenant John Dahlgren, the chief American advocate of shifting completely to shell guns. As for the British position, it was effectively summed up in 1837:

> So long as the maritime powers with which we were at war did not innovate by improving their guns, by extending the invention of carronades, or above all, by projecting shells horizontally from shipping, so long was it in the interest of Great Britain not to set the example of any improvement in naval ordnance, since such improvements be adopted by other nations, and not only would the value of our immense materiel be depreciated if not forced out of use, but a probability might arise that these innovations might tend to render less decisive our great advantages in nautical skill and experience.[4]

In 1821, France approved production of two 80-pounder bomb cannon (86.5-pounder English) developed by Paixhans. The guns were cast and transported to Brest for trial in 1823 and 1824. In the first trial, a charge of 19.75 pounds of powder threw an 86.25-pound shot a distance of 4,100 yards. It was the second trial that proved the destructive power of shell. Fired at ranges of up to 1,280 yards, it tore holes several feet in diameter, breeching the side of the target vessel entirely. Shell not only had a long range but was also quite accurate. The tests had been conducted under optimum conditions, of course, but the implications were still obvious. With a few heavy Paixhans guns, a large, fast frigate could defeat a ship of the line.

In 1824, the Paixhans was introduced into the French navy as regular armament; in 1837, a general regulation established the 22-centimeter (80-pounder) shell gun as a part of every ship's battery. Six were placed on board each French line-of-battle ship.

The French navy's first Paixhans was the *canon-obusier* of 80, no. 1, 1841. It could be distinguished from every other gun in a ship's battery by its peculiar form and straight muzzle. The gun was of medium length, 9 feet 4 inches or about 12 calibers, and large bore. It weighed about 74 cwt, the same as the 36-pounder truck gun. With a charge of 19 pounds 6 ounces of powder,

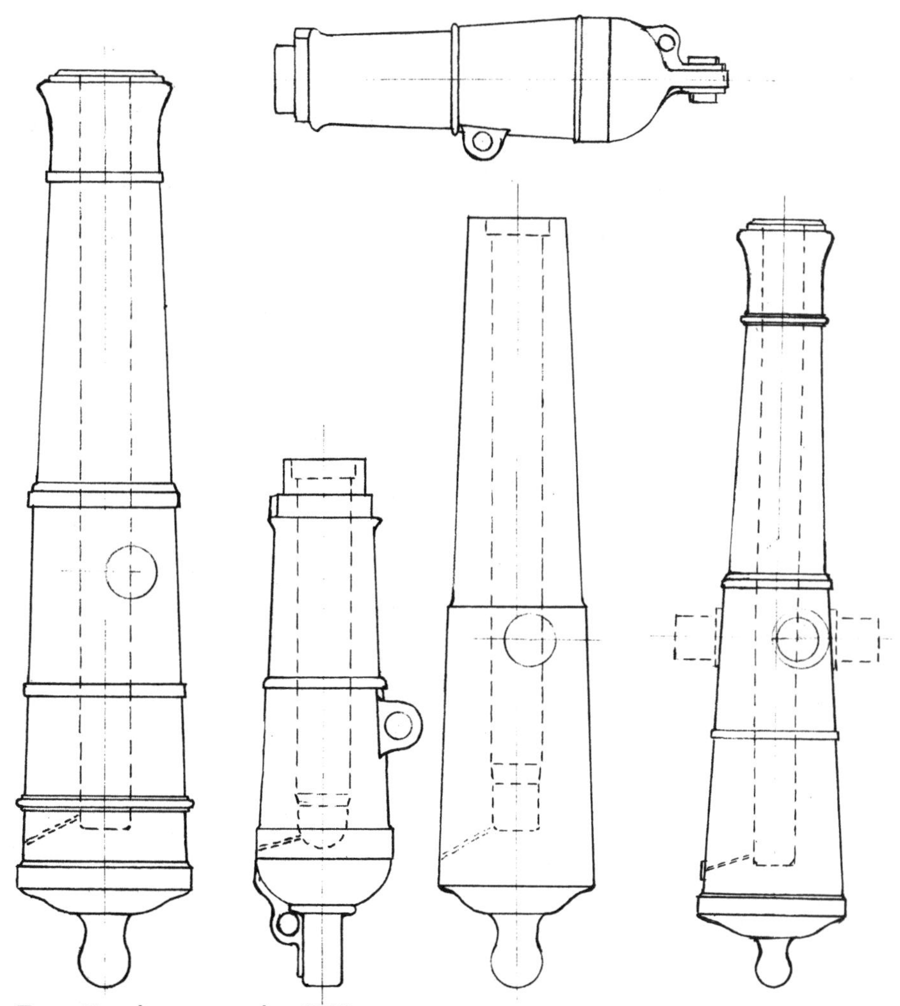

Top: **18-pdr carronade, 1818**

Bottom, left to right: **36-pdr, in use; 36-pdr carronade; 36-pdr, proposed; 18-pdr, in use**
Scale 7⁄16″ = 1′

Fig. 80. French Guns, 1818–22. (Drawing by C. S. Tucker.)

it fired concentric shells of 60.5 pounds English weight (56 livres French) and solid shot of 86.5 pounds (80 livres). The diameter of the bore was 8.95 inches with windage reduced to 0.09 inch. The ratio of gun weight to shell weight was 137 to 1.

In the Paixhans all unnecessary metal and ornamentation were absent. The outside diameter sharply increased just forward of the trunnions to a point back about two-thirds the distance to the base ring. Here the gun shrank to a diameter narrower than normal because the chambering at the end of the bore held what was, for the size of the gun, a small charge of powder. The

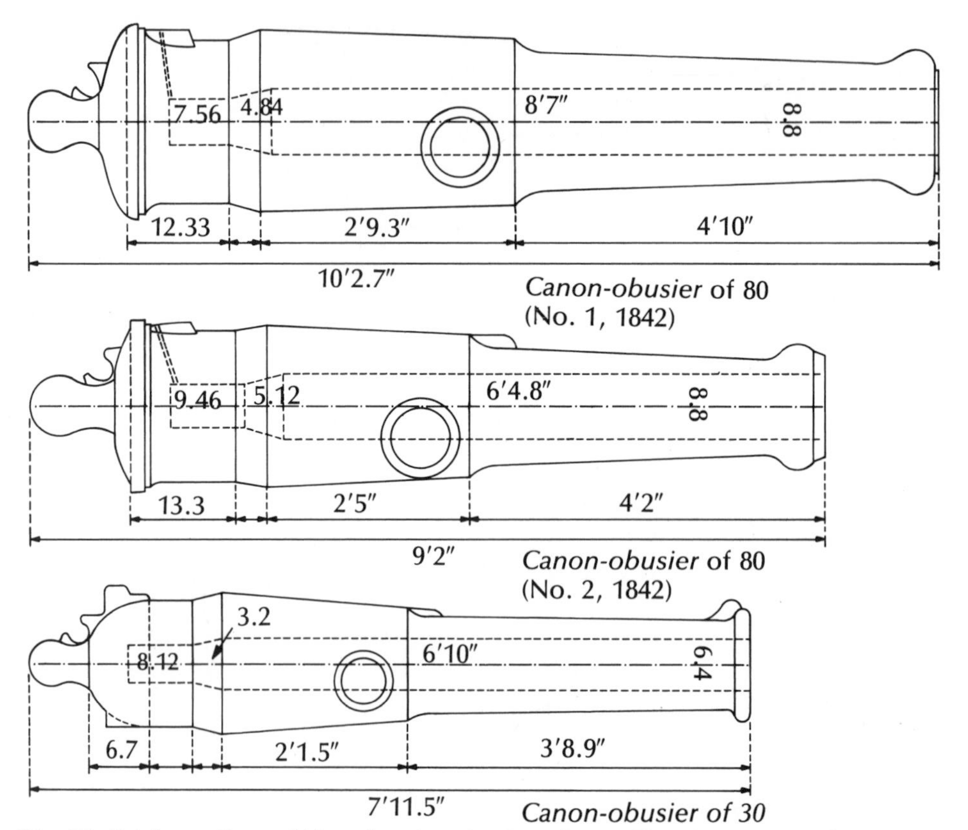

Fig. 81. Paixhans Guns. (After drawings in Douglas, A *Treatise on Naval Gunnery* [London, 1851].)

diameter of the cylindrical part of the chamber almost equaled that of the bore of a French 24-pounder.

Some difficulties were experienced with the first *canon-obusier* in service, but these were remedied in a new model in 1842, the *canon-obusier* of 80, no. 1, 1842. The diameter of the chamber was made larger, equal to that of a French 30-pounder, and hence the gun was easier to load and slightly shorter, 9 feet. Other models of the 80-pounder appeared in 1842 and 1848. Another gun with a bore of 10.6 inches (27 centimeters) was tried, but it and its projectile were found too heavy and it was not adopted. Finally, there were *canon-obusiers* of 30 livres for solid or hollow shot. These were 7 feet 4 inches long with a bore of 6.4 inches and were fired with a charge of 4 pounds 6 ounces (2 kilograms) for solid shot.

When the Paixhans guns joined the fleet, they did not replace the standard 30-pounder long gun firing solid shot. There were still the old guns for solid shot of 24, 36, and 50 livres as well as carronades for firing live shells on French ships of the line.

French success goaded the British into action. In 1824, the year the

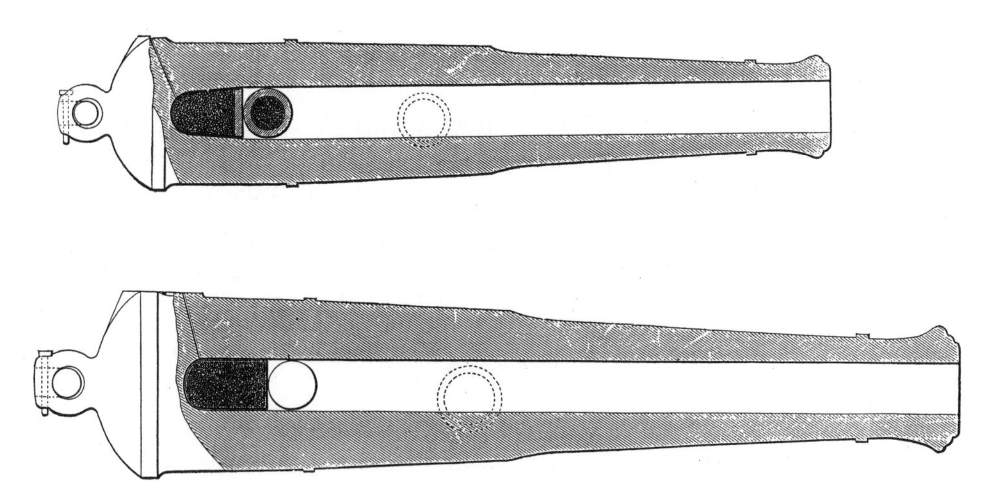

Fig. 82. British 8-Inch Shell Gun and 68-Pdr (8-Inch) Shot Gun. Note the gomer chamber on the shell gun, *top*. (Alexander Holley, *A Treatise on Ordnance and Armor* [New York, 1865].)

Paixhans was accepted by the French navy, the British tried out a 10-inch gun of 9 feet 4 inches and 85 cwt. They found this too heavy for ordinary ships, which led to the 8-inch gun of 5 feet 8.5 inches and 50 cwt, too light and short for the bigger ships. Finally, in 1838, they adopted the 8-inch shell gun of 65 cwt, 9 feet in length, as part of their standard armament. By 1851, it had become the favorite gun of the Royal Navy and belonged to the armament of ships of all rates and classes for broadside batteries and, in steamers, for pivot guns.

Still, for a number of reasons shell guns formed only part of the armament in the world's navies. There was insufficient proof of their effectiveness, and immense stockpiles of shot discouraged governments from changing the ammunition of their navies. Shell guns misfired more frequently because cartridges did not always seat properly in the chambers. For this reason, great care had to be taken in loading. In addition, the unfortunate legacy of switching to all-carronade armament lingered, and many felt that shells were simply unsafe. In 1799 HMS *Theseus* blew up after her shells, supposedly captured from a French frigate, exploded. Another factor was certainly simple resistance to change. Seamen and officers alike were apprehensive, as Dahlgren observed:

> I had the opportunity of firing the first shot from the "Cumberland." There are four Paixhans, or shell guns, in the ship, and these have been assigned as my division. The Captain gave me orders to fire a shell from each piece. Accordingly I had the heavy 68-pound shot drawn and the shells substituted. . . . It was amusing today, when about to fire, to notice that the crew had left the gun, as if desirous of avoiding any accident from the shell, which is new to them and seems alarming. I at once ordered them to stand

to their quarters in their proper places at the gun. Shot they do not mind, but shell they dread.[5]

The new shell guns apparently did not meet with much favor from officers of the old school either. Captain William H. Parker, writing of a voyage aboard the ship of the line *Columbus* from Madeira to Rio de Janeiro, noted:

> Shells were a great bother to us; as they were kept in the shell-room, and no one was allowed even to look at them; it seemed to be a question with the division-officers whether the fuse went in first or the sabot; or whether the fuse should be ignited before putting the shell in the gun or not! However, we used to fire them off, though I cannot say I ever saw them hit anything.[6]

Resistance to shell guns intensified when proponents also advocated steam vessels to carry them. The ideal combination, in their eyes, was a steam frigate mounting a few powerful shell guns. They argued that such vessels would be more maneuverable, less vulnerable to enemy fire, draw less water, require small crews, and yet be able to defeat the old ships of the line.

By 1848, the proportion of 22-centimeter shell guns in French naval batteries had increased; again the British followed suit, in the regulation of July 1848, although the percentage of shell guns in their ships varied greatly from one vessel to another. A 92-gun ship of the line such as the *London* had twenty-four 8-inch guns, an 84-gun ship of the line only eight. In 1849, the French officially did away with the carronade and substituted 50-pounders for some of the 22-centimeter guns.

By 1849, as many as seventy-six British warships were armed or were to be armed with an increased number of shell guns. Between them these ships had nearly 4,000 guns, of which some 1,200 were 8-inch shell guns. For the hundred steam vessels in the Royal Navy in May 1849, there were 112 10-inch shell guns. By the time of the Crimean War, 8-inch shell guns had taken the place of 32-pounders as the lower-deck battery of British line-of-battle ships and comprised the main-deck battery of five new frigates.

Little is known of the columbiad, the first American shell gun. It was apparently a short, rather light gun designed as an alternative to the carronade and usually designated an 18-pounder. It may have been a rebored cannon, mounted on slides in gunboats and on broadside carriages in ships. Lieutenant George Bomford (1750–1848), later colonel and head of the Army Ordnance Department, is generally credited with inventing the columbiad. William James, the English naval historian who was a prisoner of war in the United States during the War of 1812, wrote that the columbiad was developed by the Americans in response to the Congreve gun and was so named "probably from its having been cast at the cannon-foundry situated in the District of Columbia, in the United States."[7]

The columbiad, a chambered gun that combined certain qualities of the gun, howitzer, and mortar, was capable of firing both shot and shell. It was employed for coastal defense during the War of 1812 and was also placed

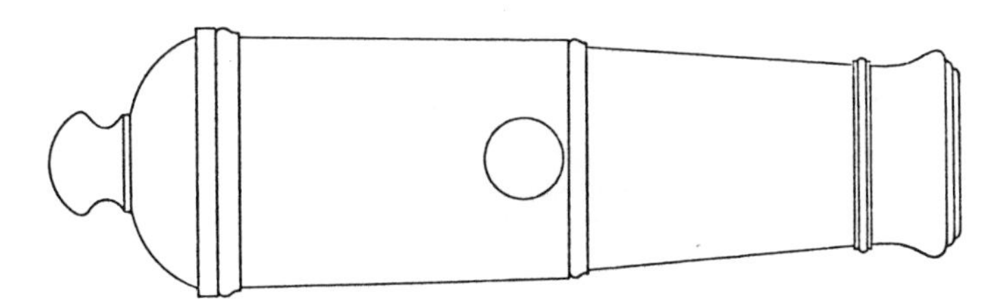

Fig. 83. The 50-Pdr Columbiad of 1811. Located at West Point, this is the only columbiad of the early period now in existence. It is 6′3.5″ overall, 21.5″ maximum diameter, and has a 16.75″ muzzle swell. (Drawing by C. S. Tucker.)

aboard some U.S. Navy vessels. Its shipboard use seems to have been limited mainly to gunboats and a few larger vessels, all on the Great Lakes. Six 18-pounder columbiads and four long 12s formed the original armament of the sloop *President* on Lake Champlain. The sloop *Montgomery,* also on Lake Champlain, was originally armed with seven long 9-pounders and two 18-pounder columbiads. It was not unusual, of course, to find land ordnance such as howitzers on naval vessels. In any case the term columbiad has always been an elusive one, for many authors designate as columbiads all large nineteenth-century American smoothbores.[8]

Some Americans charged that Paixhans had merely expropriated Bomford's idea, introducing the Bomford gun with some changes under his own name in France. A writer in 1841, while not attributing the columbiad to Bomford, said that the United States had "made use of such long howitzers for sea-coast defense years before Colonel Paixhan [*sic*] gave anything to the public on the subject. We called them columbiads."[9]

Certainly there was navy interest in the use of shells during the War of 1812. Stephen Decatur may have been the first naval officer to carry on extensive experiments with shell. Decatur told a friend in 1811 that he had designed a shell and fired it into masses of timber from a 0.25-mile range; the timber had been torn apart by the explosion. However, if there was a war with the English he would not use the shells, "as he meant to have fair play with them."[10]

After the War of 1812, the Board of Navy Commissioners authorized Andrew Oehlers to experiment with shell he had designed. Six of the shells were cased at public expense, filled with powder at the Washington Navy Yard, and fired at a target in the Potomac River. The experiment was not successful.

In 1818, a contract was let with Robert L. Stevens of New York for 1,200 "elongated shells" for long guns. Information on their construction was to be kept secret from everyone save the secretary of war, the secretary of the navy, and Colonel Bomford of the Ordnance Department. A clause in the contract provided for a test after delivery of the first 400. If the shells performed poorly, the navy had the option of refusing delivery of the remainder. Poorly meant that two of six shells would fail to explode in 6 to 20 seconds after firing. The

Stevens projectiles were not successful; fired from smoothbore guns, they had no spin and tumbled end over end.

In 1822 the navy had a total of only 3,290 shells on hand. By contrast, round shot totaled 169,671, double shot, 19,570, cannister, 8,011, and stands of grape, 18,249.

The columbiad vanished from the navy's inventory rather quickly. The 1833 inspection report of ordnance showed only two columbiads, both at Gosport Navy Yard. They were identified as 50-pounders of American manufacture.[11]

The columbiad also appears to have been discarded by the army about this time; an inventory of 1818 listed a total of only sixty army columbiads comprising 18-, 24-, 32-, 50- and 100-pounders. This probably represented the army columbiad at its peak; the guns were discarded by about 1820. The columbiad is listed in the ordnance manual of 1834 under the heading Obsolete Equipment. In the 1840s the army columbiad was revived, at least in name. A new piece appeared in 1844, possibly a different version of one of 1842 cast at South Boston Foundry. In the 1844 columbiad, the bore was lengthened and metal weight was increased to endure a heavier charge, one-sixth the weight of solid shot. Later it was discovered that the altered pieces did not always have the required strength and often burst. In 1858 they were downgraded to the status of shell guns only, to be fired with reduced charges. A new design was introduced the same year, but few guns were cast from it before the appearance of the Rodman gun in 1861.

As noted, the French established the 22-centimeter shell gun as part of all their ship batteries in 1837. In 1838 the visit to the United States of a French warship of twenty-six guns, armed entirely with new ordnance, may have had some impact on the Navy Department. Certainly there was concern over the growing firepower of European navies.

The gunnery experiments begun in 1839 at Sandy Hook and aboard the steamer *Fulton II* included trials of Paixhans-type guns, other ordnance, hollow shot, conventional solid shot, and explosive shell. The Paixhans-type 64-pounder shell gun demonstrated its superiority, an important step toward the inclusion of shell guns in the sloops *Portsmouth* and *Plymouth* (both completed in 1844) and on most large navy ships by the time of the Mexican War.

An interesting aspect of these trials concerned hollow shot—nonexplosive round shot fired at low velocity with less powder. They were employed with the larger guns coming into service in the world's navies because solid shot was too heavy and difficult to load. A 12-inch solid shot in British service weighed 243 pounds; a hollow shot of the same size weighed half as much. Hollow shot were also obtained for the smaller reamed-up guns of the Royal Navy in the belief that light guns throwing hollow shot of large caliber would be superior to smaller-caliber guns firing solid shot.

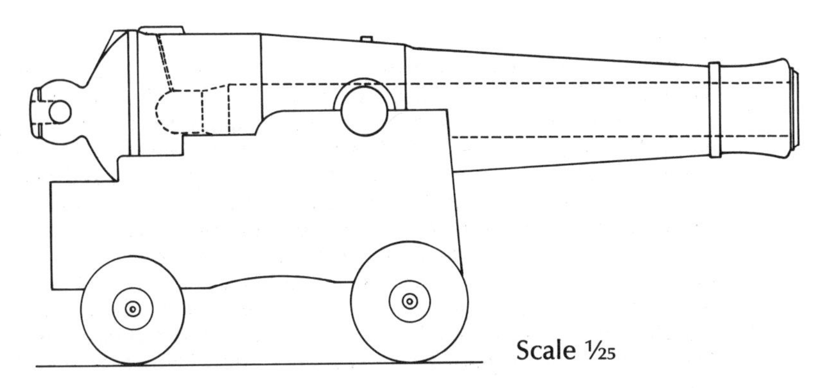

Fig. 84. An 8-inch Shell Gun of 53 CWT. (After a drawing by John Dahlgren, 1849.)

In the U.S. Navy, hollow shot was tried with the 32-pounders of 27 and 32 cwt that appeared in the mid-1840s following the shift to uniform 32-pounder armament and replaced the old 32-pounder carronades in the sloops. Since these guns recoiled violently even with a service charge of one-eighth the weight of shot, hollow shot was proposed as an alternative. Presumably it was also used in the fifty 24-pounders that in 1842 were reamed up to 32-pounders with 24-pounder chambers. Hollow shot was also tried in the first U.S. Navy shell gun, the old 42-pounder of 65 to 68 cwt, bored up to 8 inches, which could not sustain a solid ball.

Some of this shot was invented by T. N. Cochrane and ordered by the navy in 1840. Cochrane's hollow shot, according to one source, possessed "great smashing power with low velocity, and took less powder."[12] The tests also included a bronze 1,500-pound cannon ordered by Cochrane and cast by N. P. Ames of Springfield, Massachusetts. Tests were conducted with this gun in the *Fulton II.* Some three hundred shot had been fired from the cannon, which, Cochrane claimed, was still "to all appearance perfect as new. . . ." The gun was intended, he said, to be "a very heavy piece of ordnance for firing shot & shells to the greatest possible range." The experiments were expensive and not entirely successful. Cochrane claimed he had spent $2,000 on the cannon and on experiments and requested the navy to "take the Gun off my hands by paying me what it has cost. . . ."[13]

The major advantage of hollow shot was its light weight and consequent ease of handling. It had higher initial velocity—200 feet per second in the 32-pounder of 27 cwt—but neither the penetration nor the accuracy of solid shot. Hollow shot proved effective only at short ranges, where their velocity was adequate and their smashing power great. At longer ranges their flights were liable to be erratic. The experiment with them was short-lived, and by the time of the Civil War solid shot and shell came to be the mainstays of shipboard ammunition.

Perry recommended that the trials with shell be continued. He was

Key to fig. 85.

Gun no. 1: The 8-inch gun of 63 cwt. Dated January 1841, the original drawing for this shark's mouth or Paixhans shell gun calls it an 8-inch bomb cannon. It is 106" long. There is a powder chamber 6.4" in diameter and 7.45" long, tapering up to the 8" bore over a length of 5". Contracts list 208 63 cwt guns let. Both the 10-inch of 86 cwt and 8-inch of 63 cwt, cast prior to 1851, followed the Paixhans form and had the straight muzzle common to the French *canon-obusier*. The guns had no sight masses, and as they were not turned down on the exterior, their outer crust had a rough appearance. In 1851 some new 8-inch guns of 63 cwt were cast with sign masses, bell muzzles, and a stouter knob. The 8-inch gun of 44 cwt cast after 1845 (see gun no. 2 below) resembles the "new" 8-inch guns of 63 cwt.

Gun no. 2: An 8-inch gun with a 32-pdr chamber. The original drawing is dated July 1851 and lists guns 370 to 407 as being cast at West Point Foundry. The gun is 106" long.

Gun no. 3: An 8-inch columbiad. The original drawing is dated 1856. Typical of the army-pattern ratchet-breeched pieces of the time, this gun probably includes improvements incorporated into the columbiads made for the army about 1852. Since this piece has a chamber, it was probably a shell gun only.

Gun no. 4: An 8-inch gun modified by Rodman, 1860. Weight was computed as 8,465 pounds, and the piece had a semispherical-ended chamber 6.4" in diameter and 11" long overall, tapering to the 8" bore over a 5"-long cone. It is typical of pieces made for the army. The short trunnions indicate the use of wrought-iron carriages.

Gun no. 5: The 8-inch gun of 53 cwt (a standard type, and a shell gun). It is 100" long with a bore of 95". The trunnions were shortened in 1851 from 6.5" to 6". From March 1846 to September 1847, 157 of these guns were cast in Pittsburgh. The contracts list 112 let in 1845 and 39 in 1847, a total of 151.

Gun no. 6: A 64-pdr cannon (an 8-inch gun of 107 cwt, and a shot gun). This shows the difference between shot and shell guns. The bore is 8", but the use of solid shot required thicker metal and the piece weighed 12,000 pounds. The original drawing is dated June 1848; a note states that the ratchet-type cascabel was changed in 1854. The gun is 130" long with a bore of 124.2". Contracts show twelve of these guns let in 1848 and four more in 1854.

convinced that, despite widespread ignorance concerning its use, it could be fired with almost as much precision and safety as solid shot. In his annual report of 1841, Secretary Upshur noted the ordnance trials and said that steps had been taken to supply the navy with the new shell guns.

The first American Paixhans guns were actually 64-pounders of 60 cwt with an 8-inch bore and 32-pounder chamber; the Navy ordered these from American foundries in 1841. At the same time thirty old 42-pounders, some cast as early as 1822, were bored up to a diameter of 8 inches but retained a 32-pounder chamber.[14] Not strong enough to fire solid shot of 64 pounds, they fired hollow shot of 43 (46 filled with sand). Two of the bored-up guns broke in proof with a charge of 15 pounds of powder, another broke in the *Fulton II,* and a fourth burst at Sandy Hook in a test to determine its strength. All the bored-up 8-inchers were condemned at the end of 1847 and sold at auction.

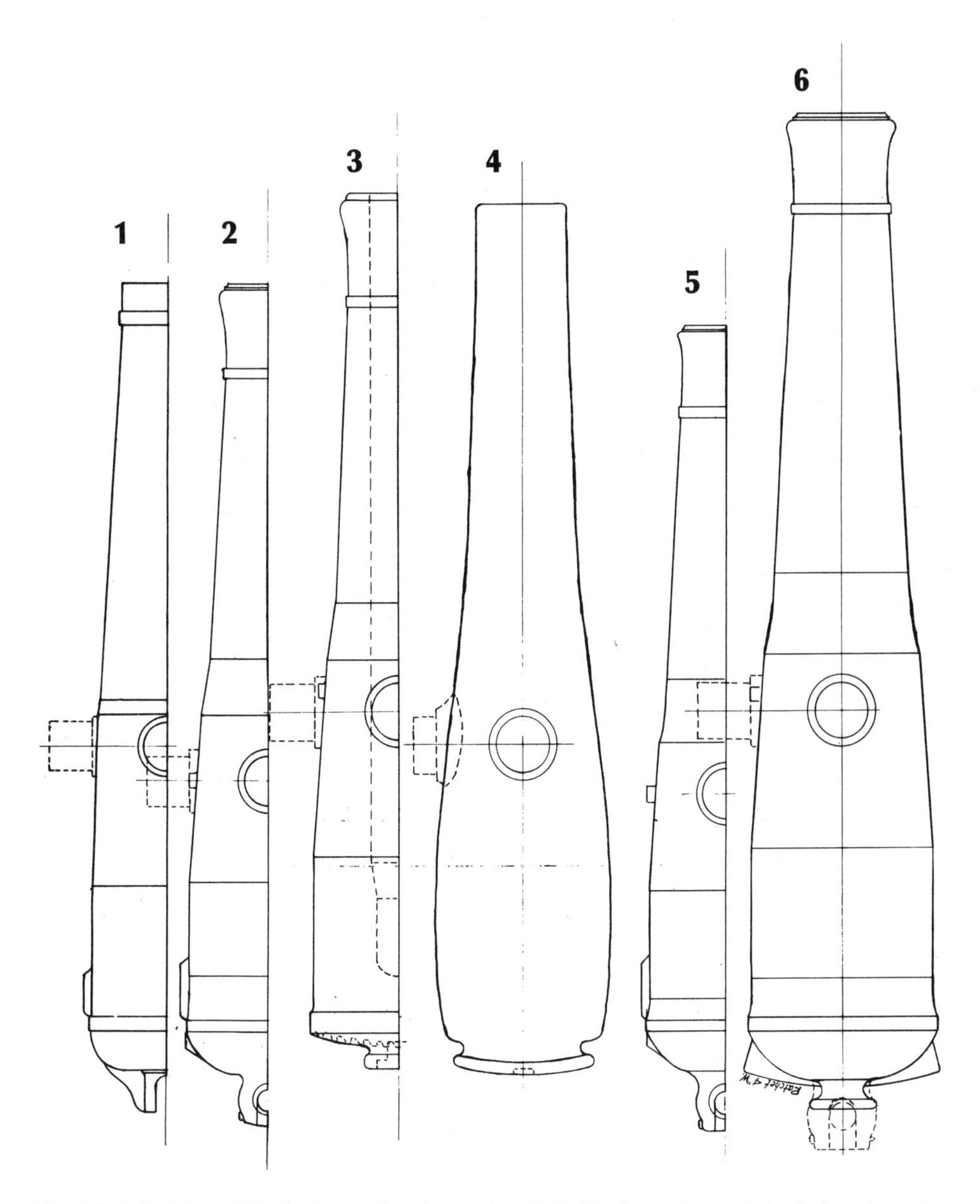

Fig. 85. U.S. Navy 8-Inch Guns. (Redrawn by C. S. Tucker after original drawings in National Archives, Record Group 74.)

Other guns were also reamed up, probably in response to British practice, for use with hollow shot and shell. In 1842 fifty 24-pounders were reamed up to 32-pounders with 24-pounder chambers. These guns, which ranged from 8 feet 7 inches to 9 feet 5 inches, were all sold out of the navy in 1847.

By August 1842, twenty-two Paixhans had been received at the Gosport Navy Yard. Twelve were put in the *Pennsylvania,* four in the *Constitution,* and two in the *Levant.* Four others remained on hand.

In the U.S. Navy, as in the British, shot guns continued to be designated by the weight of their projectile. Shell guns, however, were designated by the

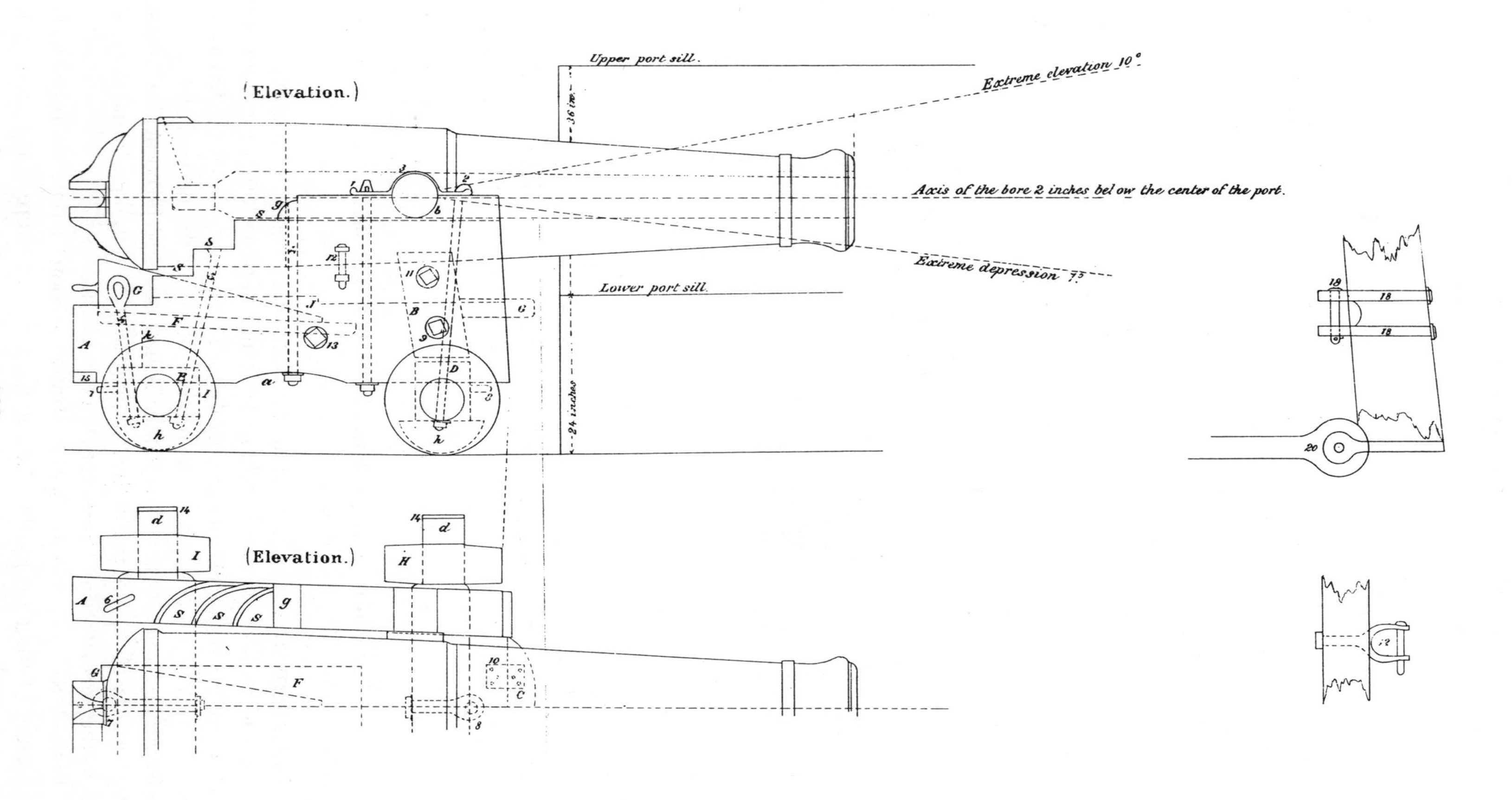
(Elevation.)
Upper port sill.
Extreme elevation 10°
36 ins.
Axis of the bore 2 inches below the center of the port.
Extreme depression 7°
Lower port sill.
24 inches
(Elevation.)

Key:

A. The cheeks (in large carriages they are composed of two pieces connected by a jog *J*). The cheeks contain the trunnion holes *b;* the arch *a;* and the steps *s,* from which the handspikes are levered when the gun is to be elevated or lowered.
B. The transom
C. The breast pieces in two parts, hinged and bolted to the cheeks
D. The outer axletree and the inner axletree *E* are composed of the square body and the arms *d.*
H, I. The trucks
h. h. The dumb trucks, which support the carriage should the trucks be destroyed or taken off to lessen recoil
F. The bed, with its stool *k*
Q. The quoin
3. The cap square secured by the chain bolt *2,* and the cap square bolt and key *1*
4. The cheek bolts
5. The inner axletree bolts
6. The side tackle bolts
7. The train bolt
8. The transporting bolt
9. The breast bolt
10. The hinges of the breast piece
11. The transom bolts
12. The breeching shackle, confined by the pin
13. The bed bolt
14. The axletree bands, which prevent the axletree from splitting
15. The chafing plates, which protect the cheeks from the handspike in training
16. The linchpins, with their washers *17,* which prevent the trucks from slipping off the axletree arms
18. The shackle bolt and shackle pin *19*
20. The thimble, into which each extremity of the breeching is spliced and by which it is attached to the shackle bolt

Fig. 86. A New-Pattern 8-Inch Shell Gun of 63 CWT and Carriage. (Jeffers, *A Concise Treatise.*)

caliber of their bores—in the British navy, by the diameter of their shot. An 8-inch gun in the Royal Navy had a bore of 8.05 inches and fired an 8-inch projectile; its counterpart in the U.S. Navy had a bore of 8 inches and fired a projectile with a maximum diameter of 7.82 inches. Had their projectiles been solid, they would have weighed 68 and 64 pounds, respectively. The 64-pounder shot gun also had a bore of 8 inches but was much heavier in the breech to sustain a larger charge.

After the appearance of Dahlgren guns in the 1850s, U.S. Navy shell guns were often designated by Roman numerals to distinguish them from shot guns. From that time on most writers referred to shell guns, regardless of their type, with Roman numerals. In this study, Roman numerals are used to designate Dahlgren guns only.

Although the British introduced their 10-inch shell gun in 1824, orders for the first such guns in the U.S. Navy were not placed until 1842. The Columbia Foundry was to cast twenty-five, each to have a 42-pounder chamber and to weigh about 86 cwt. These guns were also known as 10-inch guns of 10,000 pounds (9,632 pounds actual).

In 1844, the army tested new 8- and 10-inch columbiads. The 8-incher weighed 9,240 pounds and the 10-incher 15,400. The latter, probably the type developed for the army, was tried aboard U.S. warships during the Mexican War. Figure 87 shows drawings of a new carriage developed for use with the 10-inch gun of 15,000 pounds in the bomb vessels *Etna* and *Stromboli.* The gun shown on the carriage is a model 1844 army columbiad. (The weight is correct for that piece; the navy gun was only 86 cwt, or 9,632 pounds. The 10-inch gun of 107 cwt, 11,984 pounds, was not cast for the navy until 1854.) Trials were also conducted with a 12-inch columbiad, undoubtedly the Bomford gun of 1846, which fired a 172-pound shell and was capable of a range of 5,761 yards but whose weight of 25,000 pounds rendered it too heavy for sea service.

The new carriage, designed by Colonel Bomford, had been adopted by 1850 with modifications for use aboard U.S. Navy bomb brigs. The carriage allowed an elevation of up to 35 degrees. The slide was similar to that employed in the usual circular pivot mount. The top carriage was modified only in the application of a roller shaft under each end. By means of a lever, one man could lift either end of the carriage clear of the friction plates; six men could run out and train these large guns. Friction clamps at the sidechecked carriage recoil, and a crotch in the tail of the cheeks snatched the breeching, leaving the breech clear. This arrangement improved on the old circle mounts.

A ratchet elevated the pivot-mounted columbiad. The breech formed the arc of a circle whose center rested in the trunnions of the gun. The arc was divided by notches into which a steel check was spring-pressed. A lever on the standard the spring abutted determined elevation.

On 18 March 1845, Secretary of the Navy George Bancroft convened a

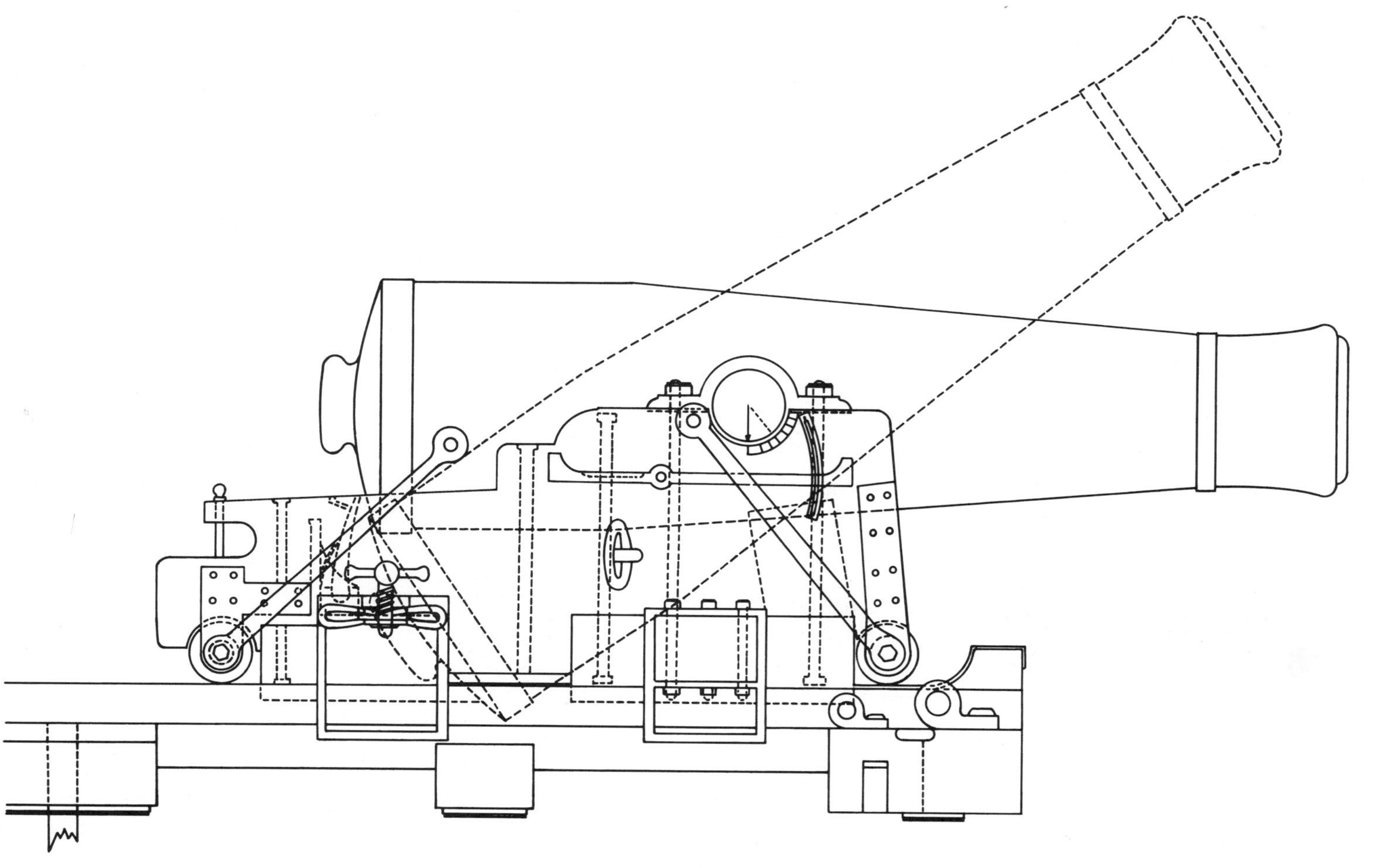

Fig. 87. Plan of the Bed and Carriage of Columbiads Fitted in the U.S. Bomb Vessels *Etna* and *Stromboli*. (After a drawing in National Archives, Record Group 74.)

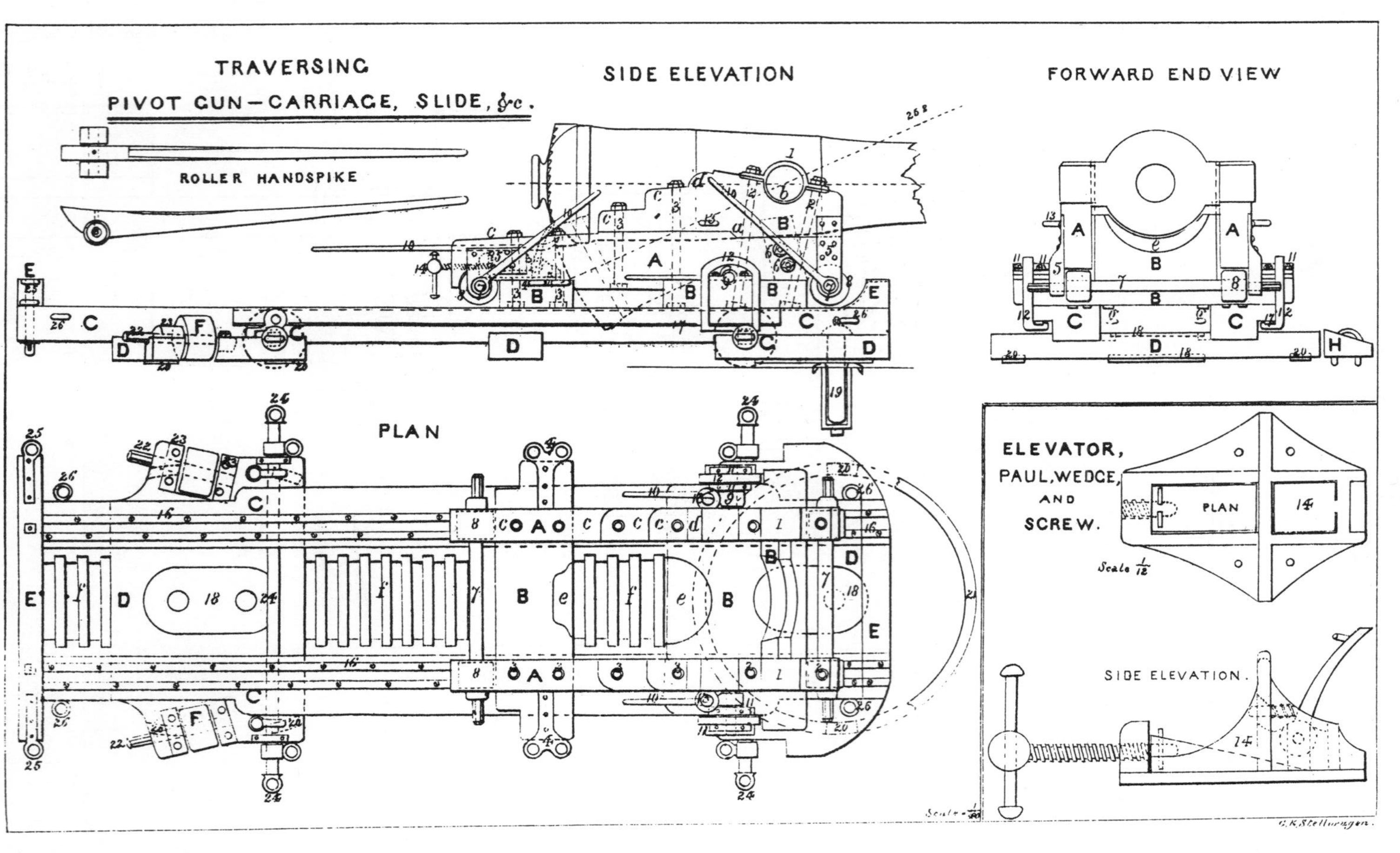

Fig. 88. Traversing Pivot Gun Carriage and Slide, 1852. (Bureau of Ordnance. *Preparation of Vessels of War for Battle.*)

Key to fig. 88.

WOODEN PARTS

Carriage

A. Brackets are each made of two pieces joined by a jog *a* and doweled. The remaining parts of the brackets are as follows: trunnion holes *b*, steps *c*, and quarter rounds *d*.
B. Breast transoms *e*, tenoned and beveled for elevation and depression. Front, middle, and rear transoms are jogged into the brackets. The front and middle transoms are joined. Guide battens *g*.

Slide

C. Rails jogged into transoms, slats *f* between them.
D. Front, middle, and rear transoms. The front and rear are each composed of two pieces.
E. Hurters forward and after. The after one has dowels and is moveable.
F. Training trucks (two)
G. Transporting trucks (four)
H. Shifting chock and dowels

METAL PARTS

Carriage

1. Cap squares (two)
2. Cap square bolts and keys (four)
3. Bracket bolts and nuts (eight)
4. Side tackle eyes (eight)
5. Journal plates for front and rear axles (eight)
6. Breast transom bolts and nuts (two)
7. Eccentric shaft and axle front and rear (two)
8. Rollers, front and rear (four)
9. Eccentric axles for compressors (two)
10. Front and rear elevating levers and compressor (seven)
11. Journal boxes for compressors (four)
12. Compressors (two) generally fitted with screws
13. Breeching bolts (two)
14. Elevator, pawl, wedge, and screw
15. Guide plates, on carriage and slide, in side rails (too small to be represented in their places between the battens and rails)

Slide

16. Rail plates (four) fastened with wood screws
17. Compressor plates (two) under flange of rail
18. Pivot plates, forward and after, upper and lower
19. Pivot bolts and socket. Sometimes the pivot bolts are fixed in the deck, in which case the slide is fitted with a moveable flap.
20. Friction plates
21. Deck circles
22. Eccentric axles for training trucks
23. Journal boxes for training trucks
24. Transporting axles with eyes for tackles
25. Side tackle eyes
26. Training tackle eyes

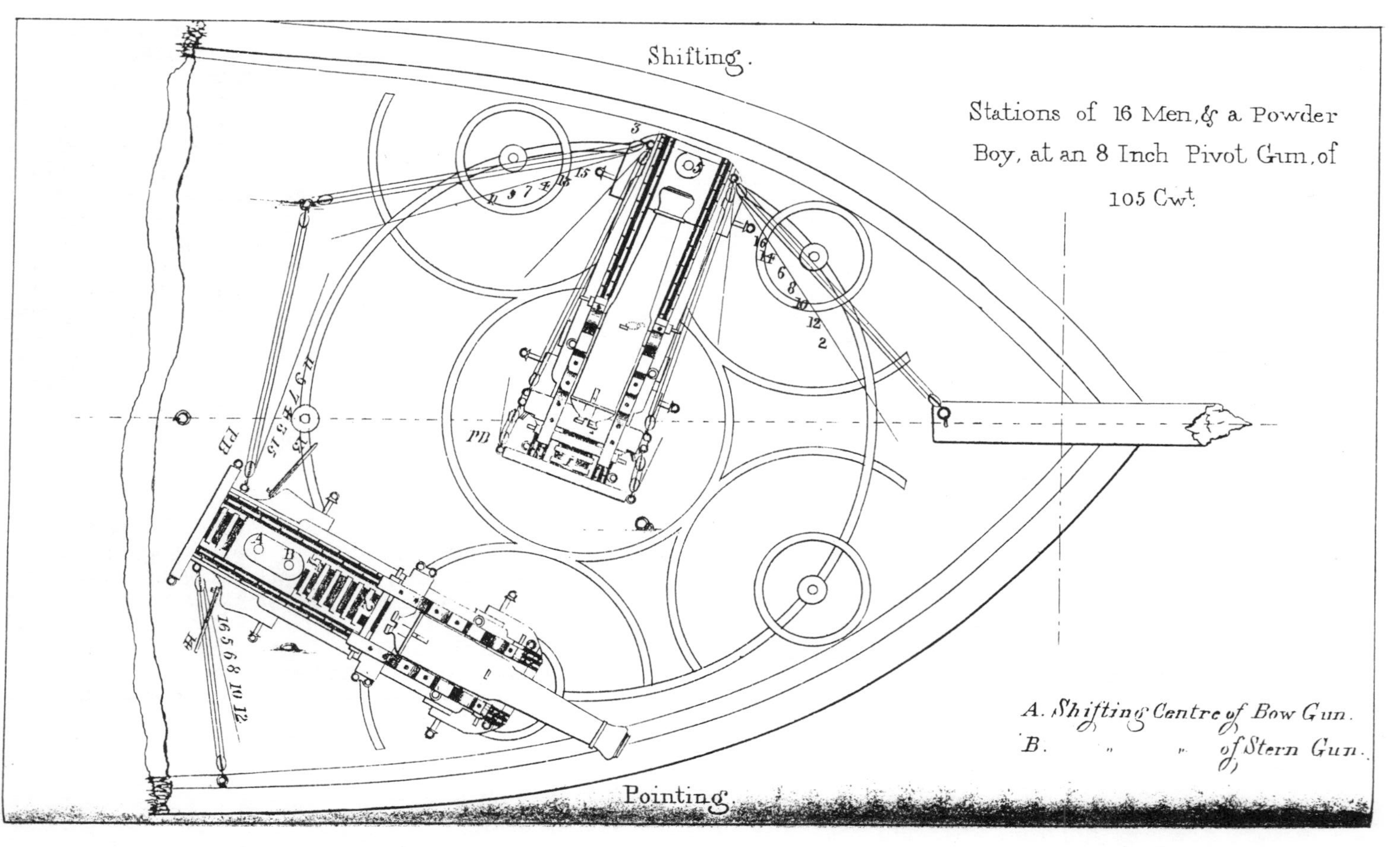

Fig. 89. Location of Crew at 8-Inch Pivot Gun, Bow. (Bureau of Ordnance, *Preparation of Vessels of War for Battle*.)

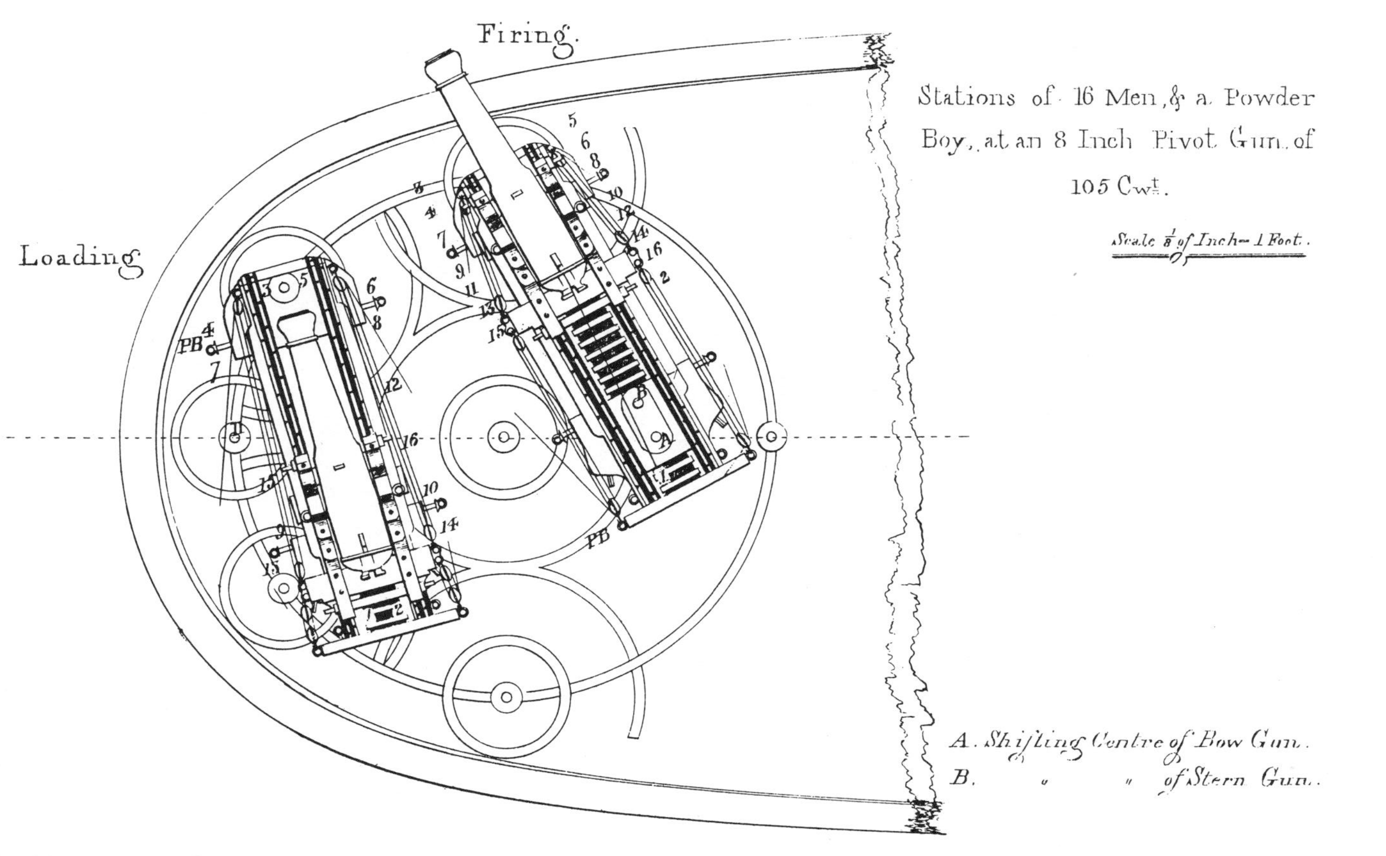

Fig. 90. Location of Crew at 8-Inch Pivot Gun, Stern. (Bureau of Ordnance, *Preparation of Vessels of War for Battle.*)

board of captains to recommend changes in armament for U.S. Navy ships. The board delivered its report on 29 May, noting that the ships of the line *Pennsylvania, Delaware,* and *Columbus* already mounted, in addition to other armament, eight 8-inch shell guns each, and that some frigates and sloops carried four 8-inch guns. The board recommended doubling the number of shell guns on all classes of ships. The 1845 regulations not only established the 32-pounder as the standard gun in the U.S. Navy (there were six weight classes) but also provided for the use of the new, lighter 8-inch shell gun with the already established 63-cwt gun. The 8-incher weighed 55 cwt.

As a result of these regulations, the lighter class of 8-inch shell guns was added to the spar decks of frigates and second-class sloops. First-class frigates carried 32-pounders of 32 cwt, four 8-inchers of 55 cwt, and two 32-pounders of 51 cwt (for chase purposes) on the spar deck. One or two of the heaviest vessels had 32-pounders of 42 cwt on their spar decks. The 32-pounders of 46 cwt were designed for a few frigates of inferior rate.

Sloops of war were armed according to size: the largest had 32-pounders of 42 cwt and 8-inch guns of 63 cwt, the next had 32-pounders of 32 cwt and 8-inch guns of 55 cwt, and the smallest had 32-pounders of 27 cwt. Sloops carried no more than four 8-inch guns.

Line-of-battle ships and frigates underwent a similar transformation. In 1853, the light 55-cwt 8-inch guns were removed from the spar decks of frigates and ships of the line, and the number of 8-inch 63-cwt pieces was increased on the gun decks, resulting in entire divisions of ten guns each. By 1856, the U.S. Navy's standard pivot guns were 64-pounders and 10-inch shell guns of 86 cwt.

At the time shell guns were installed, some older frigates were razeed or had their spar decks stripped of guns to make them into large corvettes. A corvette-armed frigate required a smaller crew than the older 44-gun frigate. The *Cumberland,* launched in 1842, was one of the best examples of the fast-sailing razeed frigate. Originally carrying forty 32-pounders and ten 64-pounder 8-inch shell guns, she was cut down between 1850 and 1856 to a corvette carrying twenty-six 32-pounders on her main deck and two 10-inch shell guns on pivot mounts, one each at bow and stern. Chase guns were mounted on slide carriages pivoting on traverse rings.

European navies were not as enthusiastic about razeeing their ships. Only a few cut-down frigates appeared in British and French service, despite the proof these ships provided that shell guns were making the old massive broadside armament of ships of the line and frigates obsolete. The U.S. Navy employed the most powerful guns possible to outrange the broadside batteries of old frigates and ships of the line.

But shell guns still made up only a small part of shipboard armament. By 1851 little use had been made of them as broadside guns, and naval officers did not favor them for the bow and stern armament of steamers. Indeed, there were those in the U.S. Navy who felt that money spent on shell guns—

TABLE 27

COMPARISONS OF U.S., BRITISH, AND FRENCH GUNS IN 1856

		Weight			Bore		Shot		
		Gun (cwt)	*Charge (lbs)*	*Shot (lbs)*	*Length (in)*	*Diameter (in)*	*Diameter (in)*	*Windage (in)*	*Charge (lbs)*
Long 32-Pounders									
United States	32-pdr	57.0	9.0	32.5	107.9	6.40	6.250	0.150	—
Britain	32-pdr	56.0	10.0	31.5	107.2	6.41	6.235	0.175	—
France	30-pdr	59.75	10.67	33.8	104.0	6.486	6.285	0.201	—
8-inch Shell Guns									
United States	8-in	63.0	9.0	51.0*	100.33	8.0	7.85	0.15	2
Britain	8-in	65.0	10.0	51.0*	105.25	8.05	7.925	0.125	—
France	*Canon-obusier* of 80 (22 cent.)	71.0	7.75	61.5*	104.0	8.794	8.774	0.12	4.75
Heavy (Pivot) Guns									
United States	10-in	86.0	10.0	104.0	106.0	10.0	9.85	0.15	4.0
Britain	10-in	84 and 86	12.0	87.0	109.33	10.0	9.84	0.16	5.5
France	50-pdr	91.0	17.67	55.67	121.84	7.64	7.44	0.197	—
Britain	56-pdr	98.0	16.0	55.5	121.87	7.65	7.475	0.175	1.75
United States	64-pdr	105.0	16.0	64.0	124.2	8.0	7.85	0.15	2.0
Britain	68-pdr	87.0	14.0	67.0	—	8.12	7.92	0.2	2.25
Britain	68-pdr	95.0	16.0	67.0	—	8.12	7.92	0.2	2.25

Source: John Dahlgren, *Shells and Shell Guns* (Philadelphia: King and Baird, 1856), 238–39 and 253.
* If completely filled with powder.

particularly for steamer armament—might be better used for heavier long shot guns. The latter were considered more accurate and effective at long range and could be double-shotted for firing at close range.

Thus by the early 1850s professional naval circles in Europe and the United States had second thoughts about the shell gun. Many agreed with the contemporary writer who concluded that "distant firing with powerful solid shot guns will be the most effectual means of avoiding or counteracting the destructive effects which hollow shot and shells would unavoidably produce if the ship which uses them were by any chance to gain the requisite proximity."[15]

Proponents of the shell gun, such as Dahlgren, maintained that the U.S. Navy's inferiority to the navies of France and Britain in numbers of ships could be offset at least in part by superior ordnance. This meant switching completely to shell guns, with which other navies were only partially armed. In the mid-1850s, however, U.S. Navy ordnance arrangements still closely followed those of the Royal Navy. British and U.S. regulations called for a broadside armament on all gun decks of long 32-pounders and 8-inch shell guns. The French utilized the long 30-pounder and the *canon-obusier* of 22 centimeters (an 80-pounder).

While the French 30-pounder was superior in size and weight of both charge and shot, its bore was shorter. French powder, moreover, was not as strong as that used in the British and U.S. navies. The American 32-pounder was almost identical to Britain's, although its shot was larger and heavier, its charge less, and its powder more powerful. For all practical purposes the guns were of about equal power. All three shot guns—the British and American 32-pounders and the French 30-pounder—were, however, inferior to the 8-inch shell gun in range and striking power and therefore were less efficient for both short and long ranges.

The 10-inch shell gun was the only pivot gun in the Royal Navy until the 56-pounder Monk and 68-pounder Dundas were introduced. Many compared these favorably with the new shell guns and indeed felt they exceeded them at longer ranges. Hence they were preferred for steamer armament.

Dahlgren believed, however, that the only shell gun in the British navy appropriate for pivot use was the 10-incher of 84 cwt. It was this piece that had been copied for the U.S. Navy and until the mid-1850s been carried on steamers. Unfortunately, in copying the British gun the Americans only exaggerated its shortcomings. The fully loaded shell weighed 104 pounds compared with the British shell's 87.5 pounds. Since the latter was considered the maximum weight at which the British gun could sustain its charge, powder in the American gun had to be reduced from 12 to 10 pounds, adversely affecting both accuracy and range.

The 10-inch shell gun had shortcomings in pivot use, which required great accuracy, range, and force, and in this respect it was inferior to the heavier 50-, 56-, 64-, and 68-pounder. The 10-inch 86-cwt gun was probably inferior to the

TABLE 28

U.S. NAVY SHIP ARMAMENT FOR LINE-OF-BATTLE SHIPS, FRIGATES, AND STEAMERS, 1 JANUARY 1850

			Guns		
Name	*Rate*	*Date Launched*	*8-In*	*32-Pdr*	*Total*
LINE-OF-BATTLE SHIP					
Pennsylvania	120	1837	16	104	120
Franklin	74	1815	64 long 32s and 20 32-pdr carr.		86
Columbus	74	1819	12	68	80
Ohio	74	1820	12	72	84
North Carolina	74	1820	12	72	84
Delaware	74	1820	12	72	84
Vermont	74	1848	20	64	84
Alabama	74	—	12	72	84
Virginia	74	—	12	72	84
New York	74	—	12	72	84
New Orleans	74	—	—	—	—
RAZEED VESSEL					
Independence	54	1814	8	48	56
FIRST-CLASS FRIGATE					
United States	44	1797	4	46	50
Constitution	44	1797	4	46	50
Potomac	44	1821	8	42	50
Brandywine	44	1825	8	42	50
Columbia	44	1825	8	42	50
Congress	44	1839	8	42	50
Cumberland	44	1842	10	40	50
Savannah	44	1843	8	42	50
Raritan	44	1843	8	42	50
St. Lawrence	44	1847	8	42	50
*Santee**	44	—	8	42	50
*Sabine**	44	—	8	42	50
SECOND-CLASS FRIGATE					
Constellation	36	1797	6	32	38
Macedonian	36	1836	6	32	38
			10-In	*8-In*	
STEAMER					
First-class steamer	10	1850	2	8	10
Second-class steamer	6	1850	—	6	6
Third-class steamer	2	1850	—	2	2

Source: George F. Emmons, *The Navy of the United States* (Washington: Gideon, 1853), 24–25.
* Projected armament. Launched in 1855.

TABLE 29

Dimensions for Shell Guns and Shot in the U.S. Navy

Gun	Weight (cwt)	Date	Length* (in)	Bore Length (in)	Bore Diameter (in)	Charges (lbs) Distant	Charges (lbs) Ordinary	Charges (lbs) Near	Shot (lbs)	Shell Load (lbs)
32-pdr	27	1846	76.6	68.4	6.4	4.0	4.0	3.0	32.5	26.25
	32	1846	84.0	75.10	6.4	4.5	4.5	4.0	32.5	26.25
	42	1847	101.2	92.05	6.4	6.0	6.0	4.0	32.5	26.25
	46	1846	107.44	97.2	6.4	7.0	7.0	5.0	32.5	26.25
	51	1846	113.4	104.0	6.4	8.0	7.0	5.0	32.5	26.25
	57	1846	117.6	107.9	6.4	9.0	8.0	6.0	32.5	26.25
8-in	55	1846	105.7	95.4	8.0	7.0	7.0	6.0	—	51.5
	63	1841	111.5	102.0	8.0	9.0	8.0	6.0	—	51.5
	63	1851	112.01	100.3	8.0	9.0	8.0	6.0	—	51.5
10-in	86	1841	117.0	106.0	10.0	10.0	9.0	8.0	—	106.0
64-pdr	105	1849	137.0	124.2	8.0	16.0	12.0	8.0	63.75	51.5

Source: John Dahlgren, *Shells and Shell Guns* (Philadelphia: King and Baird, 1856), 26.
* Length extreme from muzzle to rear of breech plate (this excludes the pomilion). Measurement is from the base ring to the face of the muzzle and may vary in individual guns.

68-pounder save at close range. It was undoubtedly to remedy this that the 10-inch gun of 107 cwt was cast for the U.S. Navy beginning in 1854.

Despite continued controversy over the relative merits of shot and shell guns, by the 1850s shell had earned a permanent place. The 1860 ordnance instructions called for captains of U.S. Navy vessels to practice firing loaded shells "in preference to shot."[16]

The mid-1850s also saw the introduction of the new Dahlgren-designed IX- and XI-inch shell guns. John Dahlgren was easily the most influential figure in the development of nineteenth-century American naval ordnance. His work marked the real beginning of scientific techniques in its design and employment. While best known for the so-called Dahlgren gun, he also developed rifled cannon, a highly successful boat howitzer, and other innovative pieces.

As a lieutenant directing ordnance activities at the Washington Navy Yard, Dahlgren designed a new gun lock, an improved primer, and sights graduated in yards. In 1848 he reported on tests with the 32-pounder of 32 cwt; a year later he did the same for the 8-inch gun of 55 cwt. This was the first time ranging data was available for these guns. Soon after he designed the first standard boat howitzer for the U.S. Navy.

The need for a boat howitzer had been demonstrated during the Mexican War, when the blockade resulted in boat operations in shoal waters for which small carronades, army field pieces, and howitzers had all been pressed into service. These had not proved satisfactory, and after the war Dahlgren was authorized to produce a new design. After a year of trial, the U.S. Navy officially adopted his boat howitzer.

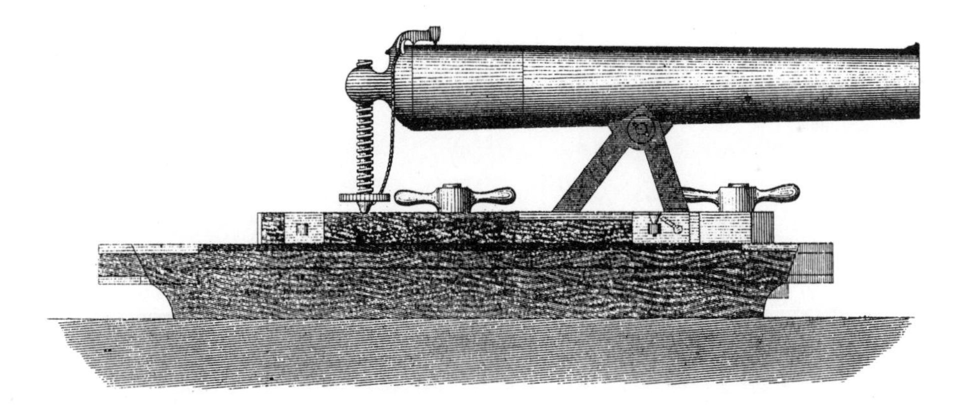

Fig. 91. Dahlgren Howitzer on Boat Carriage. (Bureau of Ordnance, *Ordnance Instructions,* 1866.)

Fig. 92. Dahlgren Howitzer on Field Carriage. (Bureau of Ordnance, *Ordnance Instructions,* 1866.)

It appeared first in three different sizes: a 12-pounder light howitzer of 4.62-inch bore and 430 pounds (with boat carriage, 600), a 12-pounder medium howitzer of 4.62-inch bore and 760 pounds (with boat carriage, 1,200), and a 24-pounder of 5.82-inch bore and 1,310 pounds (with boat carriage, 2,000). Other types appeared later, including a lighter 12-pounder weighing 300 pounds and 12-pounder (3.4-inch bore and 880 pounds) and 20-pounder (4.0-inch bore and 1,340 pounds) rifled guns.

All Dahlgren boat howitzers were chambered at the bottom of the bore. They had a smooth external form with no muzzle swell. A loop underneath secured the gun, like the old carronade, to its carriage. This was not the case with the 20-pounder of 4-inch bore, which had conventional rimbases and trunnions.

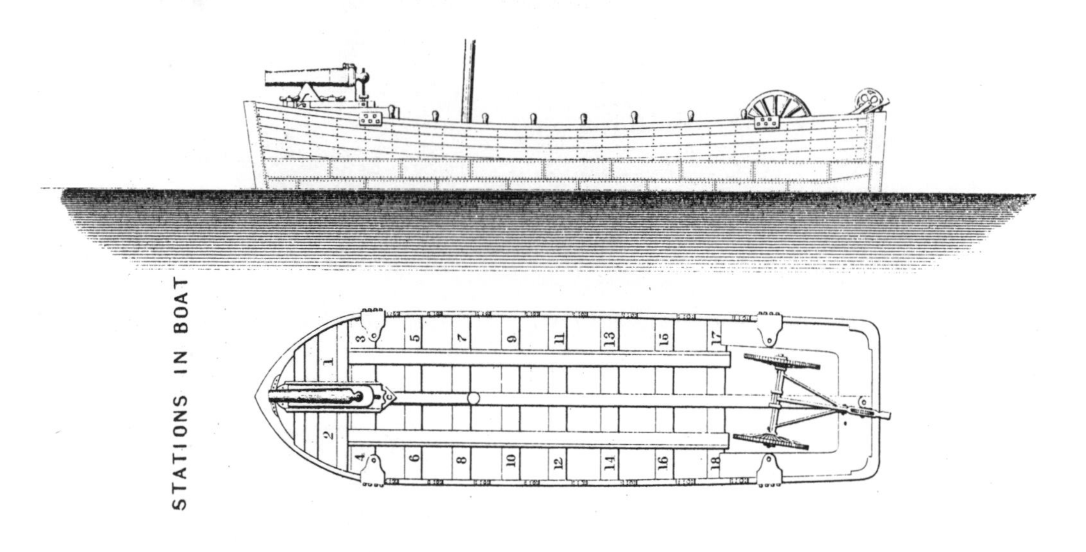

Fig. 93. Dahlgren Boat Howitzer in the Bow of a Launch. (Bureau of Ordnance, *Ordnance Instructions,* 1866.)

The 24-pounder Dahlgren howitzer was intended for the launches of both seventy-fours and frigates. The medium 12-pounder was designed specifically for the launches of frigates, while the light 12-pounder had been developed for sloops. Placed in the bow of a launch, the howitzer could be pivoted 120 degrees without altering the direction of the vessel. It provided rapid fire against small boats or light vessels and covering fire in an amphibious assault. On landing, the howitzer could be quickly mounted on a field carriage and used for ground-fire support, then changed back to its launch mode and reembarked. Eight to ten men could make these changes in two or three minutes. Slightly more time was required for land-to-boat configuration.

Field carriages of wrought-iron were carried in the stern of the launch. In contrast to normal land-service practice, a small wheel was added at the end of the trail for ease of movement since guns were hauled by sailors rather than horses. When a piece was ready to fire, a pin was removed and the wheel turned upon its trail. The carriage had no limber.

The basic ammunition for howitzers was shell, shrapnel or spherical case, and cannister, no shot. All projectiles were fixed—that is, attached to their charge. Dahlgren boat howitzers could be fired rapidly. For proof and in drill, 12-pounders were fired eight times a minute, sometimes ten times a minute or more. On the boat carriage, where the howitzer was more difficult to service, the maximum rate was five times a minute.

Powder charges weighed 2 pounds for the 24-pounder, 1 for the 12-pounder, and 0.625 for the light 12-pounder. The range for the 24-pounder was 1,308 yards with shrapnel and 1,270 yards for shell at 5 degrees' elevation.

The advantage of howitzers in combat was demonstrated at the end of November 1856, when they proved highly effective in assaults on the Barrier Forts near Canton, China.

During the Civil War large numbers of boat howitzers were cast, at least 1,087 12-pounders alone. These included 456 mediums, 177 lights, 23 small 12-pounders of 300 pounds, 424 rifled bronze 12-pounders weighing 880 pounds each, and at least seven steel ones weighing 790 pounds. One hundred rifled 20-pounders weighing 1,340 pounds and 1,009 24-pounders were also cast. The Washington Navy Yard could not keep up with the wartime demand for these guns, and as a result Charles T. Ames and Cyrus Alger both produced them under private contract for the navy.

Small and light 12-pounders were not favored during the war (the manufacture of lights was for the most part discontinued), and 24-pounders, although officially designated as boat armament, usually remained aboard ship, where they proved invaluable in operations on Western rivers, especially the Mississippi. The medium 12-pounder also proved extremely effective and was considered the best boat gun of its day in the world. In fact, it continued in service well past the Civil War.

Even as his boat howitzer underwent trial, Dahlgren was designing a new heavy shell gun for the navy. In November 1849 a 32-pounder being tested for accuracy at the experimental battery blew up, killing the gunner. Dahlgren asked for permission to design a new gun that would incorporate both greater power and safety. In January 1850 he submitted a draft for a IX-inch gun to the chief of ordnance. A week later he presented a draft for a 50-pounder. He was allowed to proceed, and the first two prototype Dahlgren guns were cast at West Point Foundry and delivered to the Washington Navy Yard in May 1850.

The original IX-inch Dahlgren had a more angular form than earlier guns and only one vent. Later the design was modified in favor of a curved shape and double vent. In 1856 side vents were restored. The purpose of the second vent was to extend the life of the gun. Repeated firings enlarged the vent opening. When this occurred the second vent, which had been filled with zinc, was opened and the original vent itself sealed off with zinc.

The new Dahlgrens had a distinctive shape. The weight of metal was concentrated at the breech, the point of greatest strain, giving them the name soda bottles. Ultimately they were cast in 9-, 10-, 11-, 13-, 15-, and 20-inch bore sizes.

A single day of testing confirmed Dahlgren's preference for the heavier IX-inch gun (9,000 pounds) over the 50-pounder (8,000 pounds). He believed the extra weight of the IX-incher was manageable. In July 1850, he proposed the arming of frigates with six 10-inch pivot guns on the spar deck and IX-inch

Fig. 94. A IX-Inch Dahlgren Gun, 1859. This piece, located at the Mariner's Museum in Newport News, is 9′ long and weighs 9,020 pounds. On the breech appears the markings "No. 243" and "C.A. & Co."; on the left trunnion, "P" and "W.R.T."; and on the right trunnion, "IX In." and "1859." (Photo by the author.)

guns in broadside on the gun deck. Six months later he had prepared a detailed report for a new ordnance system.

Dahlgren had three principal ideas regarding naval ordnance: first, most effective were "the heaviest pieces that can be mounted on truck carriages, and those throwing the heaviest projectiles that can be conveniently handled"; second, shells should be the primary projectile, shot being used "only in exceptional cases and then with low charges"; and third, testing should be done to ascertain "the precise term of velocity that ought not be exceeded . . . in order to obtain the greatest practicable accuracy."[17]

The heart of Dahlgren's plan was to transfer the main artillery to the spar deck, the best place to mount heavy guns. He proposed that the armament of a first-class frigate consist of six 10-inch guns on pivot mounts on the spar deck and twenty-six IX-inchers on the gun deck. He also suggested building a new vessel of about 240 feet in length that would cost only half as much as a first-class steamer but would mount twenty-eight IX-inch guns on the gun deck and seven XI-inch shell guns of about 15,600 pounds on pivots on the spar deck. This would give a broadside shot weight of 1,960 pounds, compared with 2,114 for the *Pennsylvania,* the largest vessel in the U.S. Navy, and only 1,488 for the *Ohio,* a representative 74-gun two-decker.

But total weight of broadside did not give an adequate picture of real firepower. As Dahlgren subsequently proved, an 11-inch shell produced far greater damage than three 32-pounder shot, even if the latter hit near one another. An 11-inch shell made a hole equal to that of two 8-inch shells, and its explosive power was greater.

Dahlgren also concluded that his ordnance arrangement would result in

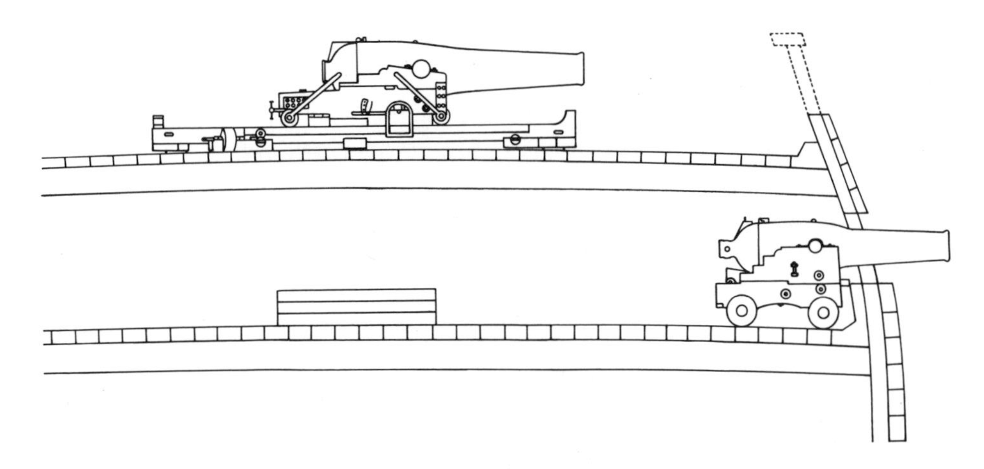

Fig. 95. Dahlgren's Proposed Armament for a First-Class Frigate, August 1850. Section of a first-class frigate with a proposed armament of six X-inch guns on pivot mounts on the spar deck, and twenty-six IX-inch guns on the gun deck. This drawing was submitted by Dahlgren to Commander Warrington in August 1850. (The carriage of the IX-incher was to be that used for an 8-incher of 63 cwt, widened to take the larger gun; the pivot carriage of the X-incher was similar to that used for steamers.) (From an original drawing in National Archives, Record Group 74.)

substantial savings in manpower. It could be manned by half the number of men required for the *Pennsylvania* and one-third less than the number assigned to batteries of seventy-fours such as the *Ohio*.

In March 1851, Dahlgren submitted a design for an experimental XI-inch gun that was approved. The first, cast by Cyrus Alger in July, took part in a parade through the streets of Boston on 17 September when President Fillmore visited that city. It was delivered to the Boston Navy Yard in October. The new gun weighed 15,890 pounds.

There was considerable opposition in the early 1850s to Dahlgren's XI-inch gun for use in ships, and it grew after the death in October 1851 of Dahlgren's supporter, Commodore Warrington, chief of the Ordnance Bureau. His successor, Captain Charles Morris, did not agree with Dahlgren, and from this point on his efforts met with increased official opposition.

Support for Dahlgren's ideas was, however, growing in Congress. In February 1851 the House Committee on Naval Affairs recommended adoption of his system, citing its financial advantages. But in the summer of 1852, when Congressman Frederick B. Stanton, chairman of the House Committee on Naval Affairs, reported a bill out of his committee to construct a warship testing the improved heavy ordnance suggested by Dahlgren, it failed to pass.

Tests with the Dahlgrens continued. In the summer of 1852, the first XI-inch gun was fired 500 times with shell and 655 times with shot of 170 pounds. Bursting did not occur until July 1855, on its 1,959th fire. The trial of another Dahlgren, a IX-incher cast in 1857, was also remarkable. It fired 1,500 rounds of 72-pound shell before being intentionally burst, then with only ten shot and a charge of 20 pounds of powder.

These highly successful trials at last brought official if grudging support. In 1854, when Congress authorized six new screw-propelled frigates, the *Merrimack* class, Dahlgren's guns were included in the armament but his proposed system was modified. Gun deck armament was to consist of IX-inchers, as he had recommended, but spar deck armament of only two heavy pivot guns, one each at the bow and stern, and they were to be X-inchers rather than XI-inch guns. Twenty 8-inch, 63-cwt shell guns would make up the broadside armament of the spar deck, not six XI-inchers between the fore and main masts. Contracts let in December 1854 called for the manufacture of 156 IX-inch, 14 X-inch, and 14 XI-inch guns.

The five frigates of the *Merrimack* class were the finest and most powerful in the world. Despite the modification of Dahlgren's plan, they were armed entirely with shell guns. This was an innovation, since in both England and France shell guns had merely been auxiliaries in batteries composed largely of 32-pounders. The British were quick to react, building five frigates of their own, the *Diadem* class, all armed with batteries of 10-inch shell guns.

By the second half of the 1850s Dahlgren had reason for satisfaction. Writing to a friend he noted, "I have dislodged the 32-pdrs, and only a few of the old 8-inch guns find place in the new ships. . . ." But their presence was "a blemish and a weakness."[18]

The *Merrimack* was commissioned in early 1856. Dahlgren noted that "after delays and opposition and objections that have lasted six years, I had the satisfaction of seeing one of the largest ships in the world armed with the guns of my own model."[19] The IX-inch Dahlgrens were the mainstay of the armament of the rest of the *Merrimack* class—the *Wabash, Minnesota, Roanoke,* and *Colorado*—except for the *Niagara,* which evolved as a large sloop of war armed with twelve XI-inch guns.

Dahlgren was not satisfied, however, with what he regarded as a halfway approach to the *Merrimack*'s battery. Repeatedly he had argued for a uniform broadside armament rather than a mixed battery. The greater the number of gun types, the greater the risk in battle of mismatching powder charges and projectiles. A uniform armament would also simplify carriage and equipment manufacture.

Dahlgren pushed for a spar deck armament consisting entirely of XI-inch pivot guns. Arguments against this centered on the great weight of these pieces and the difficulties of working them and handling their projectiles. But, as Dahlgren pointed out, such problems were offset by the great firepower of XI-inch pivot guns and their economy. Smaller guns required more men to project the same weight of shot.

The demonstrated success of the *Merrimack* weakened navy opposition to Dahlgren's proposals, and in 1857 money was forthcoming to arm the sloop of war *Plymouth* under his direction as an experimental ordnance vessel.[20]

Modifications enabling the *Plymouth* to carry the heavier Dahlgren ordnance proceeded. Finally, in June 1857 the sloop left Washington on a cruise that took her to the Azores, Portugal, the Netherlands, Great Britain, and Bermuda. During the cruise her armament consisted of four IX-inch shell guns in broadside, one XI-inch pivot gun, and two 24-pounder and one 12-pounder howitzers. The crew practiced day after day in different conditions handling the IX-inch and XI-inch guns and conducting target practice. With the IX-inch gun, the men achieved a record of one firing every 40 seconds. This compared quite favorably with gunnery ship HMS *Excellent*'s record of 43 seconds for each of eleven rounds from a 32-pounder and 46 seconds for each of eleven rounds from an 8-inch gun.

The five-month cruise of the *Plymouth* was extremely important in demonstrating the feasibility of employing large ordnance in U.S. Navy ships. As Secretary of the Navy Isaac Toucey noted, 121 shells had been fired from the XI-inch pivot gun without "any of the difficulties usually supposed to render such heavy ordnance nearly unavailable on shipboard."[21]

Dahlgren's IX-inch broadside guns were mounted on a Marsilly carriage designed by the French. In the 1750s, John Muller had noted that the French used a carriage nearly the same height as the common truck carriage but with only two large fore trucks. There were no steps in the brackets, and the stool bed rested on a transom at the rear (instead of on the hind axletree, as in the common carriage). Muller observed that "these carriages do not recoil so much, and are more readily pointed, because the trucks are not tight to their axle-tree. When they are traversed but a little, the carriage will move without the truck and then fall back again so soon as the handspike is taken away."[22] The French navy adopted the modern Marsilly carriage for its heavy broadside guns and the U.S. Navy followed suit, selecting it for all IX-inch shell guns in broadside.

The roller handspike made the Marsilly carriage easier to train. Additional weight was put on the hind dumb trucks during recoil to check it. The Marsilly carriage would damage decks made of anything but oak or hard yellow pine. With the gun to windward or on an even keel, the roller handspike was used to return it to battery; with the gun to leeward and with a lot of heel, the handspike was not necessary because the friction of the hind dumb trucks checked the movement of the gun, which would then bump into the side of the ship.

A Marsilly carriage and its IX-inch Dahlgren gun—the largest used in broadside by the time of the Civil War—together weighed upwards of 5 tons, yet they could be moved from one side of a frigate to the other in less than 2 minutes. This carriage was, in fact, the only one ever to compete seriously with the old four-truck carriage in the U.S. Navy.

One complete turn of the elevating screw of the IX-inch-gun Marsilly carriage equaled a degree of the quadrant. The screw could elevate the gun 19 degrees and depress it 8 degrees, but as the gun ports would allow only 10

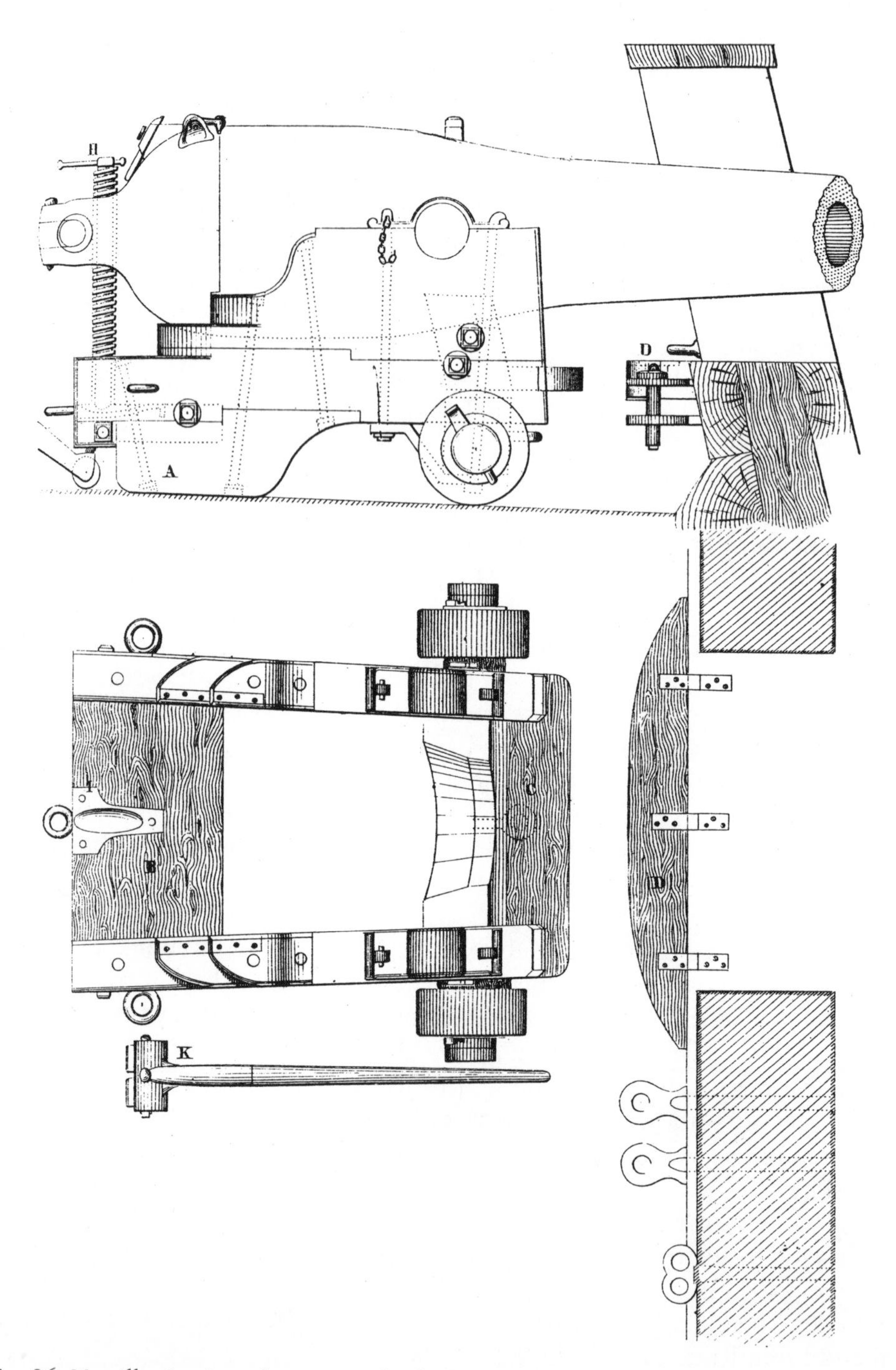

Fig. 96. Marsilly Carriage for a IX-Inch Shell Gun. (Bureau of Ordnance, *Ordnance Instructions*, 1860.)

Key to fig. 96.

NOMENCLATURE OF PARTS

A. Lowest piece of bracket, in place of rear truck of ordinary carriage
B. Rear transom, in place of rear axle
C. Breast piece
D. Sweep pieces fixed below port sill
H. Elevating screw and lever, with saucer *I*, in place of bed and quoin
K. Roller handspike
L. Loop for handspike

degrees of elevation and 7 of depression, the transom was scored to keep the gun within limits and prevent the muzzle from striking wood at either the top or bottom of the port.

By 1860, a slightly modified version of the pivot carriage had been introduced for the XI-inch Dahlgren gun. Front, middle, and rear transoms replaced the axletrees in the top carriage. The lower part of the transoms formed a plane that rested on the slide and, by creating friction, modified the recoil. There was also a fourth or breast transom, located in about the same position as the transom in the old truck carriage. The top carriage also had front and rear metal friction rollers attached to the carriage with journal plates.

The slide consisted of two rails on an inclined plane with slats extending from the lower edge of the one to the lower edge of the other. The rails were fitted into front, middle, and rear transoms. Attached to the lower part of the front and rear transoms were rollers on axles. The rear rollers were used for training and the front ones for shifting. At first there was no roller under the middle transom, but as the length of the slide caused it to sag at that point, by 1860 a single roller had been added there as well.

Projecting from the outside of the rails were flanges or compressor battens, one on each side. The lower lip of the compressor extended under the batten, and the upper bearing rested in a socket in the upper surface of the middle transom. A screw compressed the batten between the carriage and the lower lip of the compressor.

A preventer breech kept the gun from rolling too far on its carriage when it was run out to leeward. To run the gun to windward the carriage was released from all checks and the crew pulled on the out tackles, taking advantage of the roll. Care was necessary—an XI-inch gun and its pivot carriage weighed 20,000 pounds.

In 1856, Dahlgren recommended the manufacture of rifled guns for the navy. Work on such a project was not approved until the spring of 1859, and the Civil War had begun before a Dahlgren rifled gun was introduced. Another pre–Civil War project was armor for ships, but nothing came of it until later.

Although Dahlgren retained an interest in these projects, he still concentrated on the development of an ordnance system for the navy based on his IX-inch and XI-inch shell guns. Despite his failure to get the system adopted

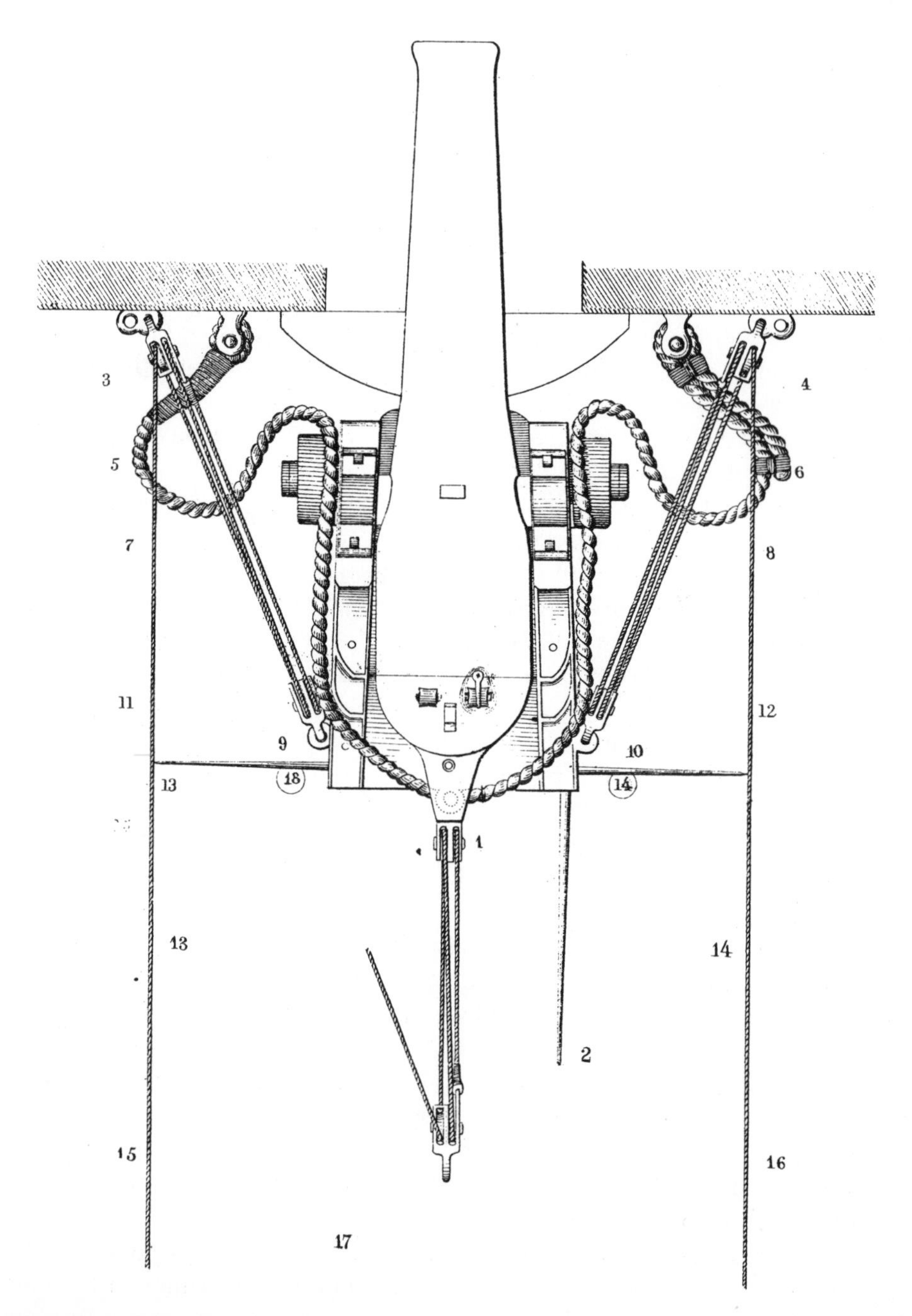

Fig. 97. Marsilly Carriage and IX-Inch Dahlgren Gun, Showing Location of Crew. (Bureau of Ordnance, *Ordnance Instructions*, 1866.)

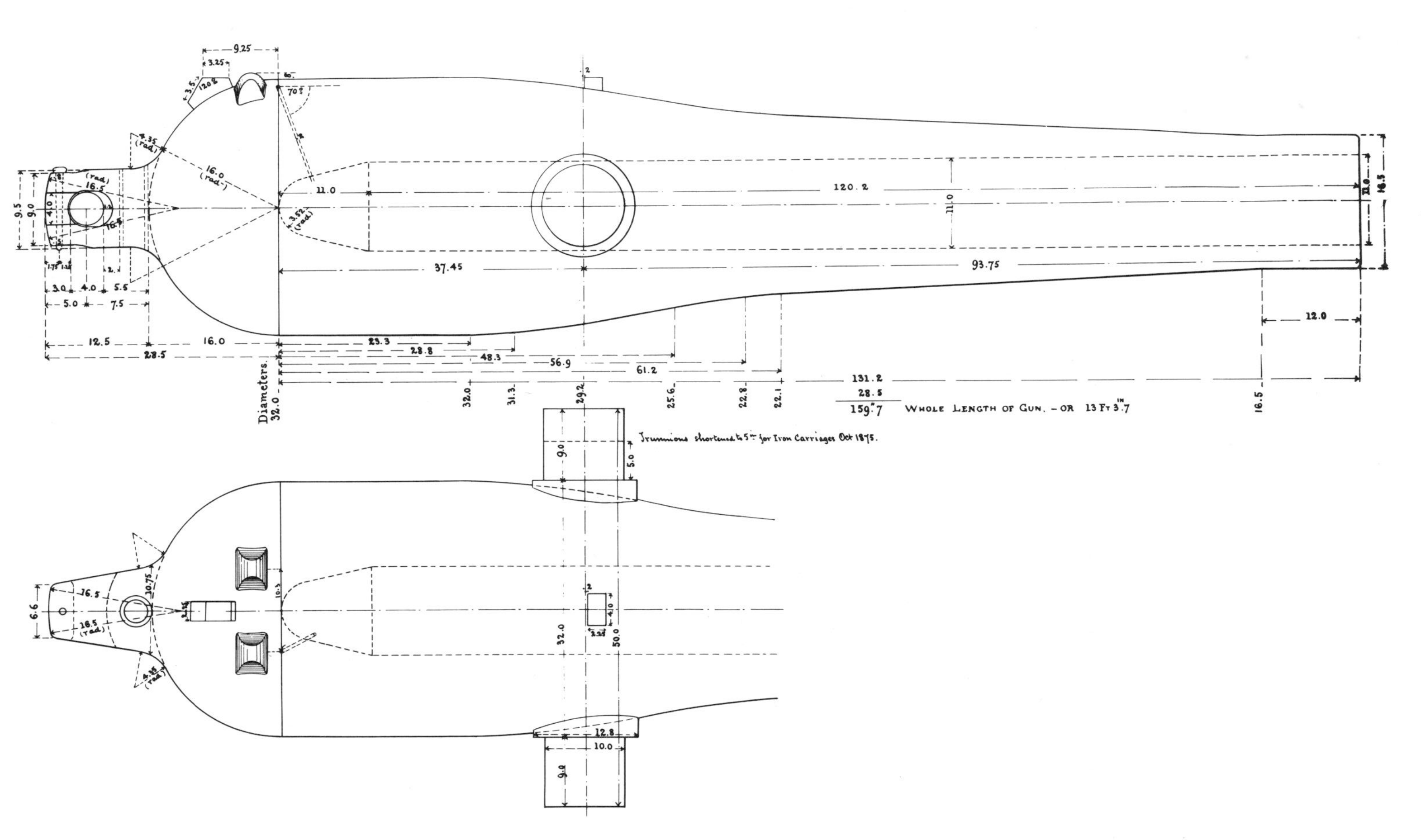

Fig. 98. XI-Inch Shell Gun of 1851, Showing Changes Made up to 1869. (National Archives, Record Group 74.)

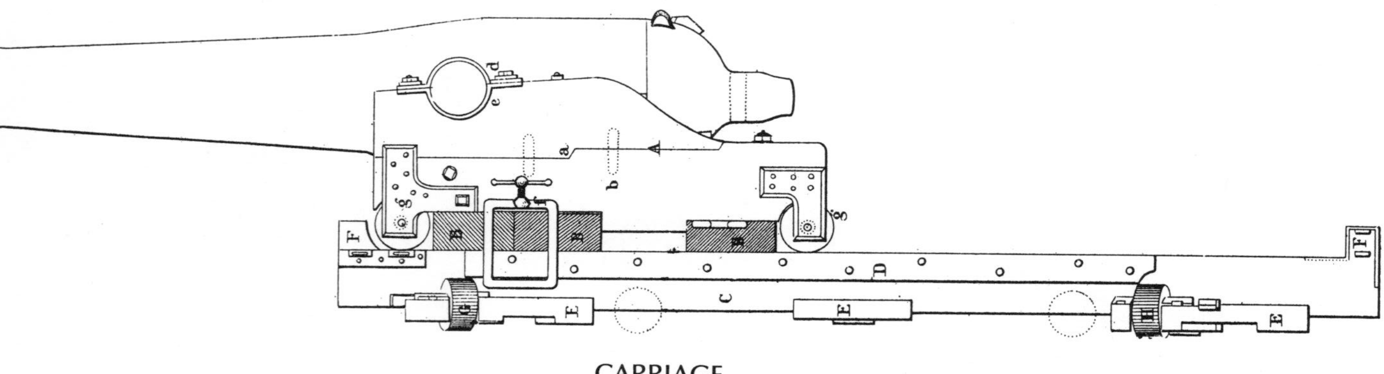

CARRIAGE

Wooden Parts

A. Brackets of two pieces with jog *a* and dowels *b*
B. Front, middle, and rear transoms (projecting be-young the rails and jogged into brackets)

Metal Parts

d. Cap squares
e. Trunnion plates
f. Compressor with screw and lever
g. Rollers and journal plates

SLIDE

Wooden Parts

C. Rails
D. Compressor battens
E. Transoms (front and rear in two parts, middle in one part)

Metal Parts

F. Hurters, front and rear
G. Shifting trucks
H. Training d°, both with journals and eccentric axles

Fig. 99. Side Elevation of an XI-Inch Carriage and Slide. (Bureau of Ordnance, *Ordnance Instructions*, 1866.)

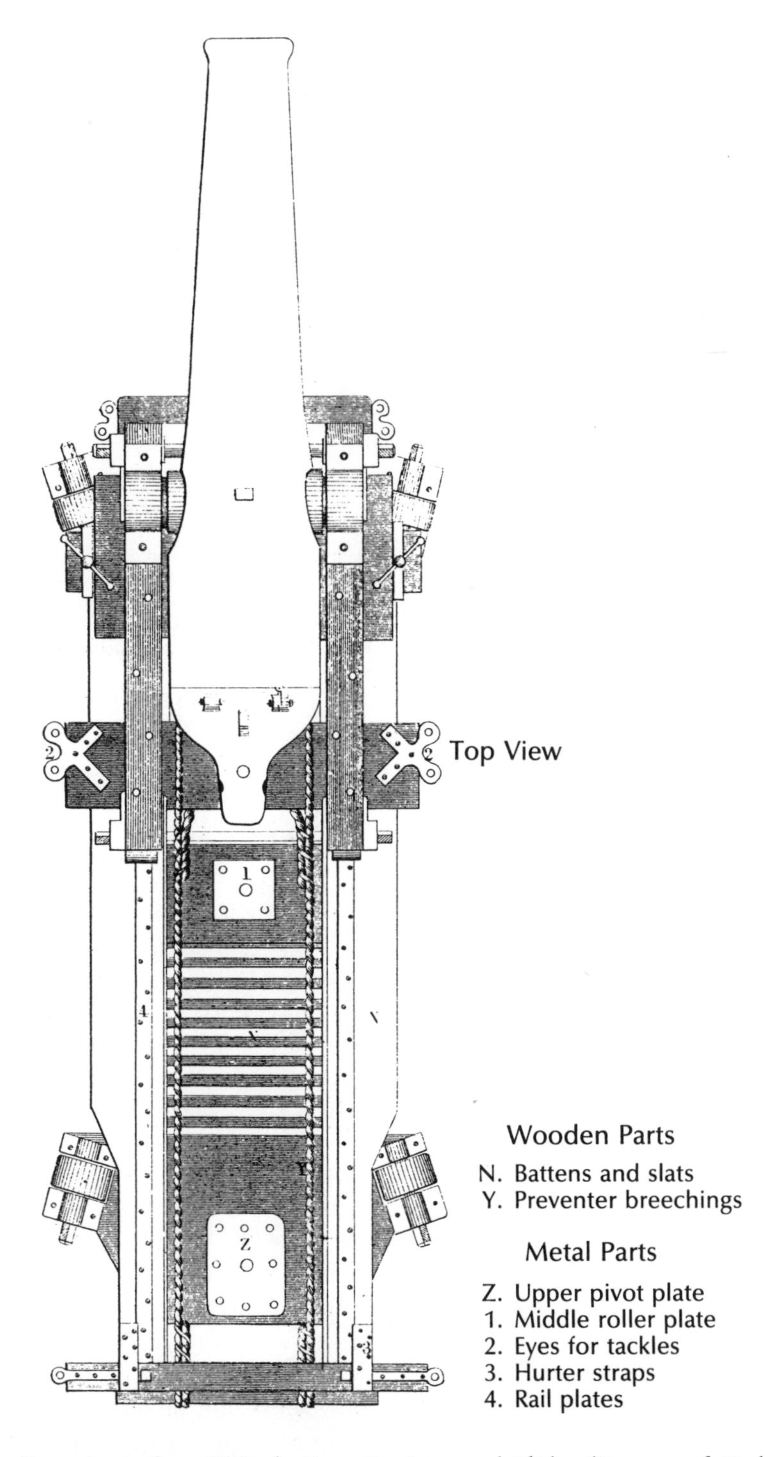

Fig. 100. Top view of an XI-Inch Gun Carriage and Slide. (Bureau of Ordnance, *Ordnance Instructions*, 1866.)

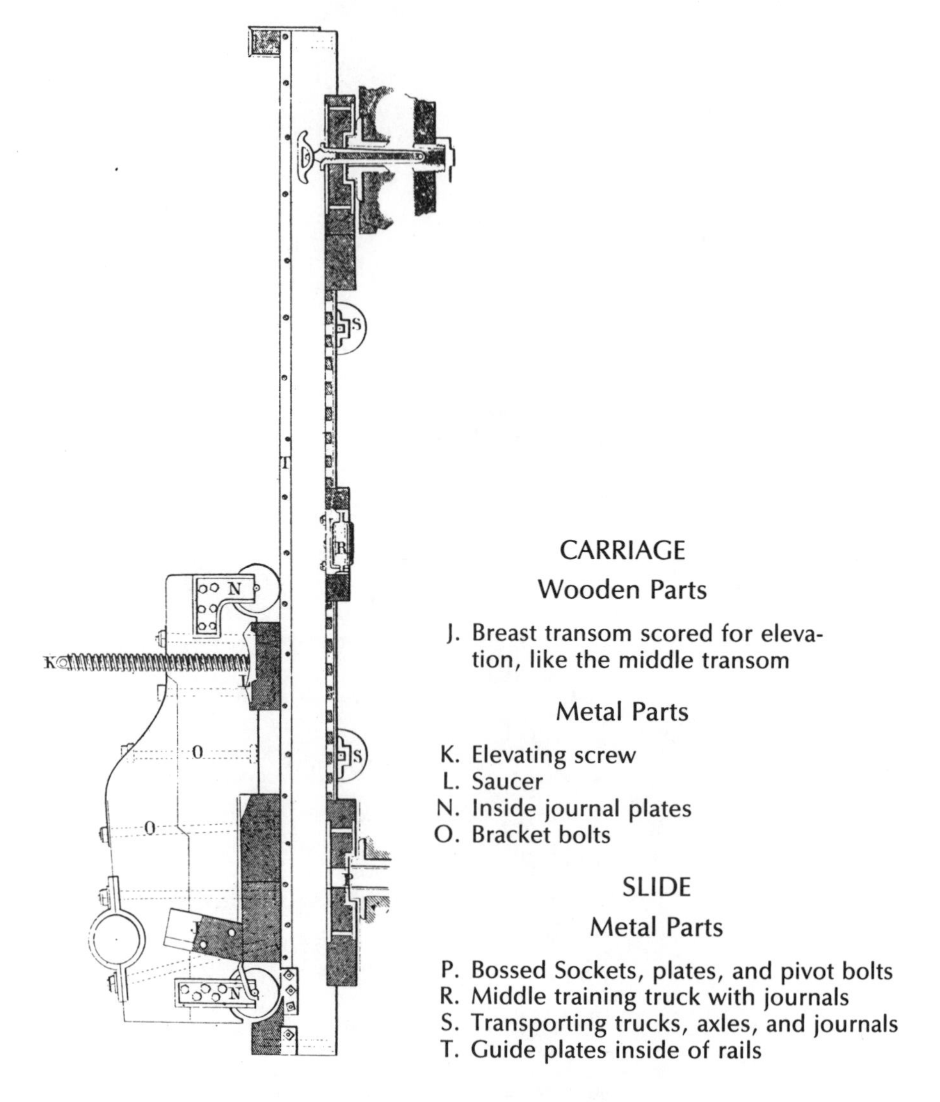

Fig. 101. Sectional View of an XI-Inch Gun Carriage and Slide. (Bureau of Ordnance, *Ordnance Instructions*, 1866.)

in toto by the time of the Civil War, Dahlgren's work was immensely important in the history of naval ordnance. Paixhans may have been responsible for introducing the system of firing shells from long guns, but John Dahlgren was the first to incorporate it into naval armament on a widespread scale.

Dahlgren himself summed up the difference between Paixhans' system and his own when he wrote, "Paixhans' guns were simply shell-guns, and were not designed for shot, nor for great penetration or accuracy at long ranges. They were, therefore, auxiliary to, or associates of, the shot-guns. This made a mixed armament, was objectionable as such and was never adopted to

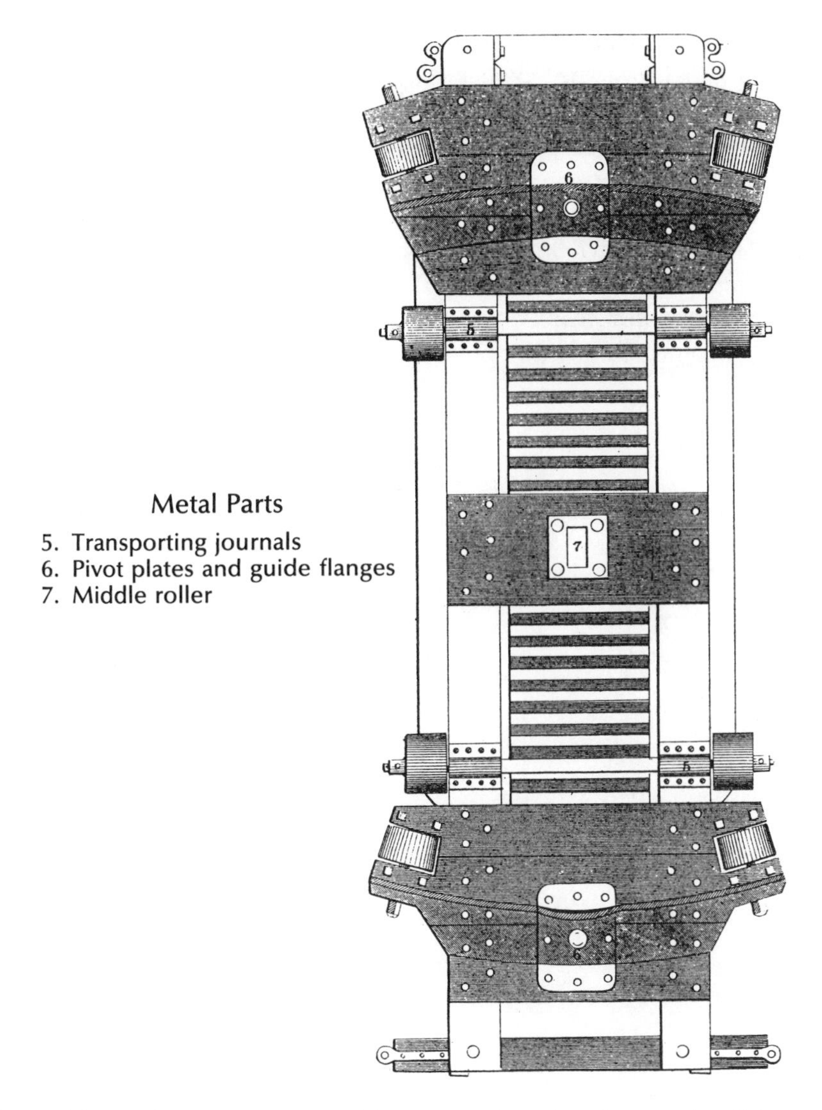

Note: All metal parts are composition except the axles, levers, elevating screw, and bracket bolts.

Fig. 102. Plan of Slide for an XI-Inch Gun Carriage. (Bureau of Ordnance, *Ordnance Instructions*, 1866.)

any extent in France." The same was true in England and the United States. Dahlgren's system, on the other hand, was "to have a gun that should generally throw shells far and accurately, with the capacity to fire solid shot when needed. Also to compose the whole battery entirely of such guns. The omission of shot is thus accounted for. The proclivity to fire them was such, and the avoidance of shell practice so great, that I asked that no shot should be put on board, and then the practice with shells would be compulsory. . . ."[23]

Dahlgren's many critics had missed the point—not only to fire shell but also to propel it at the correct velocity so that it would penetrate with the lowest possible velocity and explode with maximum effect. Ironically, during the Civil War Dahlgren guns were often employed to fire solid shot rather than shell at ironclad opponents.

The XI-inch shell could pierce 4.5 inches of iron plate backed by 20 inches of solid oak. One Civil War captain said that Dahlgren IX-inch guns were "the best ... ever made" and noted that crews handled them "with as much confidence as they drink their grog."[24] Dahlgren's achievement cannot be underestimated. He laid the foundation for subsequent developments in naval ordnance.

CHAPTER VII

The Civil War

WHEN THE CIVIL WAR began the Union navy had three key objectives: to enforce a blockade stretching along 3,500 miles of Confederate coastline, to carry out operations against Southern ports along the Atlantic and Gulf coasts and on the Mississippi and other rivers, and to sweep the seas free of Confederate commerce and privateers. To accomplish all of this the Union had only forty-five ships in commission. Particularly harmful to its cause was the loss, after the secession of Virginia, of the largest prewar navy yard, the one at Gosport (Norfolk). With more resolute action the Union could have held on to it. In any case, an effort to destroy the yard to prevent the Confederates from capturing it intact was hasty and unsuccessful. (The action did, however, testify to the strength of the new Dahlgren guns, for sledgehammers could not knock off a single trunnion.) Lost in the fiasco were eleven ships, including the old ships of the line *Pennsylvania*, *Delaware*, and *Columbus* as well as the frigates *Merrimack*, *Columbia*, and *Raritan*. One of the two sloops lost was the *Plymouth*. Within two months, the Confederates had repaired much of the damage to the yard and raised the *Merrimack*, which was being rebuilt as an ironclad. The Union also lost a total of 1,195 heavy guns in the action.

Over the next few months the North made considerable strides in replacing lost ordnance and acquiring ships. In all the Union navy purchased 313 steamers, about half its fleet. Another 184 vessels, most of them sailing ships, tugs, and the like, were acquired from the War and Treasury Departments. But converted merchant vessels, while suitable for the blockade, were not capable of offensive operations against Confederate forts or the Confederate cruisers that had appeared at sea by 1862. Therefore two new classes of gunboats were designed and heavy screw sloops ordered. In the West a fleet of wooden gunboats, ironclads, and mortar boats took shape. The Union army and navy shared initial control of the western flotilla, but after a year this was transferred entirely to the navy. By the end of 1862, 52 steamers were either completed or under construction and contracts for another 71 had been let, including 3 experimental ironclads. Two of the ironclads, the *Galena* and *New Ironsides*, were conventional wooden ships with attached iron, but the *Monitor*, designed by John Ericsson, was a radically different vessel. She had been approved, at least in part, because her designer promised quick construction.

In the course of the conflict, both sides invested heavily in ironclad vessels. In the North, the success of the *Monitor* produced a "monitor-mania" for ships with iron hulls below water and turrets holding the heavy guns. Already in February 1862, a month before the epic battle between the *Monitor* and the *Virginia*, Congress had appropriated money for twenty ironclads.

The problems with monitors were many. They were slow, difficult to manage in heavy seas (the *Monitor* herself succumbed to a storm off North Carolina), and they had a slow rate of fire, one shot every 5 minutes or so for the largest guns. But they were virtually invulnerable to enemy fire and were cheaper and faster to construct than conventional ironclads with guns in broadside. Slowness, furthermore, did not hinder blockade duties or army support operations ashore, particularly along rivers. And to help offset the slow rate of fire, a new class of double-turreted monitors was built.

Coastal schooners were acquired for use as mortar boats against New Orleans, and an impressive force of gunboats was assembled for riverine operations in support of the army. By the end of 1864 the Union navy numbered more than 600 ships; at its peak it had some 700 vessels of all types, including 208 new ships, 60 of which were ironclads. Indeed, at war's end the U.S. Navy was second in size only to that of Great Britain. This force had captured 1,151 blockade runners and destroyed 355 ships, including 20 Confederate navy vessels.

During the war many older guns such as 32-pounders remained in service, although new ordnance was introduced. The 24-pounders and 42-pounders were largely discarded, at least some of the latter being ordered withdrawn from service in April 1862.

By 1864 the navy's solid-shot guns included 32-pounders of 27, 33, 42, 46, 51, 57, and 61 cwt and the 64-pounder of 106 cwt. Light 32-pounders of 27 and 33 cwt and 64-pounders (8-inch) of 106 cwt were described as "nearly obsolete."[1]

Shell guns in service were 8-inchers of 55 and 63 cwt, the old 10-incher, and IX-, X-, and XI-inch Dahlgrens. By 1864 larger Dahlgrens had also begun to appear, owing to Confederate ironclad construction. Assistant Secretary of the Navy Gustavus Fox, said to have been impressed by a 15-inch Rodman at

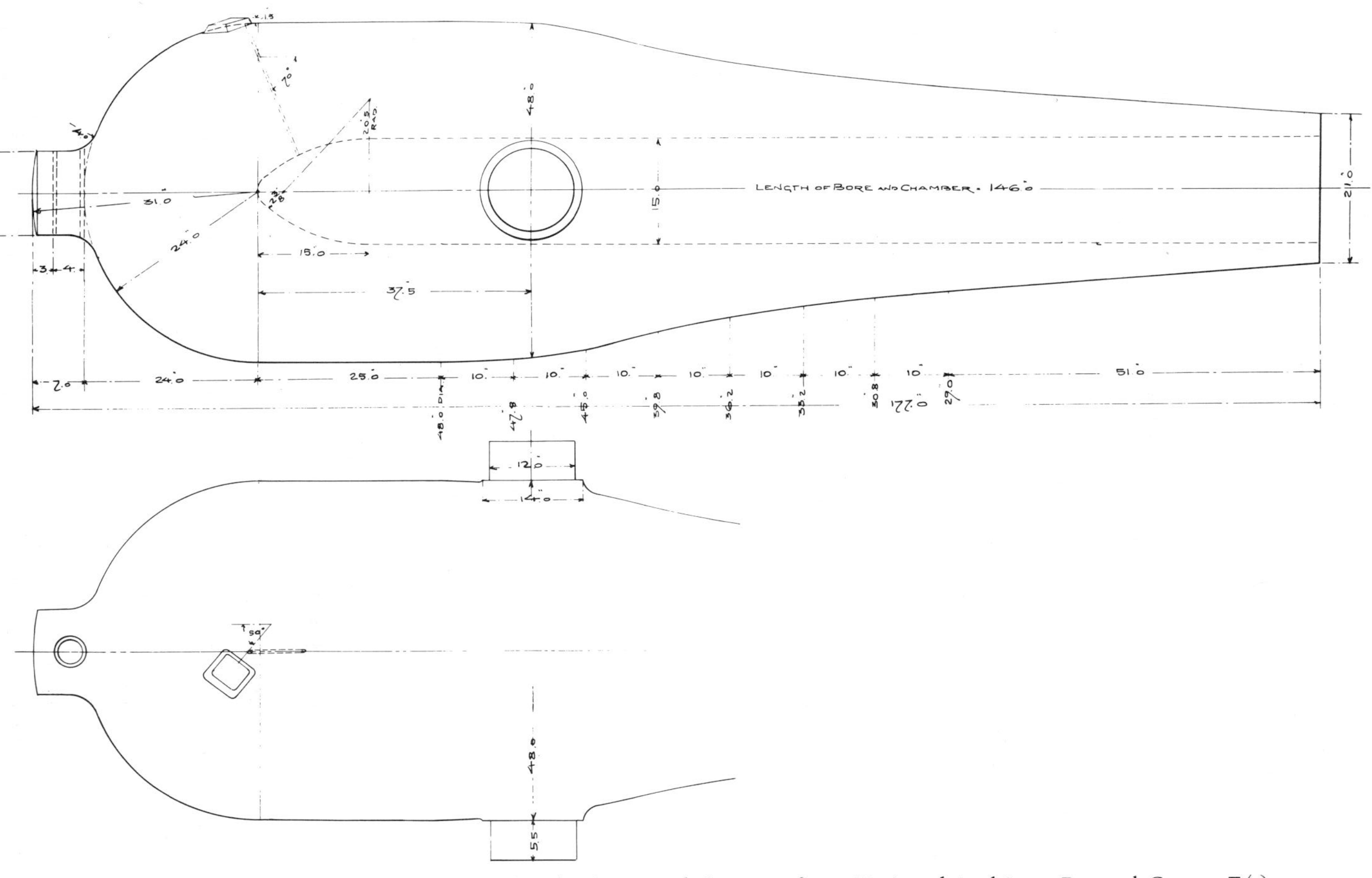

Fig. 103. The XV-Inch Dahlgren Gun of 1862. (Original drawing from National Archives, Record Group 74.)

Fort Monroe, pushed for similar-sized guns for the turrets of new monitors. The XV-inch Dahlgren was introduced only over the objections of its designer, who favored the XIII-incher. Dahlgren disclaimed any responsibility for the XV-incher. It was partly as a result of his objections that the XV-inch gun, rushed into service without the standard proof, was fired with reduced charges.

The first of the Dahlgren XV-inch guns were ordered in April 1862. The navy contracted with Fort Pitt Foundry for fifty, asking founder Charles Knap to have his men work day and night to get the guns ready within 120 days. Because there was no time for orderly testing, the guns were cast hollow according to the Rodman principle. At 42,000 pounds, too heavy for broadside use, they were intended exclusively for Ericsson's new ironclad monitors.

The desire to have a sufficient quantity of these guns on hand undoubtedly explains newspaper ads placed in nine Northern papers in June 1862 calling for proposals for the manufacture of 15-inch guns, not to exceed 50,000 pounds, and 12-inch rifles of the same exterior form and weight proportions as the 15-inch gun. With the first two XV-inch Knap-cast guns not ready for proof until the end of August, Dahlgren even proposed to Ericsson that he consider 15-inch Rodmans for turret armament in the new monitors. If they had been used, 3 feet would have had to be cut off the muzzle of the larger army pieces, resulting in excessive breech preponderance. Ericsson found this idea impractical. Finally, on 30 September, the first Dahlgren XV-inchers were delivered.

It was not until 11 October 1862 that the first XV-inch gun was test-fired at the Washington Navy Yard. It fired solid shot of 440 pounds and shell of 330, 13 pounds of which was the explosive charge. Dahlgren found that a powder charge of 30 pounds worked well in the gun. By 1864 the usual charge was 35 pounds for shell, 50 pounds maximum; little was gained by the increased charge, for maximum range at 7 degrees' elevation was 2,100 yards with 35 pounds and only 2,420 with 50. The 1864 regulations called for the heavier charge only when additional range was necessary. Cored shot of 400 pounds with a charge of 50 pounds was to be used only against masonry and at short ranges. The shot was to be supplied with a sabot, and the plug of the core hole would have to face outward in the bore when the gun was loaded. Solid shot was to be used against ironclads only, and with 50-pound charges.

Production of XV-inch Dahlgrens accelerated in the summer of 1863 as demand increased. They were mounted on iron carriages. Since the gun ports of monitors had been built for XIII-inch Dahlgrens, however, the chase and muzzle of early XV-inchers had to be turned off to fit. The bore's teat-like bottom was replaced by one of nearly parabolic form. Later XV-inchers had a chase 16 inches longer turned down 3 inches so they could enter the port opening designed for XIII-inchers; this eliminated an earlier "smoke box" of iron plating around the muzzle that protected the crew from the blast discharge. All XV-inch Dahlgrens had single vents.

The great disadvantages of the new guns were their weight and slowness of loading. Their rate of fire was something like one shot every 5 to 7 minutes, a record that improved in the double-turreted monitors, though these did not see service until late in the war. The XV-inch gun proved highly effective against ironclads at short range, as was demonstrated when its shot smashed through 4 inches of armor plate and compelled the surrender of the Confederate ironclad *Atlanta* in June 1863. The gun also played a key role in the surrender of the Confederate ironclad *Tennessee* in August 1864.

The XIII-inch Dahlgren, supplanted by the XV-incher, came much later in the war. A model was made as early as January 1863, but the gun was still not in service by April 1864, though one XIII-incher had been proved to 500 firings. By the end of the year only three were in service. The XIII-inch gun weighed 36,000 pounds and with a powder charge of 50 pounds fired a shell of 224 pounds. The charge for its 280-pound shot was 70 pounds of powder. It and the subsequent XX-inch Dahlgren were designed primarily to deal with Confederate ironclads.

The first XX-inch Dahlgrens were cast in 1864, but none saw service in the Civil War. They weighed about 100,000 pounds and used a powder charge of 100 pounds to fire a cored shot of 1,080 pounds.

Controversy continued during the war over the design of Rodman and Dahlgren guns. Each service thought its gun the better. Dahlgren was greatly upset about the similarity between the Rodman XV-inch columbiad of 1860 and his own XI-inch model. As early as October 1860 he protested to the secretary of war, claiming that Rodman had simply copied his design. Unlike the Rodman the Dahlgren was chambered, and the latter was longer by about 1 caliber. Aside from this and the fact that the guns had different elevating mechanisms—the Rodman, intended for land service, was cast with a rack of teeth at the breech, while the Dahlgren retained the shark's mouth cascabel—they were much the same. Dahlgren contended that "the proportions distribution, and form of the metal were so nearly similar in the two guns as to make their exterior form substantially identical."[2] Rodman argued that his gun was the product of his own ordnance experiments and a natural evolution from earlier army guns. But Dahlgren noted that his rival had also designed new 8- and 10-inch guns to replace old columbiads of these calibers, and that there was greater variation between these two guns and the 15-inch than between the latter and his own XI-inch model. An unstated irritant was probably the fact that, unlike Rodman, Dahlgren did not receive any royalties on his ordnance work.

In addition to those already mentioned, there were navy smoothbores on Dahlgren's design: a 32-pounder weighing 4,500 pounds, an VIII-inch weighing 6,500, and a new pattern of X-inch gun weighing 16,500 pounds. The first X-inch Dahlgren weighed 12,000 pounds and fired a shell of 97 pounds and shot of 130, but the heavier, later piece was designed to fire solid shot alone, as was a IX-inch gun of 12,280 pounds. It is likely that few of these new types

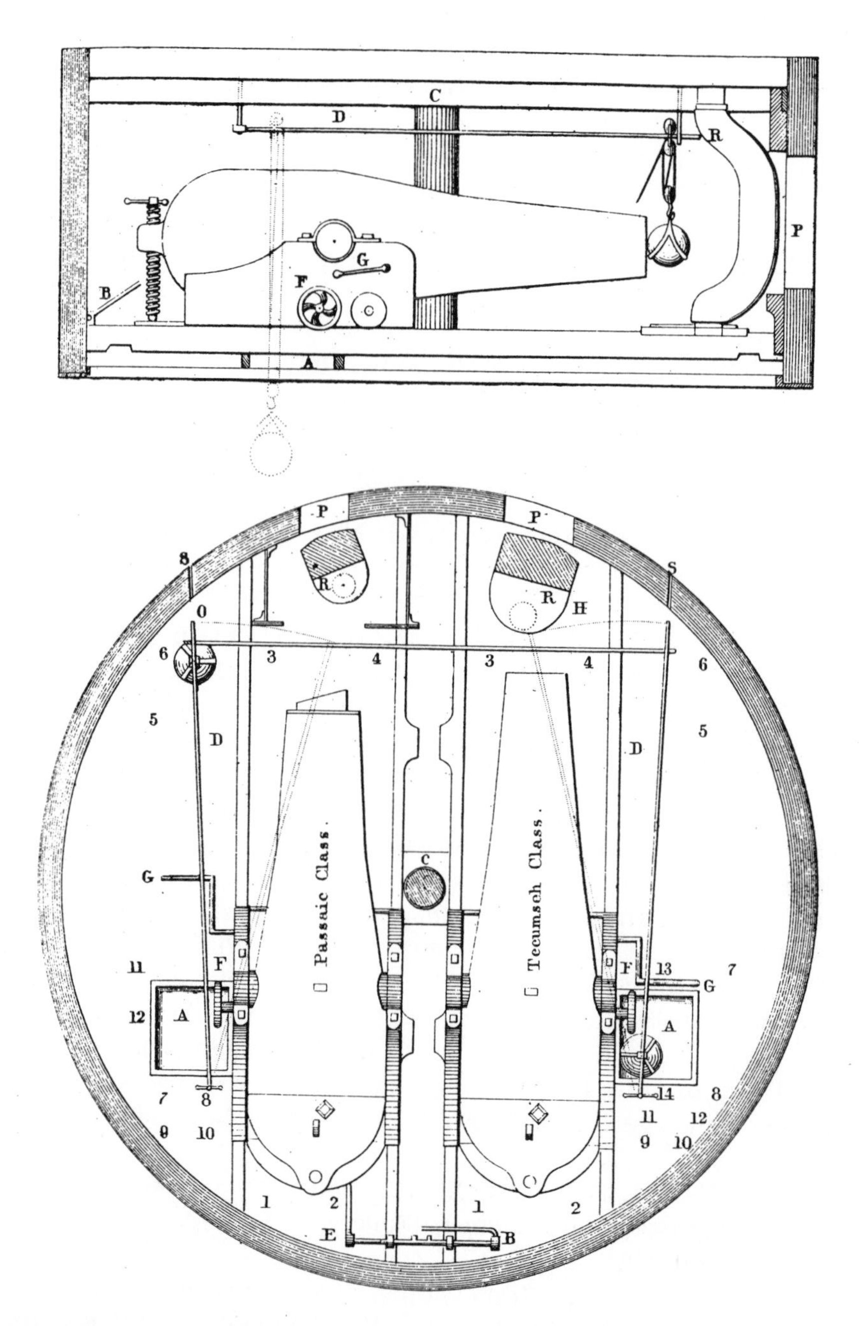

Fig. 104. Dahlgren XV-Inch Guns in Monitor Turret. (Bureau of Ordnance, *Ordnance Instructions*, 1866.)

Key to fig. 104.

A. Ammunition scuttle
B. Starting bar for revolving turret and training gun
C. Shaft on which turret revolves
D. Traveling bar on which shell whip moves
E. Position of engineer stationed at bar to revolve turret and train guns
F. Compressor wheel to check recoil, hove taut before firing
G. Crank for running gun in and out
H. Smoke box of XV-inch (*Pessaic* class)
O. Officer at sight hole
P. Port hole
R. Port stopper
S. Sight hole

In the *Pessaic*-class monitors the gun was fired entirely within the turret. The smoke box was designed to protect the crew from the muzzle blast. While largely accomplishing this, it slowed down the loading process. *Tecumseh*-class (also known as *Canonicus*-class) monitors had an enlarged port to allow the face of the gun muzzle to run out flush with the exterior of the turret. For this class, the XV-inch gun was lengthened 16″ and the muzzle turned down to minimum size. The contracted space, however, required additional mechanical aids for running out, loading, and checking recoil.

The XV-inch gun was normally worked by fourteen men but could be handled by only eight; some captains preferred the smaller number, feeling it was equally efficient, gave more room in the turret, and provided relief crewmen in case of a protracted engagement.

were assigned to warships before the end of the conflict. The IX-inch solid-shot gun was not received until May 1865.

One source estimates production of Dahlgren smoothbores through the Civil War as 1,185 IX-inch, 10 X-inch, 34 new X-inch, 465 XI-inch, 11 XIII-inch, 113 XV-inch, and 1 XX-inch gun.[3] None of the IX-inch solid shot, X-inch, XIII-inch, or XX-inch guns survive. Two XV-inchers survive in Sweden.

All U.S. Navy Civil War guns were muzzleloaders, but some experiments were being conducted with breechloaders, of which the Englishman William Armstrong was an advocate. By the end of the Civil War, however, breech-loading Armstrongs as well as Whitworths and Blakelys had not proved successful. In 1851 one authority wrote, "Breech-loading cannon to command the settled confidence of military men, never has, and never will be made at least in considerable numbers for general service.... Popular favor now sustains the Armstrong breech-loading cannon. In time it will sink to a level corresponding with its true merit."[4] A year later another writer concluded in a similar vein that "the endeavor to produce breech-loading cannon is an effort to obtain uncalled for and superfluous facility in gunnery."[5] Dahlgren apparently believed the muzzleloader was here to stay when he wrote in December 1865, "The plan of loading at the breech is exploded and dismissed."[6] Breech-loading heavy ordnance would have to await advances in technology and manufacturing.

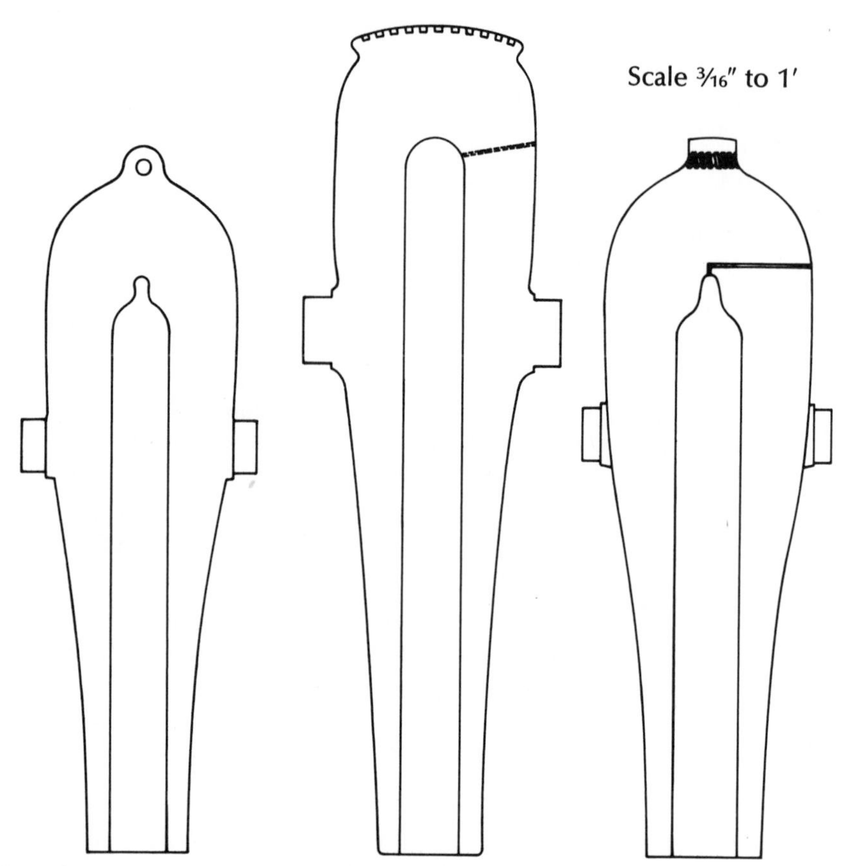

Fig. 105. Comparison of Rodman and Dahlgren Guns. (After drawings in Alexander Holley, *A Treatise on Ordnance and Armor* [New York, 1865].)

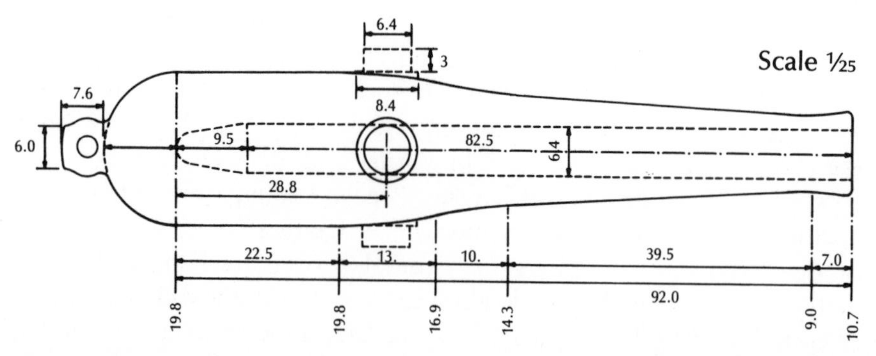

Fig. 106. Dahlgren 32-Pdr of 4,500 Pounds. (Original drawing from National Archives, Record Group 74.)

By 1864, U.S. Navy frigate and sloop armament consisted mainly of IX-inch Dahlgrens in broadside and X- and XI-inch Dahlgrens and Parrott rifles in pivot. There were a few exceptions to this. Fourteen XI-inch Dahlgrens, for example, were employed in broadsides in the frigate *New Ironsides*, and they produced a devastating effect in ricochet fire against Charleston's Fort Wagner. In their turrets monitors carried XI- and XV-inch Dahlgrens and 8-inch (150-pounder) Parrotts. Dahlgren howitzers and rifles also saw boat and deck service. Some old 32-pounders and 8-inchers continued in service.

The 64-pounders and larger shell guns were almost always mounted as pivot guns on slide carriages. Other guns, with the exception of XV-inch Dahlgrens, which had special metal carriages designed by Ericsson, were mounted on the Marsilly carriage or common truck carriage in broadside.

Breeching was snatched in the slot or shark's mouth at the breech of the gun. A chock secured by a pin closed the shark's mouth. Breechings had thimbles to shackle them to the starts on the bulwarks. Old-style navy guns had their rings cut out so they could be snatched. This greatly facilitated the replacement of breeching when necessary.[7]

The Civil War also saw the use of large rifled guns at sea. The accuracy of the infantry rifle compared with its counterpart smoothbore had already been sufficiently demonstrated. Utilizing the new Minie ball, it had a musket's ease of loading and three times its range, 400 to 600 yards as opposed to only 100 to 200. If this principle could be applied to heavy ship ordnance, the effects would be revolutionary. But the difficulties, not the least of which was getting cast iron to withstand the strain, were formidable and the cost was great.

Rifling had found an enthusiastic advocate in the Englishman Benjamin Robins, who in 1742 published his important book, *New Principles of Gunnery*. Robins invented the "ballistic pendulum," which measured the velocity of projectiles. His theories of atmospheric resistance to the flight of a projectile led him to favor rifled, elongated projectiles and larger-caliber guns at the expense of range; in 1745 he conducted experiments with rifled field pieces. Robins predicted that "whatever state shall thoroughly comprehend the nature and advantages of rifled barrel pieces, and, having facilitated and completed their construction, shall introduce into their armies their general use, with a dexterity in the management of them; they will by this means produce a superiority which will almost equal anything that has been done at any time by the particular excellence of any one kind of arms."[8] But he was largely ignored. It was not until the 1820s that serious efforts were made to apply rifling to cannon.

The pioneering guns in this process were the Wahrendorff of Sweden, Cavalli of Sardinia, and Lancaster of England. The Wahrendorff and Cavalli were unsatisfactory breechloaders, but the Lancaster, developed in England in 1850, offered promise. Lancaster's gun weighed 95 cwt (10,640 pounds) and had an elliptical bore of 8 inches with a spiraled rifling of one-quarter rotation. The elongated projectile of this gun and all other rifles was heavier than round shot of comparable diameter; and since it was in greater contact with the barrel and fit it more tightly, the projectile developed more friction. Consequently, rifled gun barrels were under considerable strain compared with smoothbore barrels firing round shot with a heavier charge. To be safe, spherical projectiles could be fired only with small charges of powder.

The first trial of the Lancaster gun took place in August 1851. The strain of the firing broke six out of seven shells, even with small charges. Better results were obtained a year later when seven shells were fired with 10 and 12 pounds of powder for a range of 5,600 yards at 17 degrees of elevation. On the eighth fire, however, the shell stuck in the gun.

After these trials the Lancaster gun was shelved until the Crimean War, when it was seen as a weapon that could strike Russian defenses at distances beyond those of Russian shore batteries. Some Lancasters installed in land batteries took part in the firing at Sevastopol beginning 17 October 1854. One of the guns, firing at the Russian line-of-battle ship *Dvenadtzat Apostolov*, failed to register a hit. Two burst in the attack on the Kinburn forts, another in England. The combination of heavy charge (16 pounds) and high elevation (18 degrees) necessary to attain a range of 5,600 yards proved to be their undoing. This less than distinguished performance resulted in the withdrawal of Lancasters from service and a decision to arm British gunboats in the future with 68-pounder smoothbores of 95 cwt.

Among the more promising experiments of the time were those conducted in France with the rifling of a 22-centimeter gun bored for a 30-pound shell. It was rifled with two spiraled grooves and fired a cylindro-conical projectile weighing 54.5 pounds. The projectile, 12.838 inches long and 6.419 inches in diameter, had two nipples that fit into grooves in the bore. Forty of these guns were ordered from the Ruellese foundry, and by 1856 thirty had been cast. They achieved ranges of more than 5,400 yards and were used on gunboats in Baltic operations the same year. The French also employed rifled pieces on land with considerable effect in the campaign against Austria in 1859.

Probably the most successful rifled cannon of this era was the breechloading English Armstrong, designed in 1854. Manufactured in 1855, this gun had a 2-inch bore, a steel interior, and a wrought-iron exterior. The breech unscrewed for loading. After the success of the prototype, a larger gun was manufactured, all of wrought-iron. In 1858 the British army accepted the Armstrong gun, and Armstrong was later knighted and made superintendent of the naval gun factory. His gun fired a projectile 9,175 yards; the largest by 1862 was one of 65 cwt, which threw projectiles of between 80 and 100 pounds. There were some problems with the gun, however, one of the main ones being its vulnerability to damage by enemy fire; even a 9-pounder shot could easily put it out of action. In 1864 cannon founder Charles Knap described the Armstrong as "a very good gun, but excessively expensive, and not very durable."[9] Later Armstrongs were also made as muzzleloaders and appeared in a variety of calibers, from 6- to 600-pounders.

The British Whitworth rifled gun was a breechloader that also appeared as a muzzle-loading gun. The bore of the Whitworth formed a hexagonal spiral.

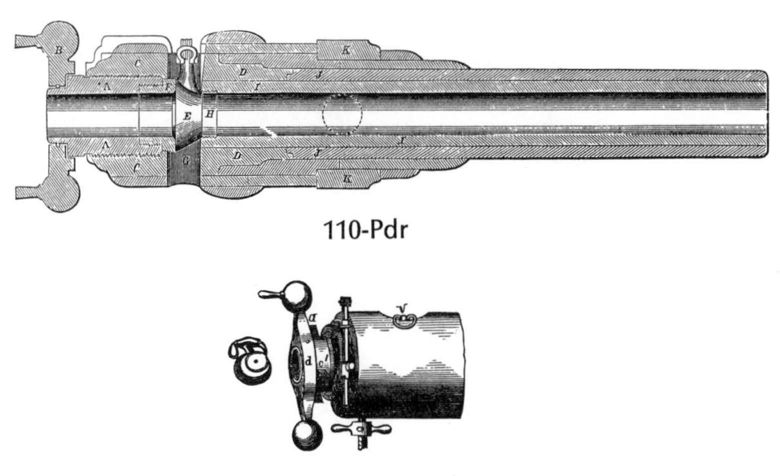

Fig. 107. Armstrong Rifled Guns. (Holley, *A Treatise*.)

It was made of cast iron bored from the solid and also from steel, with wrought-iron rings shrunk on. By 1862 Whitworth guns were of 3-, 12-, and 80-pounder sizes and ranged in weight from 208 pounds to 4 tons. The 3-pounder was capable of throwing a projectile 9,688 yards (five and a half miles) with an 8-ounce charge of powder.

A third British rifled gun was the Blakely. It was built on the same principle as the Armstrong and Whitworth with wrought-iron rings shrunk around a cast-iron core. It differed from them, however, in being only a muzzleloader.

All three of these British rifled guns as well as the inferior Clay breechloader were purchased and employed by the Confederacy during the

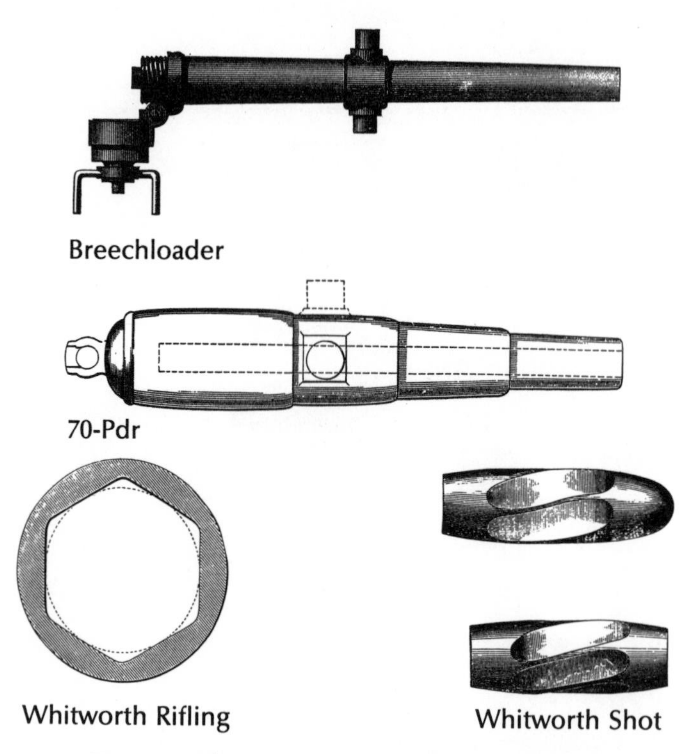

Fig. 108. Whitworth Guns. (Holley, *A Treatise*.)

Civil War. A smaller number were also acquired by the North. Among the more noteworthy of the Confederate rifles was the 7-inch (150-pounder) Blakely, one of two pivot guns in the *Alabama* during her engagement with the *Kearsarge*. It should be noted that all of these British rifles utilized the "hooped gun" principle introduced by Professor Treadwell in the United States a generation earlier.

The most noteworthy American rifled gun of the Civil War was first produced by founder Robert P. Parrott in 1860. Parrott was a former captain of ordnance in the U.S. Army who became superintendent of the West Point Foundry Association in 1836 and by 1861 advertised himself as the lessee there. His first rifle was a 2.9-inch (land diameter) 10-pounder. Prior to the Civil War he also made a 3.67-inch (20-pounder) and a 4.2-inch (30-pounder).

While the Parrott gun was not the best rifled gun of the Civil War era, it was easy to operate, durable, and inexpensive enough that it could be produced in large quantities. It was essentially a muzzle-loading cast-iron rifle with a wrought-iron band reinforcing the breech. The 3.67-inch and 4.2-inch guns were rifled with five grooves (the 2.9- and 3-inch had three, the 6.4-inch nine, the 8-inch eleven, and the 10-inch fifteen grooves), the circumference of the bore equally divided between lands and grooves.

The distinctive feature of the Parrott was its wrought-iron band, shrunk

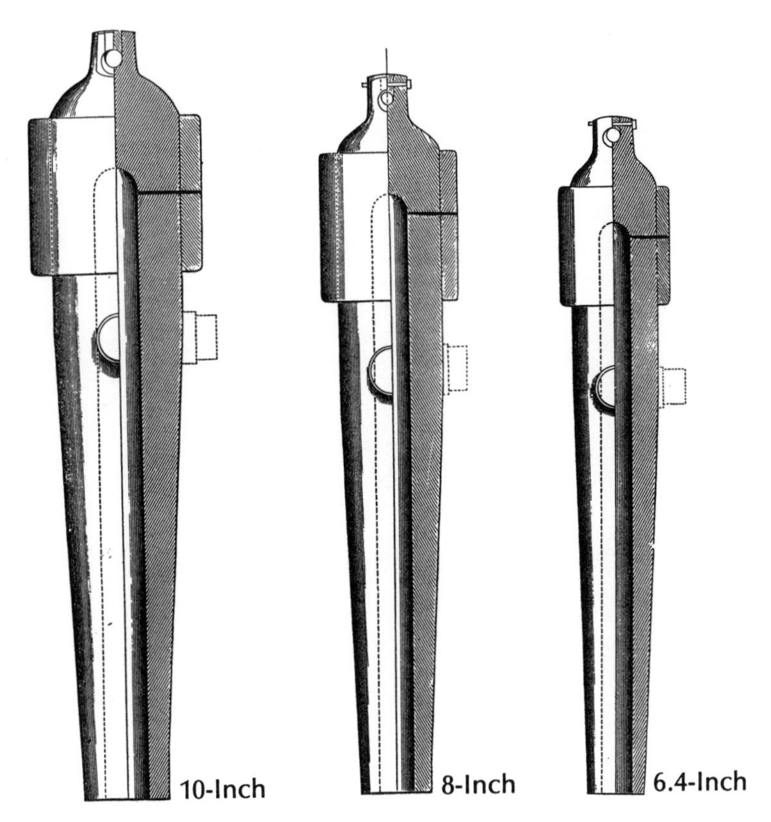

Fig. 109. Three Parrott Guns of the Civil War. All Parrotts had the same family resemblance. (Holley, *A Treatise*.)

around the breech. It had a thickness of half the diameter of the bore; in length it equaled the powder charge and projectile combined. Parrott believed that a larger reinforce was not necessary.

The band of the Parrott gun was formed by spiraling a rectangular bar of wrought-iron around a mandrel and then welding it together with a hammer. It was carefully turned to a cylindrical shape with its interior diameter a sixteenth of an inch to the foot larger than the diameter of the barrel in a cold state. The reinforce was then heated for expansion and forced over the tube, which was in a near-horizontal position with the muzzle slightly depressed. Cold water forced into the bore was allowed to run freely from the muzzle. At the same time, the body of the gun was rotated to produce uniform cooling. As the band cooled, it contracted and gripped the tube with its tensile strength. This process was believed to produce the strongest gun. Late in the Civil War larger Parrotts were cast hollow.[10]

Neither the navy nor the army adopted the Parrott until after the start of the Civil War. It was first introduced in the navy in May or June of 1861, and by 1862 the service had two different Parrotts: a 20-pounder and a 30-pounder.

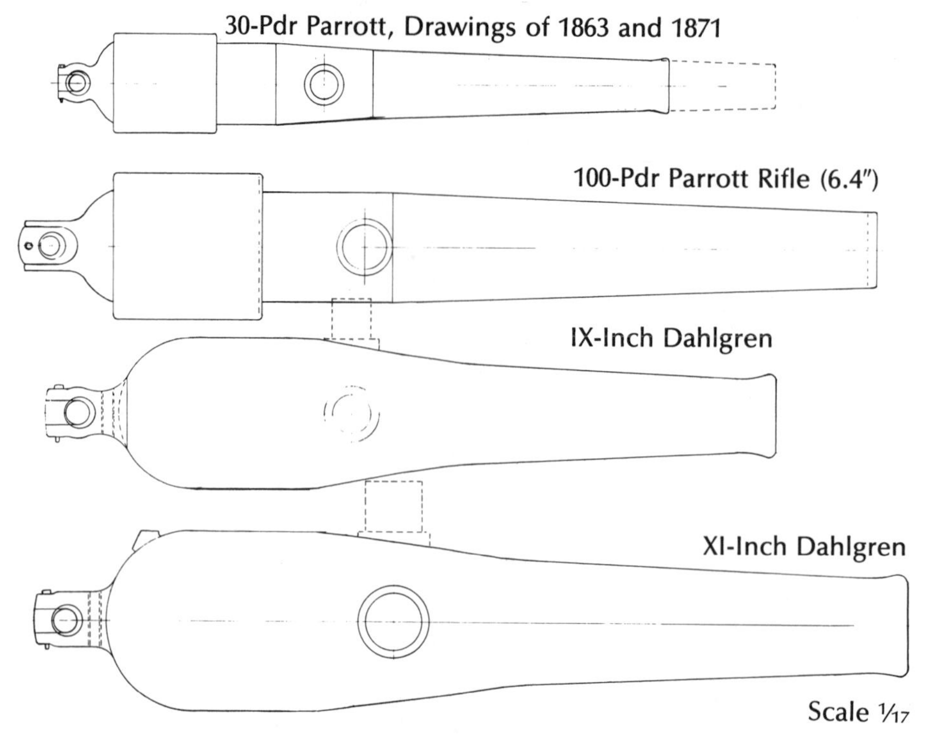

Fig. 110. Comparison of Parrott and Dahlgren Guns. (Redrawn by C. S. Tucker. After drawings in National Archives, Record Group 74.)

The former had a weight of 1,750 pounds, length of 94 inches, bore of 3.67 inches, and charge of 2 pounds; the latter, a weight of 3,500 pounds, length of 126 inches, bore of 4.20 inches, and powder charge of 3.25 pounds. The 4.2-incher (30-pounder) had a range of 4,800 yards at 15 degrees of elevation.

From the beginning of the war through 1 April 1864, nearly 2,000 Parrott guns were manufactured for the army and navy: 336 2.9-inchers, 507 3.67-inchers, 572 4.2-inchers, 10 5.3-inchers (60-pounders), 444 6.4-inchers (100-pounders), 112 8-inchers (150-pounders), and 4 10-inchers (300-pounders). By February 1864 the navy had received 790 Parrotts: 215 3.67-inchers, 250 4.2-inchers, 250 6.4-inchers, and 75 8-inchers. By January 1864 the navy had about 650 Parrotts in service, which represented a fifth of the total number of guns in the service, a ratio that chief of the Bureau of Ordnance Henry Wise thought appropriate.

Larger Parrotts more suited to naval warfare followed the smaller ones into service. Both the army and navy adopted the 6.4-incher (100-pounder) first produced in the fall of 1861. It weighed 9,700 pounds. With a charge of 10 pounds of powder and at 35 degrees of elevation, it could fire its projectile a distance of over 5 miles. Later the usual method of firing the gun was with a reduced charge of 8 pounds of rifle powder with a short shell of 80 pounds.

TABLE 30

Particulars and Ammunition of the Parrott Guns

	Bore				Grooves					
	Length (in)	*Diameter (in)*	*Diameter over Reinforce (in)*	*Weight (lbs)*	*No.*	*Depth (in)*	*Twist of Rifling 1 Turn*	*Charge (lbs)*	*Weight of Projectile (lbs)*	*Price of Gun in 1863 ($)*
10-pdr	70.0	2.9*	11.3	890	3	1/10	10	1.0	Shot, 10.5 Shell, 9.75	180
20-pdr	79.0	3.67	14.5	1,750	5	1/10	10	2.0	Shot, 19.5 Shell, 18.75	380
30-pdr, army	120.0	4.2	18.3	4,200	7	1/10	12	3.25	25 to 30	520
30-pdr, navy	96.8	4.2	18.3	3,550	7	1/10	12	3.25	25 to 30	520
60-pdr, navy	105.0	5.3	21.3	5,360	7	1/10	15	6.0	55	800
100-pdr	130.0	6.4	25.9	9,700	9	1/10	18	10.0	70 to 100	1,200
8-in	136.0	8.0	32.0	16,300	11	1/10	23	16.0	132 to 175	1,900
10-in	144.0	10.0	40.0	16,500	15	1/10	30	25.0	230 to 250	4,500

Source: Alexander L. Holley, *A Treatise on Ordnance and Armor* (New York: D. Van Nostrand, 1865), 55.
* Later 3.0.

TABLE 31

U.S. Navy Civil War Ordnance, 1862

	Average Weight	Crew	Charge (lbs) Distant	Ordinary	Near	Shell (lbs)	Shot (lbs)
Pivot Guns							
XI-in	15,700 lbs	25	15.0	—	—	135	—
X-in	12,000 lbs	20	12.5	—	—	100	—
IX-in	9,000 lbs	17	10.0	—	—	72	—
8-in	63 cwt	17	9.0	8.0	6	51	64
Side Guns							
64-pdr	106 cwt	16 + boy	16.0	12.0	8	—	—
IX-in	—	17	10.0	—	—	72	—
8-in	63 cwt	14 + boy	9.0	8.0	6	51	64
8-in	55 cwt	12 + boy	7.0	7.0	6	—	64
32-pdr	61 cwt	14 + boy	10.0	8.0	6	—	—
32-pdr	57 cwt	12 + boy	9.0	8.0	6	—	—
32-pdr	42 cwt	10 + boy	6.0	6.0	4	—	—
32-pdr	33 cwt	8 + boy	4.5	4.5	4	—	—
32-pdr	27 cwt	6 + boy	4.0	4.0	3	—	—
Parrott Rifled Guns (on ordinary carriages, or as side guns)							
100-pdr	9,688 lbs	16 + boy	10.0	—	—	100	84
30-pdr	3,520 lbs	10 + boy	2.5	—	—	—	—
Parrott Rifled Pivot Guns							
200-pdr	16,000 lbs	25	16.0	—	—	155, 200	—
30-pdr	—	12 + boy	—	—	—	—	—
20-pdr	—	10 + boy	—	—	—	—	—

Source: Lieutenant Edward Barrett, *Gunnery Instructions* (New York: D. Van Nostrand, 1862), 21–23.

The 8-inch Parrott, called a 150-pounder by the navy and a 200-pounder by the army, followed the 6.4-inch gun into production. It weighed 16,300 pounds and was used in the turrets of some monitors in place of or alongside the Dahlgren smoothbores. It began to reach the navy in the summer of 1862. Parrott stated that several 10-inch guns—navy 250-pounders and army 300-pounders—first produced in the winter of 1862–63 were also in naval service, but no evidence has been found to support this.

The Parrotts were well received in the navy. One writer noted in 1862, "Ever since the first appearance of the gun, and the first experiments made with it, it has been growing in favor, and it bids fair now to supplant all previous inventions in the line of rifled cannon."[11] In 1865 another commentator said that the 8-inch Parrott was "a favorite gun in the Navy. . . . The most formidable *service* gun extant." This was because it could sustain heavier charges than other guns such as the English 8-inch 68-pounder, the French

6.5-inch naval gun, and the American cast-iron 8-incher, IX-incher, and X-incher. The 8-inch Parrott fired a 152-pound elongated shell at 1,200 feet per second on a charge of 16 pounds. With a charge of 25 pounds of powder, the same gun fired a 68- to 70-pound cast-iron or steel spherical shot at more than 1,800 feet per second.[12]

The U.S. Navy's 3.67- and 4.2-inch Parrotts were mounted on both truck and pivot carriages. The 6.4-incher was mounted on a pivot or Marsilly carriage, the 8-incher in either pivot or monitor turrets.

The Parrott projectile was elongated, some 3 calibers in length. It was of cylindro-conical shape with a bronze ring at a contraction in the base. When the gun went off, gas expanded the bronze ring into the grooves of the bore, thus imparting a spin to the projectile, which was fitted with either a percussion or a time fuse. Parrott projectiles came in different forms, including one with a hardened nose for armor piercing.

While there were problems with his guns bursting during the Civil War, notably in operations against Charleston and Fort Fisher, Parrott blamed premature explosion of loaded shells in the bores rather than defects in the gun themselves. The greater longevity of navy Parrotts was attributed to an order of July 1863 that all rifle projectiles, particularly those of the Parrott, were to be thickly greased before being loaded in the gun. The bores of all rifled guns were also to be washed frequently and the grooves cleaned of all residuum and dirt. By 1865, nineteen of the navy's some three hundred 100-pounder Parrott guns had been lost because of bursting.

In January 1865, the navy test-fired three 6.4-inch Parrotts at Cold Spring and concluded that shells broke not by the shock of discharge but rather from lack of lubrication. Without adequate lubrication "a residuum of a slaty texture of the powder" formed rapidly in the bore and jammed the projectile. Problems with the navy's "metal-stock time fuzes" were also judged a factor in premature explosions. The examining board found Parrotts as reliable "as any Guns at present within our reach."[13]

Not one IX- or XI-inch Dahlgren gun had burst in service, and so the problems in that regard with larger Parrotts resulted in a loss of confidence in them. In January 1865 Assistant Secretary of the Navy Gustavus Fox testified, "It is a great risk to use them with the present charges."[14] Cost was another factor. In January 1864 Parrott guns cost about 17 cents per pound, while 8- and 10-inch Rodmans were about 9.75 cents and Dahlgrens about 10 cents a pound.

John Dahlgren was also attracted to the idea of a rifled gun for use at sea. As early as August 1856, he had submitted a draft for a rifled 100-pounder cannon weighing 16,000 pounds, but the chief of the Bureau of Ordnance, Captain Ingraham, had blocked it, not even bothering to reply to the proposal. Dahlgren concluded that progress toward a rifled gun would be impossible until Ingraham left the bureau. However, because of the attention that the English Armstrong gun aroused, Ingraham did authorize him to proceed with the trial of "one or two" rifled guns, which Dahlgren later noted was on a scale "too contracted to be satisfactory."[15]

In March 1859, Secretary of the Navy Isaac Toucey approved the manufacture of an experimental rifled cannon. Dahlgren submitted a design on 4 April and on the nineteenth a 10.5-pounder was bored, turned, and rifled—the first gun rifled at the Washington Navy Yard. On 19 May a second 10.5-pounder rifled cannon, longer than the first, was bored, and a 40-pounder was cast shortly thereafter. In all, five rifled cannon were made for trials.

Later in 1859 Dahlgren described those trials: "The samples of rifled cannon I cast here myself, with some variation in form from the smooth bore. The trial gun, weighing 600 pounds and bored smooth, stood 1000 fires and 12-pdr shot and 12½ pounds charge. The last, a rifled 40-pdr (5700 pounds), has been fired to a moderate extent with projectiles varying from thirty-five to forty-two pounds, and four pound charges—the wear exhibiting very favorable indications."[16]

In December 1860, Dahlgren sent a "report on rifled cannon and the armament of ships of war" to the secretary of the navy. It was forwarded to the House Committee on Naval Affairs, which ordered it printed. Dahlgren decided that the tests he had made to date would not allow him to recommend the "entire replacement of the present smooth-bore guns by rifled cannon of *any* kind." In accuracy the IX- and XI-inch shells compared well with rifled shells, at least to distances of 1,300 yards, and Dahlgren was opposed to firing at greater ranges: " . . . I am sure that in sea service no profitable end could be obtained by firing at the largest ship if distant 2,000 yards." In comparing rifled projectiles with round shell, he concluded that the former were far superior to the latter in penetrating power, that the disadvantage of a rifled projectile was that it passed through an object with far less shock effect, and that it was inferior in ricochet firing. Dahlgren therefore recommended a mixed battery of rifles and shell guns aboard U.S. Navy vessels. Ships with gun-deck batteries of IX-inch guns should have four rifled 6-inch cannon throwing 80-pound shot; their spar decks should have two such guns. In ship batteries with guns smaller than IX-inchers, there should be rifled cannon of 5-inch (50-pounder) size, and every vessel authorized more than one boat howitzer should have one rifled 12-pounder of 800 pounds.[17] In July 1861, Dahlgren recommended that half of the vessels carrying only one pivot gun have rifles. If two pivot guns were carried on a vessel, one should be a smoothbore and the other a rifle.

In February 1861, Dahlgren informed the Belgian ordnance designer General Bormann that with his rifled cannon he was able to place shells from a stationary platform within an area equivalent to a square of 17 feet at 2,000 yards' range; with a ship in motion, he was sure that "even the most exact accuracy in flight could not produce military effect beyond 2,000 yards, and even for that distance the most favorable circumstances would be needed."[18]

Developmental work on Dahlgren-designed rifles at the Washington Navy

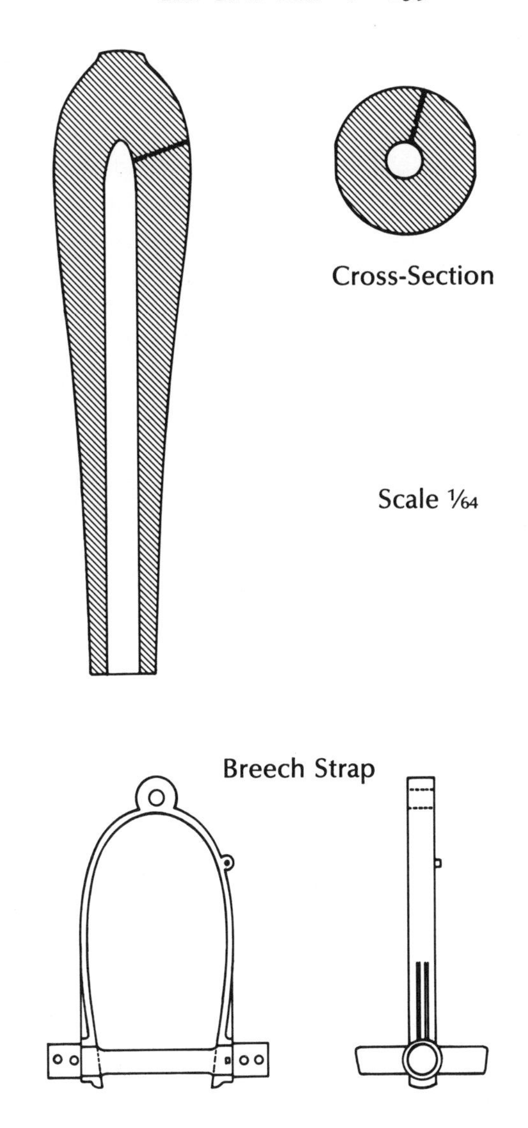

Fig. 111. Dahlgren 7.5-Inch Rifle. (Holley, *A Treatise*.)

Yard was halted until the outbreak of the Civil War. By the end of 1861 Dahlgren had completed designs for three rifled guns: a 5.1-inch 50-pounder, a 6-inch 80-pounder, and a 7.5-inch 150-pounder. The first of these, a 6-inch rifle cast by Parrott, was completed in August 1861 and put on board the USS *Underwriter*.

A number of Dahlgren rifles were cast at the ordnance foundry at the Washington Navy Yard, including in 1862 and 1863 eleven 4.4-inch (30-pounder), sixteen 5.1-inch (50-pounder), and two 6-inch (80-pounder) guns. Nine of the 4.4-inch pieces were rifled and fired. Two of them burst and none was ever sent into service. Five 5.1-inchers and two 6-inchers were also rifled.

Other Dahlgren rifles were cast elsewhere and then rifled at the Washington yard.

In their final form, Dahlgren rifles had their trunnions attached separately by means of a band. Sample Dahlgrens can be seen at the U.S. Naval Academy (a 4.4-inch 30-pounder) and at the artillery park at the U.S. Military Academy (a 5.1-inch 50-pounder). Only a few of the 7.5-inch (150-pounder) guns were ever produced, and they were never placed in service.

As with all Civil War rifles, there were problems with the Dahlgren-designed guns. On 7 February 1862 one 6-inch Dahlgren burst in the *Hetzel* during the assault on Roanoke Island. The Ordnance Board ordered the immediate withdrawal from service of numbers one to fourteen of the 6-inch gun and numbers one to twelve of the 4.4-inch. The problem with the 6-inchers, according to Dahlgren, was that they had been cast, at Fort Pitt Foundry, of inferior metal. By early 1864, however, the only rifled guns being procured for the navy were those made by Parrott.

In addition to Parrotts and Dahlgrens there were also James guns, which saw limited service on river gunboats in the first year of the war. These old army 42-pounders had been rifled and fired an 81.25-pound shot or 64.25-pound shell.

A number of experimental guns did not see service. John Ericsson contracted with the navy to build a 13-inch wrought-iron gun intended for the *Dictator* and the *Puritan*, but the prototype was not successful. The most promising of the experimental wrought-iron pieces was manufactured by Horatio Ames of Ames Iron Company in Salisbury, Connecticut. The Ames gun was made of a series of wrought-iron discs. By September 1862 at least four of them had been delivered to the navy for testing. The Ames 50-pounder rifle closely resembled the Dahlgren 5.1-inch (50-pounder) gun, even to the extent that the Dahlgren-designed breech strap secured its trunnions. Ames guns were rifled out in 30-, 50-, and 80-pounder sizes. One of the 50-pounders was fired 1,630 times with a 37-pound rifle shot and 3.5-pound service charge. Another gun of the same dimensions, bored out to 8-inch caliber, fired 438 times with a service charge of 5 pounds of powder and a 67-pound rifle shot without bursting but with some stretching at the welds. The navy concluded that the guns were too expensive and not satisfactory. Two of the fifteen guns proofed burst and blew out the breech. The basic problem was one that had always plagued wrought-iron guns, defective welds. During the war other guns, including a breechloader designed by J. Webster Cochran, were tested at the Washington Navy Yard but not adopted by the U.S. Navy.

As noted, rifled guns were fired with a smaller powder charge than guns firing round shot of the same caliber. Whereas in smoothbores the powder charge could vary from a fifth to a half the weight of shot, the general rule for rifled guns was a tenth, though this meant lower velocity and hence less penetration of armor. It was also learned in the course of the war that charges in the Dahlgren smoothbore could be increased beyond what had earlier

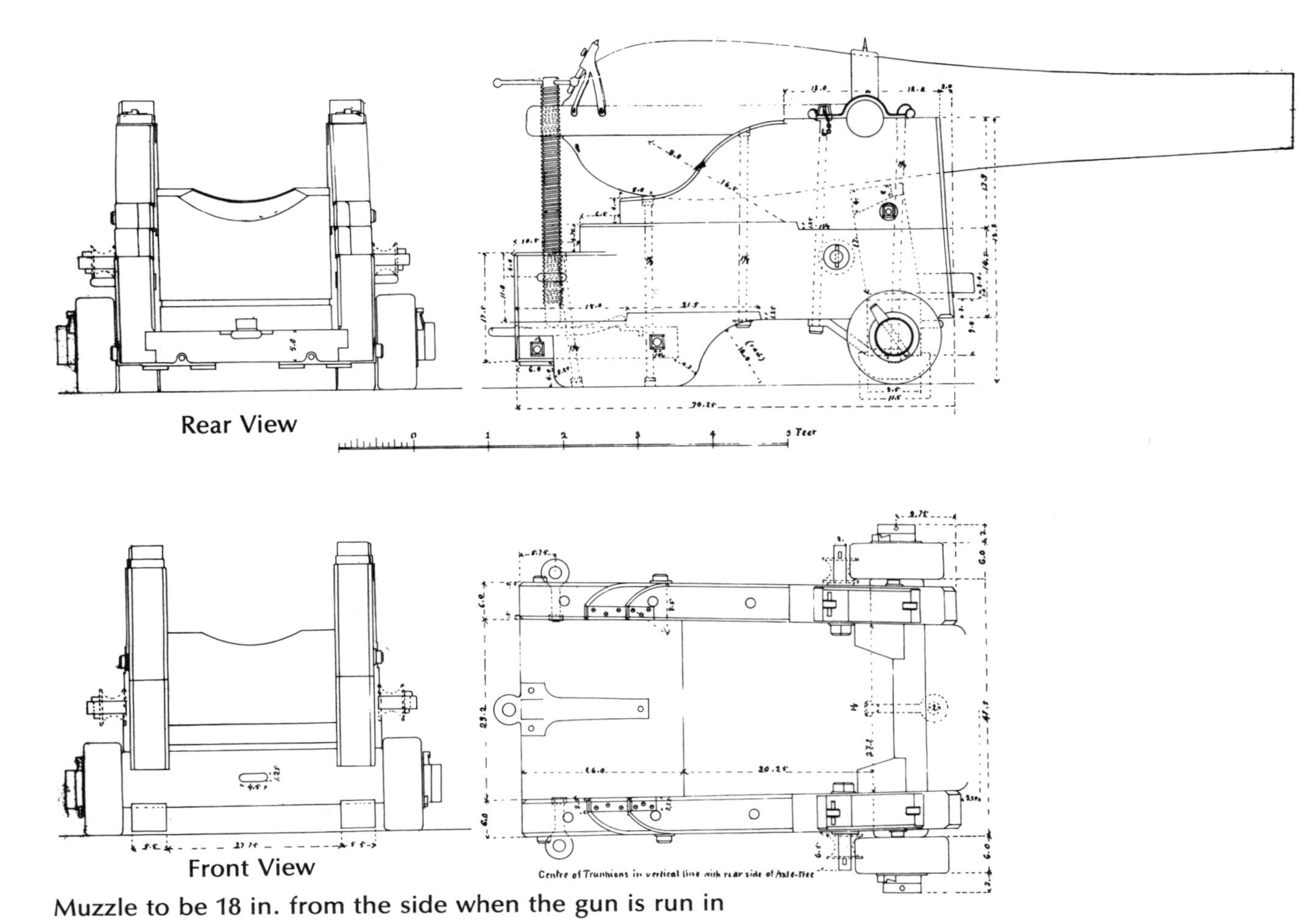

Fig. 112. The 6-Inch Dahlgren Rifle and Carriage. (Original drawing in National Archives, Record Group 74.)

Fig. 113. Dahlgren next to His 4.4- or 5.1-Inch Rifle in the *Pawnee*. (Courtesy of the News Photo Branch, U.S. Navy.)

been thought acceptable, giving far more striking power than a comparable rifled gun. As a result, the most effective weapon against ironclads during the Civil War was the smoothbore shell gun firing solid shot.

During the war, the percentage of rifled to smoothbore guns was smaller in the navy than in the army. This was in part because of the difficulty of firing accurately from a heaving deck at a moving target and of firing in ricochet. The latter was important at sea because gunners were routinely instructed to fire low for fear that shot would go high and miss the target vessel entirely. On hitting the water the round ball from a smoothbore would continue on line to the target; a rifle projectile might take off at any angle. Rifled guns were paired with the smoothbores in some monitors or in pivot, where they were used as chase guns for long-range firing.

The rifled gun represented an important step forward, nevertheless. The problem was, of course, not the idea of rifling itself but rather the weakness of the cast-iron gun, and it could be solved by a stronger metal. Friedrich Krupp of Germany, whose new guns attracted attention when they were exhibited in England in 1851 and France in 1855, led the search. The steel in his guns had four times the strength of cast iron and twice the strength of wrought iron. But they were regarded with suspicion heightened by problems such as fracturing in proof. Distrust of steel for gun making continued, but so did experimentation with it. In England, Bessemer experimented with steel after failing to produce a suitable rifled gun in cast iron.

Satisfactory rifled guns had to await the introduction of reliable steel and improved ordnance engineering; their full potential would be realized only in the 1880s with the development of slow-burning powder and extremely high velocities. Until that time, and certainly throughout the Civil War, it was the muzzle-loading, smoothbore, cast-iron gun that constituted the chief weapon at sea. Some felt this would never change. One writer spoke for many when he noted in 1861, " . . . because the rifled projectile is inferior to the ball for ricochet firing, in range, accuracy, and penetration, and because in a cannonade at sea there is no certainty of avoiding the rebound from water without a worse certainty of wasted balls in the air, it becomes doubtful if rifled cannon will ever come in use for broadside batteries in ships; however, a gun or two for accuracy in the distance may be of service."[19] Another writer reached the same conclusion in 1862. At low elevation, he said, the range of rifled guns did not exceed that of smoothbores. They were not reliable in ricochet firing and their usefulness was probably limited to the attack and defense of fortresses.[20]

Heavy mortars were also used during the Civil War in siege operations, with mixed results. The first 13-inch mortars and shells were ordered from Knap in January 1862. Knap cast at least 55 of these weapons for the navy, which by November 1863 had taken delivery of 200. They were considered essential for bombarding the forts defending New Orleans before the Union fleet could pass them. For six days and nights in April 1862, a mortar flotilla of twenty vessels pounded Forts Jackson and St. Phillip without decisive results. Farragut decided nevertheless to make a run past the forts, and he succeeded. Heavy mortars were used with greater effect in other operations.

Weighing 17,000 pounds, the 13-inch mortar was a formidable weapon. With a 20-pound charge of powder it could hurl its 218-pound shell some 4,200 yards. At this range the shell took more than 30 seconds in flight. Mortars were mounted on converted coastal schooners.

As for projectiles, shot was still used, though by the time of the Civil War it had to pass through more demanding sphericity and weight tests. Regulations required that for each gun ten shot be kept in racks located along waterways or hatches.

The technique of putting together grapeshot had changed. Because quilting around balls tended to deteriorate rapidly in the presence of iron, it

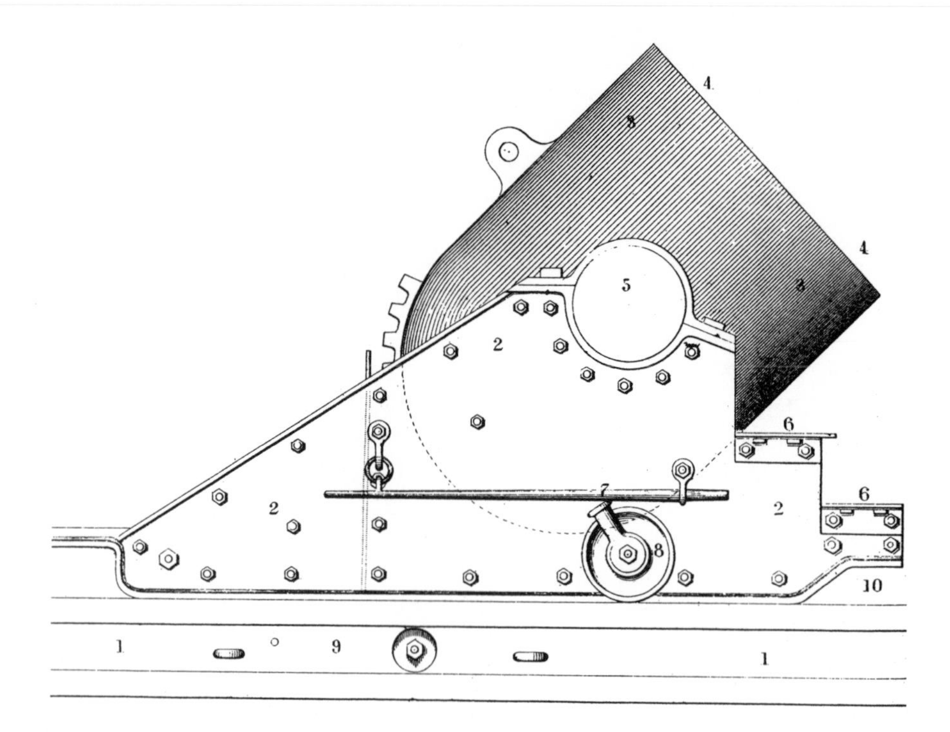

1. Circle	6. Steps of carriage
2. Bracket	7. Carriage eccentric socket
3. Mortar	8. Wheel
4. Face	9. Circle eccentric bar
5. Trunnion	10. Hurter

Fig. 114. Nomenclature of 13-Inch Mortar, Carriage, and Circle. (Bureau of Ordnance, *Ordnance Instructions*, 1866.)

was replaced in the 1850s by tier shot, which had originated in France. An iron pin secured by a nut at the end ran through a series of flat iron plates with holes to hold the shot. Between each two plates was a tier of shot. Balls numbered fewer than those in the old grapeshot, but their individual weight was greater. There were three shot to each tier—a total of nine. They ranged in weight, according to the gun, from 8 ounces to 4 pounds. The new grapeshot, more durable and cheaper in the end because there was no quilting to be replaced, enjoyed the added advantage of an increased spread in flight.

During the Civil War modifications of tier shot appeared in which there were only two plates, top and bottom, with rings of circular section replacing the earlier intermediate plates. Thus the balls of each tier nestled against those of the next, substantially lightening and shortening the stand. The number of tiers could vary. Some Confederate grape had seven or more.

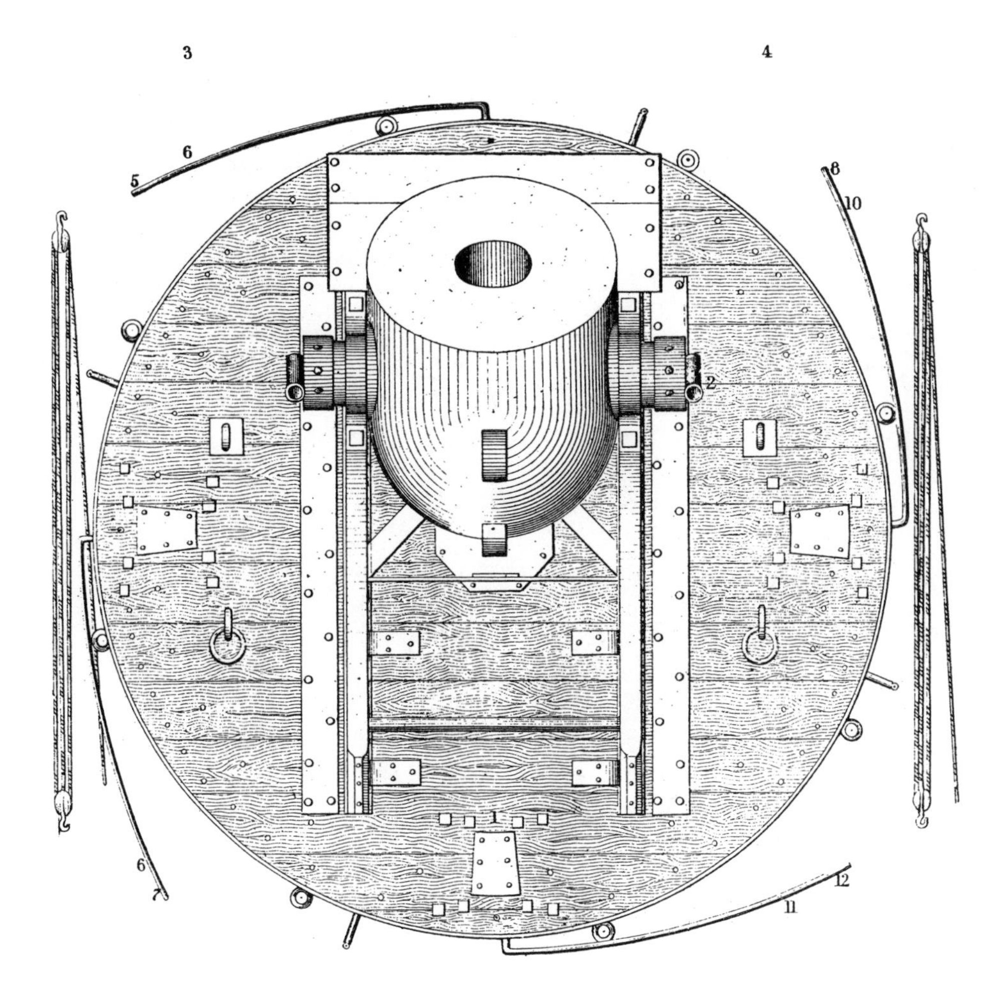

Fig. 115. A 13-Inch Mortar and Location of Crew While Mortar Is Being Trained. (Bureau of Ordnance, *Ordnance Instructions*, 1866.)

The ordnance instructions of 1860 forbade the use of grapeshot against warships beyond a range of 150 yards. It could, however, be employed against men on the spar deck of an enemy vessel at ranges of 200 to 300 yards, and at 400 yards (a double stand at 300 yards) against light vessels, boats, or masses of men, the dispersion of balls at that distance being about 30 yards.

Canister was routinely supplied for boat howitzers and, in bulk allowance, for larger guns. The decision to use canister, however, rested solely with the captain. While small amounts of both grape and canister were furnished to U.S. Navy ships, they were regarded as being of little use on vessels larger than sloops.

By mid-nineteenth century the technique of loading shrapnel shell had changed. Instead of dropping powder in to fill empty spaces between balls, it

Fig. 116. A 13-Inch Mortar in a U.S. Navy Mortar Schooner. (Courtesy of News Photo Branch, U.S. Navy.)

was confined to a chamber; this prevented it from being crushed by friction and made possible a reduction in the bursting charge. In American practice, the proper number of balls was inserted and a grooved mandrel pushed through them all the way to the other side of the shell. Melted sulphur was then poured through the fuse hole; it entered the case through the grooves in the mandrel. When the sulphur cooled, the mandrel was withdrawn and the resulting chamber could receive the bursting charge. In the absence of a mandrel melted sulphur was still used; after it cooled, it was bored out at the top along with any of the balls to receive the charge. This separated the charge from the bullets and enabled the loaded shell to be transported without danger. By this means also the powder was concentrated, making the explosion more powerful and thereby reducing the requisite amount of powder.

In British service, a sheet-iron diaphragm divided the shell into two

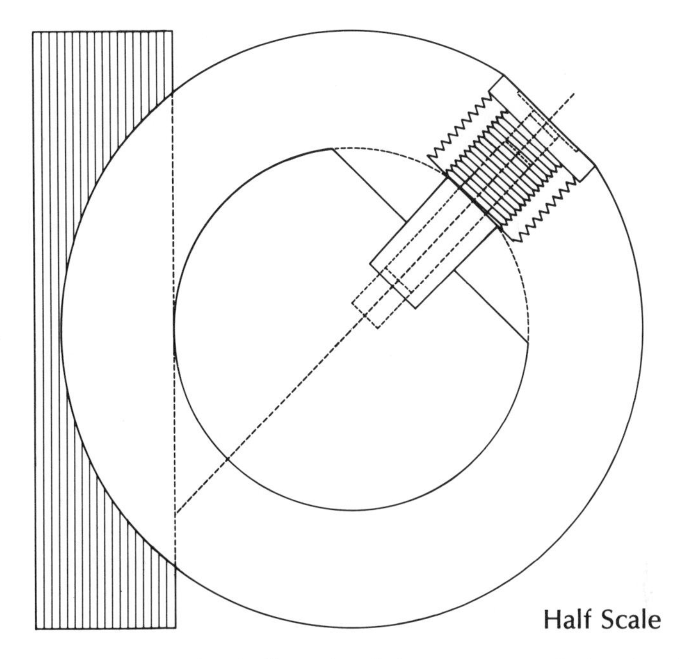

Fig. 117. Section of a 32-Pdr Shell, 1848. (After an original drawing in National Archives, Record Group 74.)

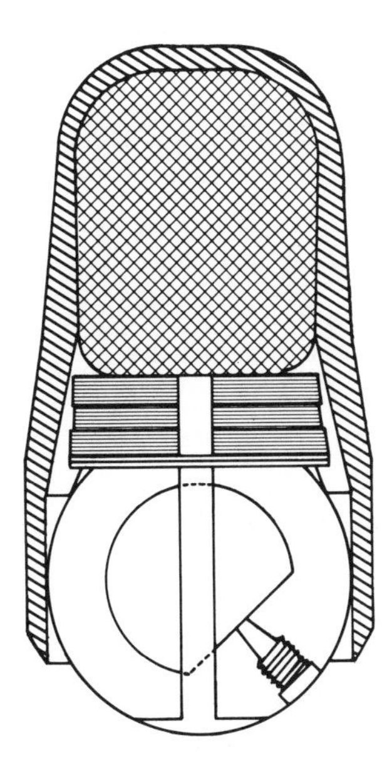

Fig. 118. Shell, Sabot, and Powder Charge. (After an original drawing in National Archives, Record Group 74.)

chambers. Spaces between balls were filled with coal dust, and the top chamber contained the powder. Again, the separation of balls and powder had the same practical effect as in American shrapnel shell, preventing a chance explosion. For uniform release of the balls, four grooves were cut in the shell's interior.

Shells evolved rapidly in the years preceding the Civil War. Wooden fuses, which tended to deteriorate in the hot, humid conditions aboard ship, were replaced in the 1850s by metal fuses. These also withstood bending better. To prevent the fuse composition from reacting with the metal case, it was put in a paper case and inserted in the metal case when ready for use. The metal fuse did not extend far into the shell—in the 8-inch shell, not beyond the metal of the shell casing.

By the time of the Civil War, U.S. Navy shell fuses came with burn times of 5, 10, and 15 seconds. The 5-second fuse was to be used with ordinary charges at ranges up to 1,320 yards. The 10-second fuse was employed with distant firing charges for ranges of 1,320 to 2,400 yards for the 8-incher and 32-pounder, 2,000 yards for the IX-incher. In 32-pounder and 8-inch guns, the 15-second fuse had a range with distant firing charges of 3,080 yards. Half the fuses for the big guns were to burn for 5 seconds, a fourth for 10 seconds, and the remainder for 15.

During the Civil War a great variety of new fuses appeared worldwide. The superior Bormann fuse, invented by Captain Bormann of the Belgian army, found its way into U.S. Navy boat howitzer shells. There were also concussion, percussion, and time fuses. The concussion fuse, set in action by the shock of discharge, and the percussion fuse, set off by impact with the target, were invented in the 1840s and 1850s. Percussion fuses were used aboard Union navy ships in the war.

Diameter and windage for shell were the same as with shot of like caliber. Shell thickness ranged from 0.80 inch for an 18-pounder to 1.5 for an 8-inch and 1.8 for a 10-inch shell. Fuse holes were all 0.60 inch by the time of the Civil War. The metal at the fuse hole was reinforced to support the fuse firmly. In earlier shells, another small hole had been made in the carcass so that powder could be inserted once the fuse was put in.

Before it was filled with powder, the shell was secured to its sabot by means of tin straps and examined to see that it was clean and dry inside and out. The powder was then inserted in the shell through a funnel, the fuse carefully screwed in place with a fuse wrench. Loaded shell was marked with red paint and placed in boxes of the same color. The length of the fuse was painted on the box in black.

By 1850 the U.S. Navy had followed French practice and added a lead patch over the fuse. The loader removed it and showed it to the gun captain as proof that the fuse was uncovered. This was done when the shell was actually in the bore of the gun. Afterward the shell was pushed (not rammed) home.

By the time of the Civil War only one shell, kept in its box, was allowed at

Fig. 119. Section of 12-Pdr Shrapnel Showing Bormann Fuse. (Bureau of Ordnance, *Ordnance Instructions*, 1866.)

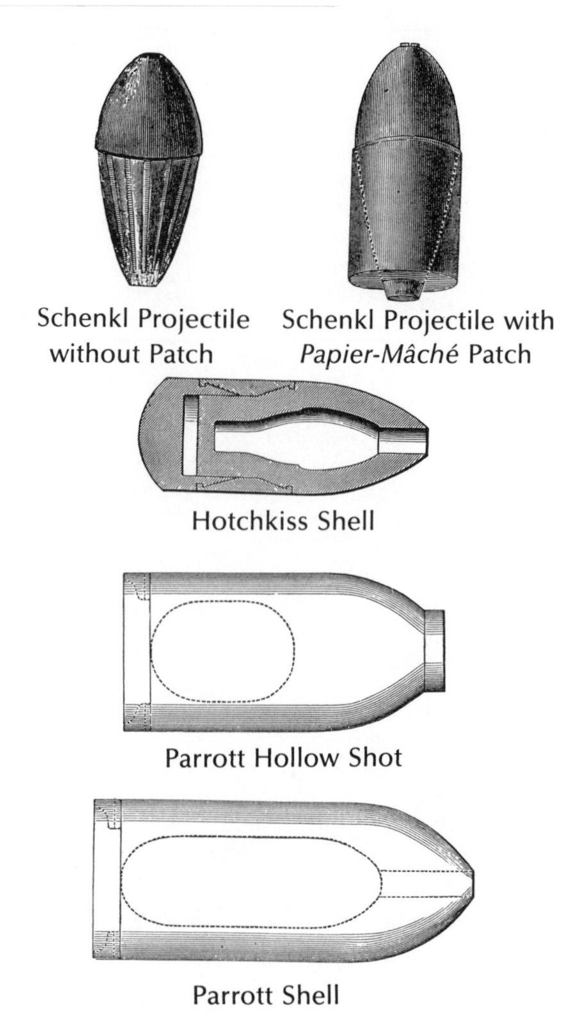

Fig. 120. Rifle Projectiles. (Holley, *A Treatise*.)

a gun, as opposed to ten shot for a shot gun. It was stored between the trucks on the gun's port side. Unlike the Royal Navy, the U.S. Navy did not allow extra shells on deck during an action. No shells were supplied from the magazine unless an empty box indicating the last shell had been used was presented in the shell room, a special storage space located apart from the magazines. Ships armed entirely with shell guns had two or more shell rooms. Regular drill was important, because even with two or more shell rooms it was difficult during battle to supply 9-inch shell weighing more than 70 pounds each. Due to the danger of fire during battle, shell rooms were located no less than 6 feet below the waterline.

There were a great many types of projectiles used in Civil War rifled guns, including those patented by Parrott, Hotchkiss, and Schenkl. The Schenkl projectile had a cast-iron body with a cone-shaped tail. A papier-mâché sabot

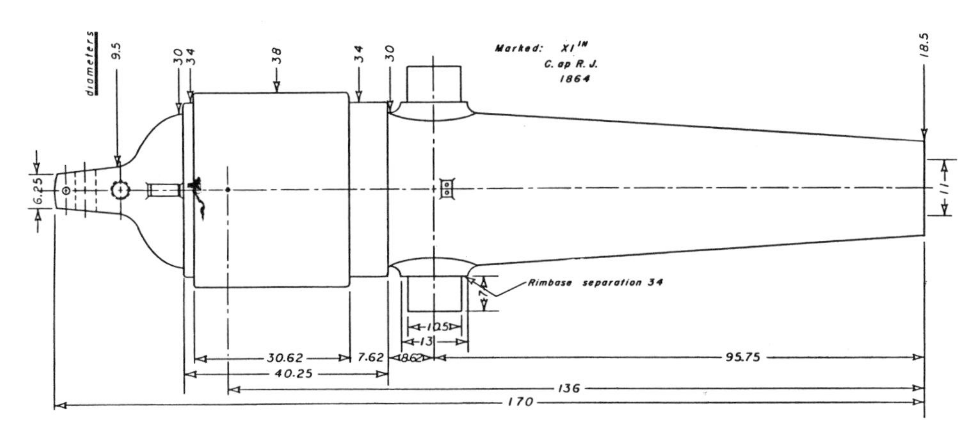

Fig. 121. Brooke XI-Inch Smoothbore Gun. (Drawing by Edwin Olmstead.)

expanded into the rifling when the action of the charge forced it forward. Projections on the cone gave a rotary motion to the projectile. The sabot material introduced a number of problems. Moisture could swell it so much that the projectile might not enter the gun or might crumble on firing. Still, the Schenkl percussion fuse was a successful design and remained in naval service for some time after the war. It had a hollow metallic stock with a plunger held in place by a small screw. The screw broke when the shell was fired, leaving the plunger free to explode the percussion cap on impact. It in turn ignited the primer in the plunger, which set off the main charge.

The Hotchkiss projectile was composed of a body, lead ring, and cup. When it was fired the cup thrust forward, compressing the lead into the grooves of the bore. If the projectile was equipped with a time fuse,

TABLE 32

U.S. NAVY SHELL, 1861

	Weight (fused and saboted, lbs)	*Bursting Charge (lbs)*
12-pdr boat howitzer	—	0.5
24-pdr boat howitzer	—	1.0
18-pdr gun	12.0	—
24-pdr gun	16.0	—
32-pdr gun	26.5	—
42-pdr gun	35.0	—
8-in shell gun	52.75	1.85
IX-in shell gun	73.5	3.0
X-in shell gun	101.5	4.0
XI-in shell gun	135.5	6.0

Source: Bureau of Ordnance, Navy Department, *Ordnance Instructions for the United States Navy*, 2nd ed. (Washington: G. W. Bowman, 1860), 135, and John Brandt, *Gunnery Catechism* (New York: D. Van Nostrand, 1864), 196.

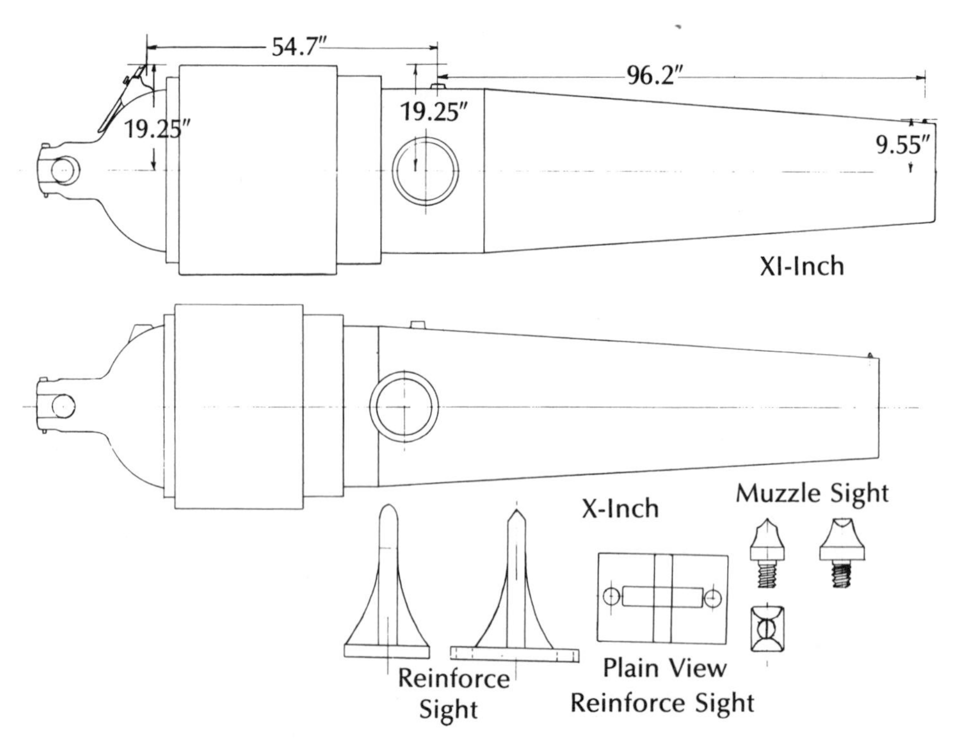

Fig. 122. Brooke XI- and X-Inch Smoothbore Guns. (Redrawn by C. S. Tucker. After an original Confederate navy drawing in National Archives, Record Group 74.)

longitudinal grooves on the outside allowed passage of the flame from the gun's discharge, which ignited the fuse.

John Dahlgren also developed a projectile specifically for his rifled guns. It had an iron body with a lead base cast over projections to the rear. Ribs along the middle of the body inclined slightly to the axis of the projectile, parallel to the rifling. Turned to a diameter 0.02 inch less than the bore, the ribs provided a finished bearing surface against the bore.

In addition to the above, a number of other rifle projectiles were tried during the war, but most of them tumbled in flight, and in any case, they could not be used in ricochet firing.

By the time of the Civil War, the U.S. Navy recommended double-shotting only at ranges of not more than 300 yards, from heavy 32-pounders of 46 cwt and up. For 32-pounders of less than 46 cwt, the range for double-shotting was not to exceed 200 yards. Shells were never double-shotted.

In 1864, windage was 0.15 inch for shot and shells from smoothbore guns, except for shot from shell guns and shells for the XV-inch gun, which were to have a mean windage of 0.20 inch.

Ordnance of the Confederate navy consisted of many different American guns including a number of obsolete types such as the carronade, as well as

British Armstrongs, Blakelys, and Whitworths, among others. Nonstandardization was much more common for the Confederacy than for the Union, a fact that exacerbated problems of ammunition, supply, administration, and training. A favorite Confederate piece early in the war was the U.S. Navy 32-pounder of 57 or 63 cwt, rifled and banded with wrought-iron.

Of great importance to the Confederate naval effort was the capture of the Gosport Navy Yard. It yielded 1,195 heavy guns ranging from carronades to modern shell guns, including 52 IX-inch Dahlgrens. In addition, the Confederacy obtained at least two thousand barrels of powder and thousands of shells. Some other cannon and ordnance stores were taken at Pensacola and elsewhere.

Unfortunately for the Confederates, they lacked naval vessels. Only one undamaged Union vessel, the *Fulton*, had been seized at Pensacola. Admittedly, the Confederacy had different naval objectives than the North, but its problems were nonetheless staggering, particularly given the agricultural economy of the South, its relative paucity of industry, and its undeveloped raw materials base. Heavy naval guns could be manufactured only at Tredegar Foundry; it was not until late in 1863 that they were also produced in Selma, Alabama. Some heavy guns were also manufactured at the Bellona foundry and elsewhere. Nevertheless, Confederate ordnance production was sufficient to meet naval demands; by late 1862, Confederate vessels were adequately armed.

The South concentrated on wooden-hulled ironclads like CSS *Virginia* carrying guns in a central casemate and fitted with a ram. The South also did more experimentation with new forms of naval warfare such as the submarine and mines.

Fortunately for the Confederate cause, a brilliant young ordnance officer, Lieutenant John M. Brooke, resigned his commission in the U.S. Navy on the secession of Virginia. Although he was only thirty-four years old and had no particular expertise in ordnance work, Brooke was placed in charge of naval ordnance experiments and was later made chief of naval ordnance for the Confederacy. Not only was he responsible for the unique design of the *Virginia*, whose bow and stern extended under water, but he also developed fuses, shells, a flat-headed bolt for use against ironclads (an idea borrowed from Whitworth), a percussion cap for small arms, and submarine mines. He challenged the established notion that air space created by not properly ramming home the projectile and charge increased the chance of a gun's exploding. He believed this actually lessened the strain.

But Brooke is best known for his naval ordnance. He designed 32-pounder and 10- and 11-inch smoothbores, probably based on standard U.S. Navy patterns, and 6.4-, 7-, and 8-inch rifles that bear his name. The Brooke rifle has been described as "the most powerful and accurate gun used in the Confederacy," and "the best weapon of its kind by either side in the War."[21]

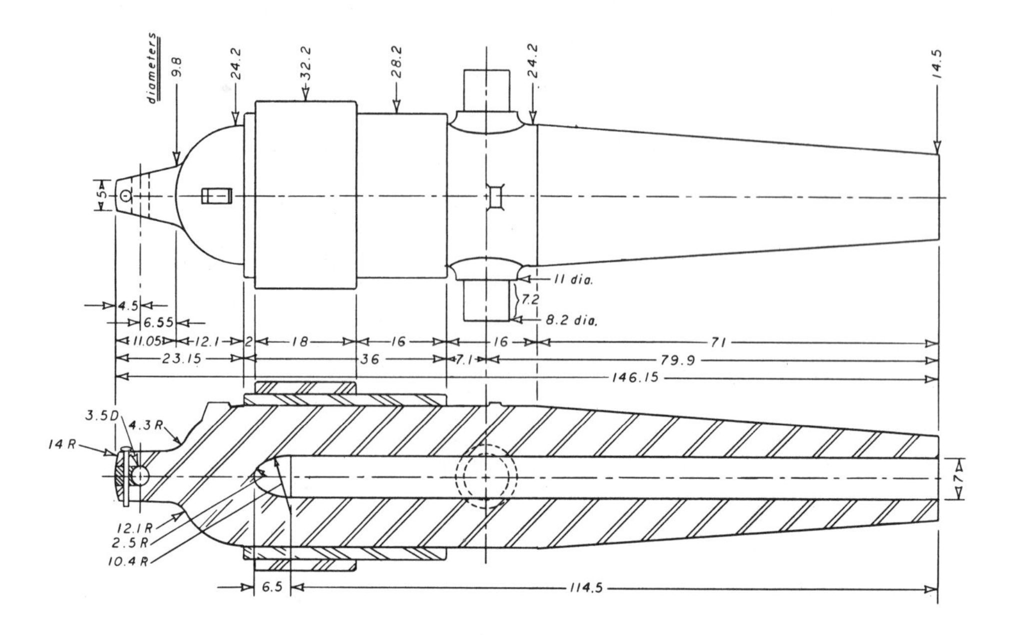

Fig. 123. Brooke 7-Inch Double-Banded Rifle. (Drawing by Edwin Olmstead.)

Certainly 7-inch Brooke rifles firing armor-piercing bolts inflicted much of the damage on Union monitors in the naval assault on Charleston in 1863.

The first Brooke rifle was a 7-inch gun. Six were ordered from Tredegar Foundry: two for the *Virginia* and the remainder for Mississippi River boats. Between September 1861 and March 1862 Tredegar cast fourteen 6.4- and 7-inch Brooke rifles. The 7-incher weighed 15,000 pounds and was intended for pivot use. The 6.4-incher weighed 9,000 pounds and was to be a broadside gun only. The latter took shells of 65 pounds and bolts weighing 80. The 7-incher threw shells of 110 pounds and bolts of 120. Brooke rifles, with their bands about the breech, greatly resembled the Union's Parrott rifles in form. Later Brookes differed from Parrotts in appearance because they were given a second and even a third series of bands, and the bands, instead of being solid, were made up of a succession of rings. The bands were approximately 6 inches wide. Brooke rifles weighed more than comparable Parrott pieces.

The additional banding on Brooke rifles necessitated design changes, so the 6.4-incher was produced in two patterns, the 7-incher in four, and the 8-incher in one.[22] Brookes had seven lands and grooves in the bore in the "hook slant" fashion of English Blakelys. The 6.4-inch rifle was from 141 to 144 inches long, the 7-incher from 143 to 147.5 inches long.

Brooke also designed a number of different rifle projectiles. Some had raised rings and a ratchet sabot of bronze or copper with its base divided into seven equal sections. Others had a soft metal ring cast on the base of the projectile. Yet another was wrought-iron with a groove turned in the base to form a lip. This expanded into the rifling, giving the projectile its rotation.

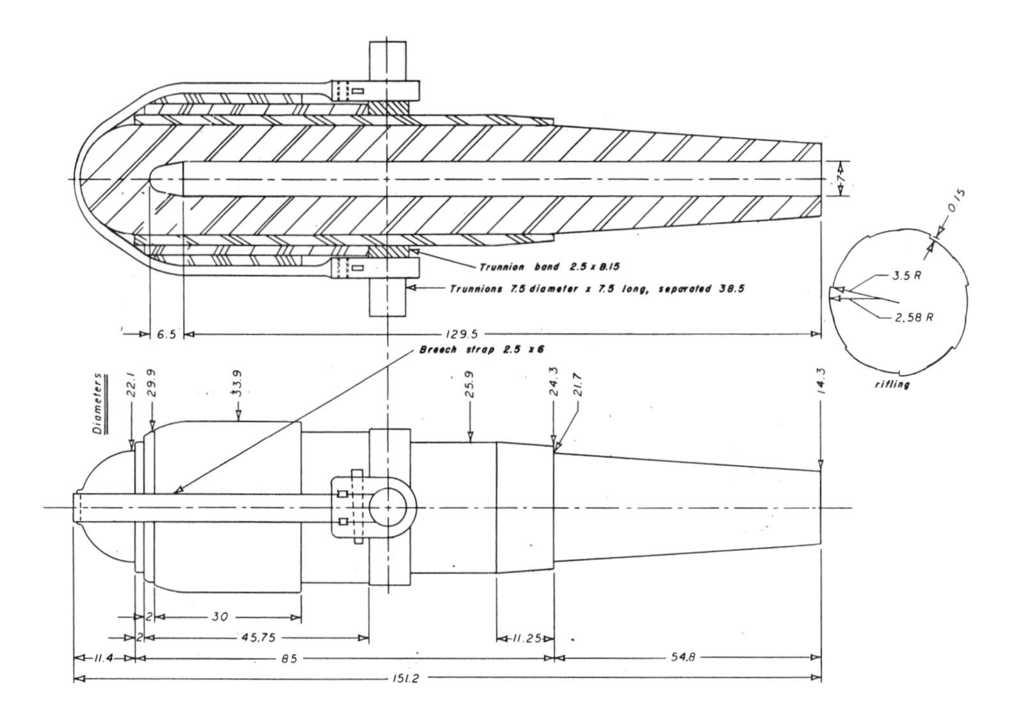

Fig. 124. Brooke 7-Inch Triple-Banded Rifle. (Drawing by Edwin Olmstead.)

The output of Brooke guns during the Civil War was quite small, particularly when compared with the production of ordnance by Northern foundries. Tredegar cast something less than 83 rifles. Only one of these was an 8-inch gun; most were 7-inch types. The same foundry also cast 16 Brooke smoothbores, but these were only a fraction of the 1,099 cannon it produced during the war.[23] At Selma an additional 55 Brooke rifles and 18 smoothbores were cast during the period from January 1864 to March 1865; 53 were sent to Mobile. Some Brooke rifles were reamed up to make larger caliber smoothbores. The 6.4-inch gun, for example, became an 8-inch piece, and the 8-inch gun a 10-inch piece.

The first dramatic test of naval ordnance and naval constructors during the Civil War came in the epoch-making engagement between the *Monitor* and the *Virginia*. It was the first clash between ironclad warships in history and one of the first between steam warships.

Retreating Union forces partially destroyed the powerful steam frigate *Merrimack* at the Norfolk Navy Yard, scuttled her, and set her on fire. Within a month, the Confederates had raised and begun to rebuild her as an ironclad warship for use in breaking the Union blockade and preventing an advance toward Richmond. Renamed the *Virginia* by the Confederates, she was cut down (although not sufficiently, for she rode too high in the water) and a 4-inch iron-plated casemate was added. She was 262 feet 9 inches long,

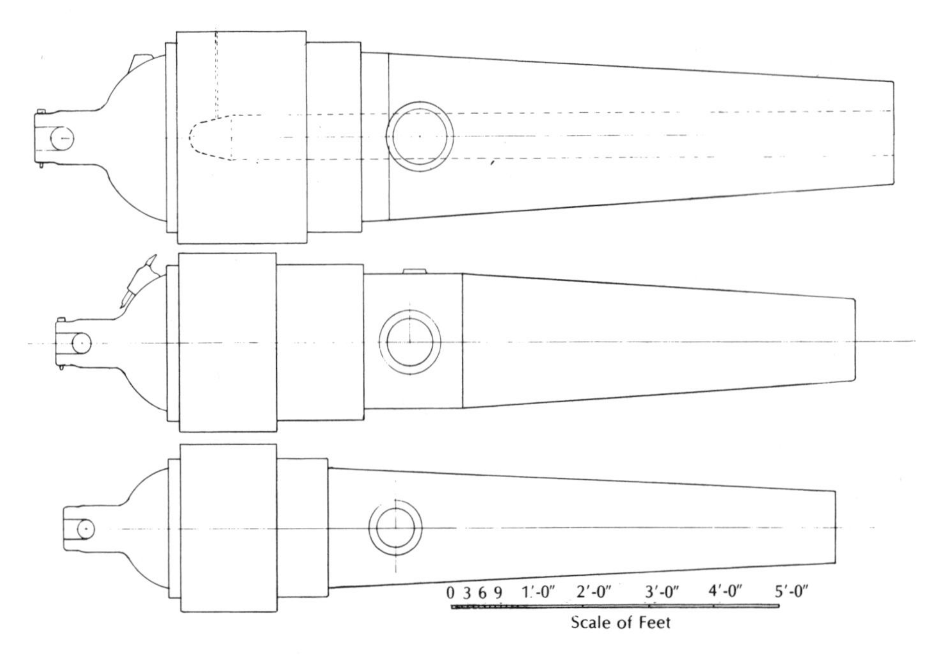

Fig. 125. Brooke 8-, 7-, and 6.4-Inch Rifles, 1864. (Redrawn by C. S. Tucker. After Confederate drawings in National Archives, Record Group 74.)

displaced 3,500 tons, and carried ten heavy guns. Eight of these, six IX-inch Dahlgrens and two Brooke 6.4-inch rifles, were in broadside; Brooke 7-inch rifles rested on pivot mounts at the bow and stern. The *Virginia* also had a 1,500-pound cast-iron beak installed to ram wooden ships. Steam-driven warships revived interest in the ancient tactic of sinking ships by ramming.

Belatedly, the federal government responded by pushing its own ironclad construction, the fruit of which was John Ericsson's *Monitor*. This craft, 172 feet long with a 776-ton displacement, was much smaller and radically different. Her hull sat so low in the water that she looked like a raft, and in fact was referred to as a tin can on a raft and a hat floating on the surface of the water. With all her vital machinery below the waterline, she did not make much of a target. Armor plate 4.5 inches thick protected the deck and projected over the side. Amidships was her most novel feature—a revolving 15-inch oak frame turret protected by 8 inches of rolled iron plate. The first armored turret to see action in history, it mounted two XI-inch Dahlgrens side by side. The ship was conned while in battle from a small armored pilot house forward of the turret.

The *Monitor* was far more maneuverable than her Confederate opponent, but as she was only a fraction of the *Virginia*'s size and mounted but two guns, there were serious doubts about her abilities.

On 8 March 1862 the *Virginia* sailed from Norfolk to attack Union blockaders accompanied by two light steamers, the *Beaufort* and *Raleigh*, each

Fig. 126. Brookes at the Washington Navy Yard. *Left:* The 12-inch wrought-iron replacement gun for the Peacemaker. *Center foreground:* A 7-inch Brooke (no discernible markings) from the CSS *Tennessee*. *Right background:* A X-inch Brooke smoothbore of 1864 (Tredegar) from the CSS *Columbia*. *Far background:* The restored commandant's house. (Photograph by Malcolm Muir, Jr.)

mounting one gun. The three vessels made for the frigate *Congress* and sloop *Cumberland*, which lay off Newport News. Two other Union warships, the steam frigates *Minnesota* and *Roanoke*, were off Fort Monroe. After an exchange of fire the *Virginia* rammed and sank the *Cumberland*, then forced the *Congress* to surrender. The latter was then set on fire by hot shot and exploded later that night. The *Virginia* now turned against the *Minnesota*, which along with the *Roanoke* and sailing frigate *St. Lawrence* had run aground and lay helpless. With low tide and the approach of dark, however, the *Virginia* retired to Sewell's Point, her crew confident they could complete destruction of the Union vessels the next day.

The *Virginia* appeared largely unscathed, but she had suffered some damage. Her beak had been lost while she was ramming the *Cumberland*. Union shot had broken the muzzles off two of her guns, she was leaking, and there were at least ten casualties, including her captain.

As the sounds of battle ended help arrived for the Union side. The *Monitor*, having survived a difficult passage from New York during which she almost sank, put into Hampton Roads. Illuminated by light from the burning *Congress* and visible to the crew of the *Virginia*, she anchored near the grounded *Minnesota*.

Next morning, 9 March, the *Virginia* steamed out to engage the *Minnesota*. The *Monitor* appeared and the two began their historic engagement at 8:00 A.M. The four-hour battle was fought at close range, from a few yards to about 200. Both vessels were constantly in motion. The *Virginia* rammed the *Monitor* but because of her lost beak did little damage. The *Monitor*, meanwhile, tried to cripple the vulnerable propeller and rudder of her antagonist. She was not able to fire her guns more than once every 7 or 8 minutes but rotated her turret so that her guns became targets only when they were about to fire. Most of her shots hit the *Virginia* and inflicted damage. The more numerous Confederate guns fired more often but shot high and did little damage outside of nearly blinding the Union vessel's commander when a shell scored a direct hit on the pilot house. In the resulting confusion the *Monitor* drifted away from the battle, and when her new commander brought her back into position he saw the *Virginia* in retreat. Her commander had interpreted the *Monitor*'s actions to mean the Confederates had won and decided to return to Norfolk for repairs.

Thus the battle ended in a draw. That might not have been the case if the *Virginia* had concentrated fire on the *Monitor*'s pilot house or if her rifles had fired solid shot rather than shell (Confederate officers had ordered from Tredegar only shell, the projectile best suited against the wooden warships that the *Virginia* expected to engage at Hampton Roads). On the other hand, the *Monitor*'s fire should have been concentrated against the *Virginia*'s waterline, where her armor was weakest, and her XI-inch guns should have employed 30-pound powder charges instead of 15. (Ericsson had protested against the light charge, but Dahlgren insisted.) The *Virginia* had been hit fifty times and was leaking. The *Monitor* had sustained only twenty-one hits and was virtually undamaged.

Though the battle between the two vessels was not renewed, it signaled a new era in naval warfare. Both the Union and Confederacy now augmented the construction of ironclads. It also led to a frantic push to manufacture larger-caliber guns capable of penetrating iron plating. The Confederate ram *Tennessee* was given a third more armor than the *Virginia*, 6 inches on the casemate and 4 on the overhang. After holding off virtually the entire Union fleet in the Battle of Mobile Bay on 5 August 1864, the *Tennessee* fell prey to design flaws, unreliable machinery, and one 15-inch shot when Commander J. W. A. Nicholson in the monitor *Manhattan* disregarded the established 35-pound service charge and on his own authority upped it to 65 pounds. The battle demonstrated that IX- and XI-inch guns were useless against 6 inches of iron heavily backed, even at close range.

Another test for U.S. Navy ordnance came on 19 June 1864, when the *Kearsarge* engaged and sank the notorious Confederate commerce raider *Alabama* off Cherbourg, France. It was the first decisive battle between steam warships at sea and a trial between American and British ordnance.

The two vessels were closely matched in size and number of guns. The

Kearsarge mounted four 32-pounders in broadside, one 30-pounder rifle on the forecastle, and two XI-inch guns in pivot, one each bow and stern. The *Alabama* was armed with British ordnance: six 32-pounders in broadside and one 7-inch Blakely rifle and one 68-pounder 8-inch smoothbore in pivot mounts. The latter gun was the favorite pivot piece in the Royal Navy. The *Kearsarge's* weight of broadside was some 20 percent greater than that of the *Alabama*, an advantage offset at least in part by the Confederate's more rapid firing. (The *Alabama*'s gunners had been trained in the Royal Navy gunnery ship *Excellent*.) All guns were fought except for a 32-pounder mounted on the stern of each ship. The *Kearsarge* enjoyed one other advantage: iron chain had been suspended vertically in her machinery areas to help protect against Confederate shot.

The battle lasted about one hour. The sea was calm and the ships circled between 700 and 1,200 yards apart, allowing full use of the broadside guns of both. These guns inflicted minimal damage. Decisive fire came from the XI-inch Dahlgrens. Their shells, with a time fuse and a powder charge just sufficient to propel them through the side of the Confederate vessel, inflicted the heavy damage that sank the *Alabama*.

Although some continued to favor broadside batteries alone, this engagement vindicated Dahlgren in his premise that ships should be armed with a mixed battery of broadside and pivot guns, and that these should be the heaviest and most powerful a ship could safely carry.

By the end of the Civil War the Dahlgren system of large smoothbore guns seemed enshrined, and they remained the principal armament of the U.S. Navy for some years. Not only through his designs, but also by his insistence on high standards of manufacturing and proof, Dahlgren had practically done away with the bursting of guns in action. As Chief of Ordnance Captain Wise wrote in November 1865, "Not a single gun of the Dahlgren system burst prematurely, and none of the XVin. guns, even when fired with their heaviest charges, have ever failed, except in the case of two or three which had their muzzle ruptured by the premature explosion of shells—the body of the gun, even then, remaining uninjured."[24]

Although Dahlgrens were undoubtedly the best of their kind in the world at the time, the epitome of the smoothbore gun era, two basic problems continued to plague ordnance designers and ship constructors: for the former, penetrating the increasing thickness of armor plate, and for the latter, developing armor to defend against new and powerful guns. During the Civil War, at least, the advantage appeared to rest with ordnance designers.

APPENDIX A

Nomenclature of Muzzle-Loading Ordnance

IT SHOULD BE pointed out that few sources agree on terms or their application. What follows will differ from some sources, but the terms are believed to be representative for most of the period.

NOMENCLATURE, EXTERIOR OF THE GUN

The gun was divided by cross sections into five parts (see figure 127):

1. The cascabel *AO* was measured back from the rear of the base ring *r*. This space was divided into the base of the breech (1), the neck (2), and the knob (3) of the cascabel. The last two made up the pomillion.

2. The first reinforce *AE* was measured from the rear of the base ring *r* to the first reinforce ring *PQ*. In all old guns the first reinforce was conical in form; by the mid-nineteenth century it was usually cylindrical.

3. The second reinforce *EF* was measured from the first reinforce to the second reinforce ring. It contained the trunnions.

4. The chase *FB* was measured from the second reinforce to the muzzle ring *Z*.

5. The muzzle *HB* was measured from the muzzle ring to the face of the muzzle *N*. It included the muzzle ring *Z*, the swell (4) or tulip of the muzzle, and the face of the muzzle *N*.

NOMENCLATURE, INTERIOR OF THE GUN

The gun interior included the bore cylinder, slope of the chamber, chamber, and vent. Carronades had a flash rim at the muzzle, where the size of the bore was enlarged; this increased gun length and protected the ship's rigging from the blast of firing.

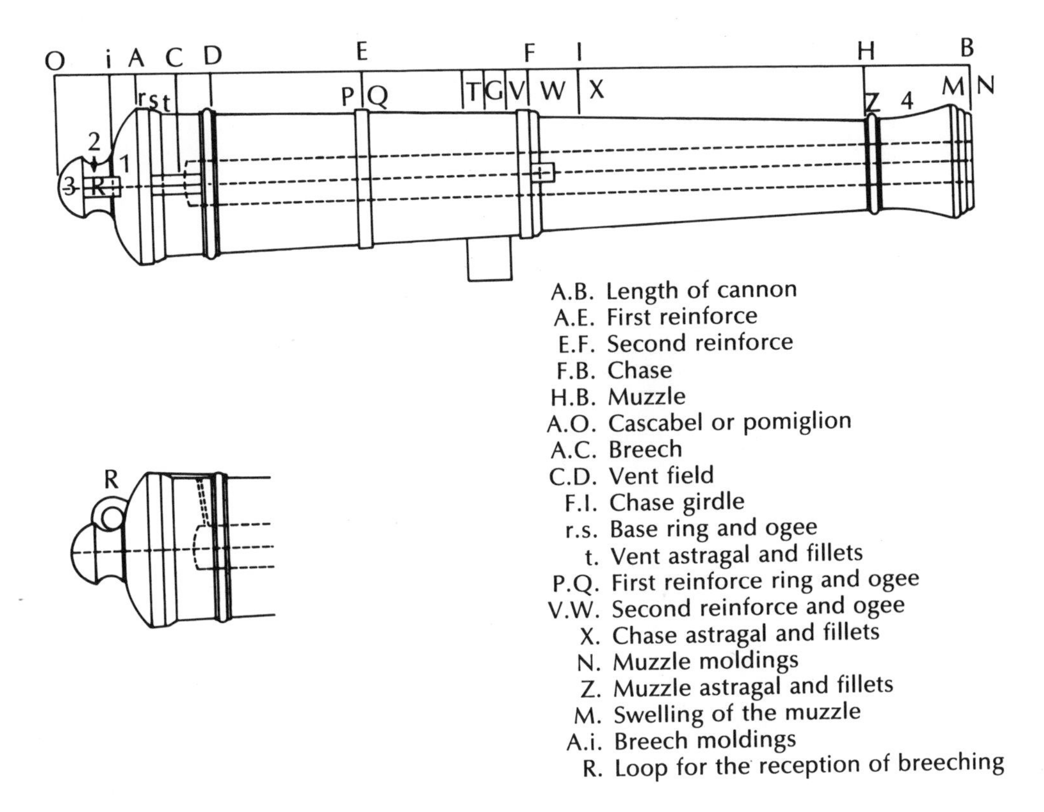

Fig. 127. Nomenclature of a War of 1812 Gun. (After a drawing in Atkinson and Clarke, *The Naval Pocket Gunner*.)

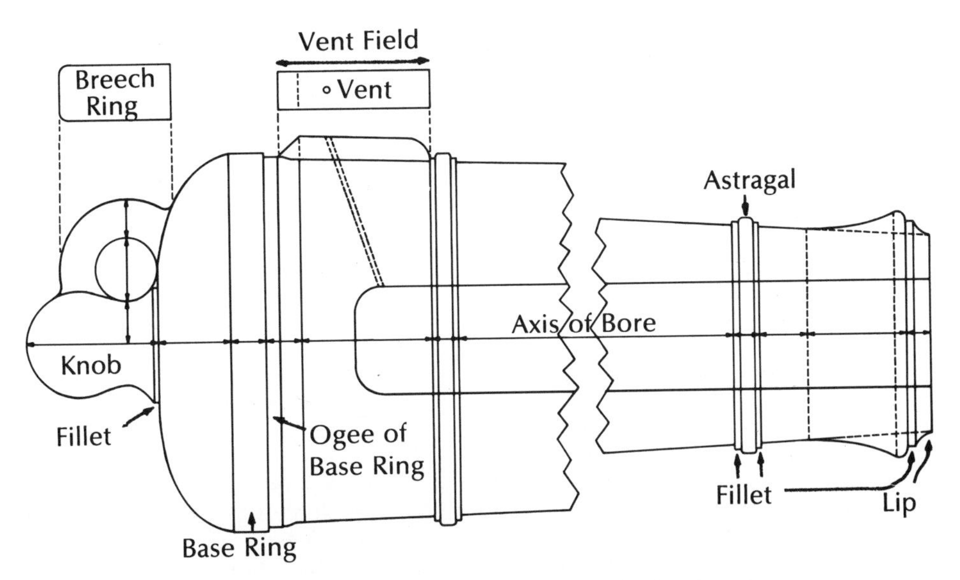

Fig. 128. Nomenclature of a U.S. Navy 24-Pdr of 1823.

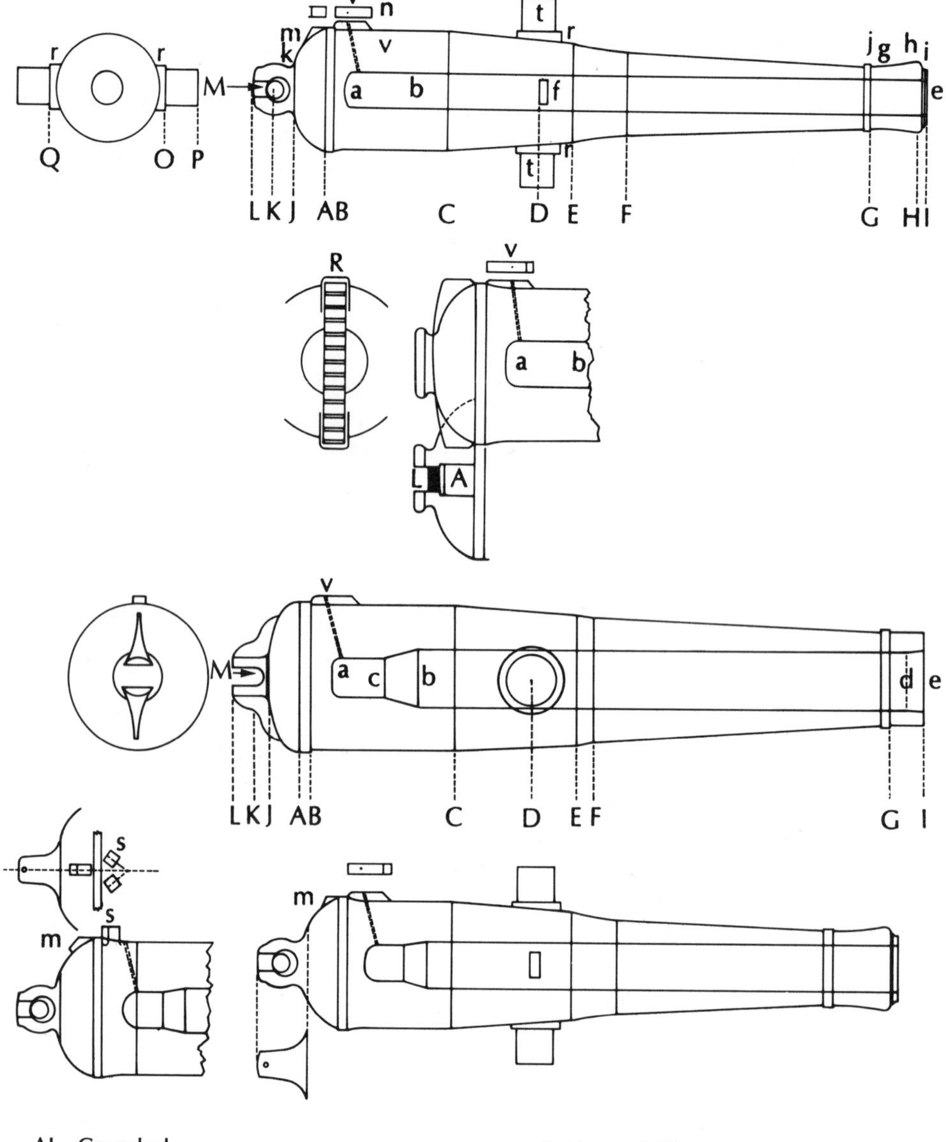

AL. Cascabel
GI. Muzzle
aJ. Breech
BC. First reinforce
CE. Second reinforce
EF. Curve of reinforce
FG. Chase
GI. Muzzle (there was a straight muzzle on some shell guns, but from 1845 all guns except the boat howitzer were cast with tulip muzzles)
AJ. Base of breech
k. Neck
M. Jaws
g. Neck
h. Swell
i. Lip and fillet
e. Face
ab. Chamber
de. Flash rim or cup
rr. Rimbases
m. Breech sight mass (also s)
v. Vent
a. Bottom of bore
R. Ratchet (found on 64-pdr of 105 cwt)
cb. Slope of chamber
tt. Trunnions
f. Reinforce sight mass
n. Lock piece
ae. Length of bore
j. Chase ring

Fig. 129. Nomenclature of Guns, 1852 Ordnance Instructions. (After drawings in Bureau of Ordnance, *Preparation of Vessels of War for Battle*, 1852.)

TABLE 33

DIMENSIONS OF U.S. NAVAL ORDNANCE, 1852

					LENGTHS OF (IN)										
	Date	*Form*	*Length (ft-in)*	*Weight (cwt)*	*AB**	*AC*	*AD*	*AE*	*AF*	*AG*	*AH*	*AI*	*AJ*	*AK*	*AL*
Shell Guns															
10-In	1841	Fig. 1†	9-4	86	2.0	28.0	42.0	50.0	53.0	106.0	—	112	5.0	8.2	12.0
8-In	1841	Fig. 1	8-10	63	2.0	20.5	40.5	45.0	47.0	102.0	—	106	5.5	8.0	11.5
8-In	1851	Fig. 3a	8-10	63	8.0	21.2	35.59	45.1	53.0	94.0	104.3	106	6.01	9.66	13.31
8-In	1846	Fig. 3a	8-4	55	4.6	20.0	35.07	41.8	50.0	88.4	98.1	100	5.7	10.25	14.15
64-Pdr	1819	Fig. 4b	10-10	105	7.5	26.0	45.56	53.56	65.0	117.25	128.2	130	6.95	—	10.95
32-Pdr	1816	Fig. 4	9-4	57	6.35	22.4	39.53	45.9	56.0	101.81	110.05	112	5.59	9.715	13.34
32-Pdr	1816	Fig. 4	9-0	51	6.3	21.6	38.32	44.7	54.0	98.02	106.5	108	5.38	9.48	13.08
32-Pdr	1816	Fig. 4	8-6	46	7.0	20.4	36.0	42.4	51.0	92.08	100.5	102	5.44	9.94	13.69
Cannon															
No. 1 32-Pdr	1842	Fig. 1c	8-0	42	5.5	20.0	38.0	45.0	52.0	92.0	—	96	3.0	5.75	9.0
No. 2d 32-Pdr	1843	Fig. 1d	8-0	42	5.5	20.0	38.0	45.0	52.0	90.0	94.5	96	3.0	5.75	9.0
No. 3c 32-Pdr	1845	Fig. 1d	8-0	42	5.5	20.0	38.0	45.0	52.0	90.0	94.5	96	3.0	6.5	10.0
No. 4 32-Pdr	1817	Fig. 1c	8-0	42	6.2	19.2	34.05	40.45	48.0	86.25	94.5	96	5.15	8.9	12.4
No. 1 32-Pdr	1846	Fig. 1c	6-7	32	5.8	15.8	28.1	34.5	39.5	69.4	77.5	79	5.08	9.08	12.83
No. 2 32-Pdr	1846	Fig. 1c	6-7	32	5.8	15.8	28.1	34.5	39.5	69.4	77.5	79	5.0	8.5	12.0
No. 1 32-Pdr	1844	Fig. 1d	6-0	27	4.0	19.0	25.0	32.5	35.0	66.0	70.5	72	4.5	6.5	9.6
No. 2 32-Pdr	1846	Fig. 4	6-0	27	6.4	14.4	25.5	31.4	36.0	62.6	7.3	72	4.55	8.05	11.55
No. 3 32-Pdr	1816	Fig. 4	6-0	27	5.6	14.4	25.5	31.4	36.0	62.6	7.3	72	4.55	8.05	11.55

TABLE 33

(CONTINUED)

	Diameters at (in)											
	A	*B*	*C*	*E*	*F*	*G*	*H*	*I*	*J*	*K*	*L*	*M*
Shell Guns												
10-In	26.25	25.5	25.2	23.0	22.0	16.0	—	16.0	8.5	—	7.0	3.6
8-In	22.6	22.0	22.0	20.5	19.5	13.4	—	13.4	7.2	—	6.3	3.3
8-In	24.04	23.25	23.25	19.78	17.16	12.4	14.0	11.0	12.02	8.6	6.8	3.3
8-In	23.2	22.4	22.4	19.45	17.0	12.85	14.0	11.6	12.0	8.5	7.0	3.3
64-Pdr	28.2	27.0	27.0	23.3	19.9	14.25	16.2	12.75	13.9	12.0	—	—
32-Pdr	22.36	21.56	21.56	18.5	15.88	11.25	12.8	10.19	11.18	8.25	6.5	3.25
32-Pdr	21.52	20.72	20.72	17.9	15.4	11.1	12.7	9.98	10.76	8.0	6.2	3.2
32-Pdr	21.28	20.48	20.48	17.5	15.2	11.0	12.5	9.92	10.88	8.0	6.5	3.0
Cannon												
No. 1 32-Pdr	20.5	19.2	19.2	17.0	15.0	11.5	—	11.5	7.0	—	6.0	3.0
No. 2d 32-Pdr	20.5	19.2	19.2	17.0	15.0	11.5	13.0	11.0	7.0	—	6.0	3.0
No. 3c 32-Pdr	20.5	19.2	19.2	17.0	15.0	11.5	13.0	11.0	7.0	7.0	5.5	3.0
No. 4 32-Pdr	20.6	19.8	19.8	17.1	14.8	10.8	12.3	9.75	10.3	7.6	6.0	3.0
No. 1 32-Pdr	20.0	19.2	19.2	16.3	14.4	10.8	12.0	9.6	10.16	7.5	6.0	3.0
No. 2 32-Pdr	20.0	19.2	19.2	16.3	14.4	10.8	12.0	9.6	10.0	7.6	6.0	3.0
No. 1 32-Pdr	18.4	17.6	17.6	15.8	14.8	10.5	11.6	9.6	8.5	—	5.5	3.0
No. 2 32-Pdr	19.2	18.4	18.4	15.8	13.9	10.7	11.8	9.4	8.0	7.3	6.0	3.0
No. 3 32-Pdr	19.2	18.4	18.4	15.76	13.9	10.57	11.4	9.4	8.0	7.3	6.0	3.0

TABLE 33

(*CONTINUED*)

	Trunnions				Bore and Chamber						
	Length OP (in)	*Span of Rimbase QO (in)*	*Diameter at (in)*		*Length of (in)*				*Diameter at (in)*		
			P	*O*	*ae*	*ac*	*cb*	*de*	*b*	*c*	*e*
Shell Guns											
10-In	7.0	25.5	9.0	11.0	106.0	9.5	5.5	3.0	10.0	7.0	10.25
8-In	6.5	22.2	7.018	8.518	102.0	7.45	5.0	4.0	8.0	6.4	8.5
8-In	6.0	23.25	7.0	9.0	100.3	7.45	4.0	—	8.0	6.4	—
8-In	6.5	22.4	7.0	9.0	95.4	7.0	4.0	—	8.0	6.4	—
64-Pdr	8.0	27.0	8.0	10.0	124.2	—	—	—	8.0	—	—
32-Pdr	6.0	21.56	6.4	8.4	107.9	—	—	—	6.4	—	—
32-Pdr	6.0	20.72	6.4	8.4	104.0	—	—	—	6.4	—	—
32-Pdr	6.0	20.48	6.4	8.4	97.2	—	—	—	6.4	—	—
Cannon											
No. 1 32-Pdr	5.5	19.2	6.4	8.4	90.5	—	—	3.0	6.4	—	6.65
No. 2d 32-Pdr	5.5	19.2	6.4	8.4	90.5	—	—	1.5	6.4	—	6.65
No. 3c 32-Pdr	5.5	19.2	6.4	8.4	90.5	—	—	1.5	6.4	—	6.65
No. 4 32-Pdr	5.5	19.8	6.4	8.4	92.05	—	—	—	6.4	—	—
No. 1 32-Pdr	5.5	19.2	6.4	8.4	75.04	—	—	—	6.4	—	—
No. 2 32-Pdr	5.5	19.2	6.4	8.4	75.1	—	—	—	6.4	—	—
No. 1 32-Pdr	5.0	17.6	5.82	7.4	70.0	6.0	2.5	1.5	6.4	5.82	6.65
No. 2 32-Pdr	5.0	18.4	5.82	7.82	67.65	5.0	2.5	—	6.4	5.82	—
No. 3 32-Pdr	5.0	18.4	5.82	7.0	68.4	5.4	2.5	—	6.4	5.82	—

Source: Navy Department, Bureau of Ordnance, *Instructions in Relation to the Preparation of Vessels of War for Battle* (Washington, 1852).
* Letters refer to figure 129.
† Figure numbers refer to illustrations on figure 129.

TABLE 34

GENERAL DIMENSIONS OF THE PARTS OF A SHIP'S GUN CARRIAGE*

	Gun-Size Proportion	*4-Pdr*	*6-Pdr*	*9-Pdr*	*12-Pdr*	*18-Pdr*	*24-Pdr*	*32-Pdr*	*42-Pdr*
Brackets									
Length	12.522	38.22	43.76	50.09	55.13	63.11	69.46	76.45	83.70
Thickness	1.000	3.05	3.50	4.00	4.40	5.04	5.55	6.11	6.68
Breadth Before	4.686	14.30	16.37	18.75	20.63	23.62	25.99	28.61	31.32
Behind	2.343	7.15	8.19	9.36	10.32	11.81	13.00	14.30	15.66
Distance at Trunnions	2.992	9.13	10.46	11.97	13.17	15.08	16.60	18.27	20.00
Distance at Middle of Hind Axtrees	3.695	11.28	12.91	14.78	16.27	18.62	20.50	22.56	24.70
Distance, Center of Trunnion from Front	1.983	6.05	6.93	7.93	8.73	9.99	11.00	12.11	13.26
Diameter of Trunnion Hole	1.082	3.30	3.78	4.30	4.76	5.45	6.00	6.61	7.23
Center Sunk in Side	0.045	0.14	0.16	0.18	0.20	0.23	0.25	0.27	0.30
Radius of Ovolo	0.500	1.53	1.75	2.00	2.20	2.52	2.77	3.05	3.34
Excavation, Length of Chord	5.000	15.26	17.47	20.00	22.01	25.20	27.73	30.53	33.42
In Bottom, Distance from Front	3.500	10.68	12.23	14.00	15.41	17.64	19.41	21.37	23.40
Axtrees									
Whole Length	9.735	29.72	34.02	37.50	42.86	49.06	54.00	59.43	65.07
Arms' Length	1.767	5.39	6.17	7.06	7.78	8.91	9.80	10.79	11.81
Diameter	1.118	3.41	3.91	4.47	4.92	5.63	6.20	6.83	7.47
Breadth Between Brackets at the Fore	1.226	3.74	4.28	4.90	5.40	6.18	6.80	7.48	8.20
at the Hind	2.163	6.60	7.56	8.65	9.52	10.90	12.00	13.21	14.46
Breadth Between Brackets and Arms	1.226	3.74	4.28	4.90	5.40	6.18	6.80	7.48	8.20
Depth in Middle of Fore	1.659	5.06	5.80	6.64	7.30	8.36	9.20	10.13	11.09
Hind	1.226	3.74	4.28	4.90	5.40	6.18	6.80	7.48	8.20
Distance Between Middle of Axtrees	8.684	26.51	30.35	34.75	38.23	43.76	48.17	53.02	58.05
Distance of Middles from the Fore	1.622	4.95	5.67	6.50	7.14	8.17	9.00	9.90	10.84
Bracket Ends, Hind	2.215	6.76	7.74	8.85	9.75	11.16	12.29	13.52	14.80
Depths of Axtrees Let into Brackets	0.432	1.32	1.51	1.73	1.90	2.18	2.40	2.64	2.89
Trucks									
Thickness	1.000	3.05	3.50	4.00	4.40	5.04	5.55	6.11	6.68
Their Diameter Fore	3.245	9.91	11.34	13.00	14.29	16.35	18.00	19.81	21.69
Hind	2.884	8.80	10.08	11.54	12.70	14.53	16.00	17.61	19.28
Cap Square									
Whole Length	2.974	9.08	10.39	11.90	13.09	14.99	16.50	18.16	19.88
Breadth	0.721	2.20	2.52	2.88	3.17	3.63	4.00	4.40	4.82

TABLE 34

(CONTINUED)

	Gun-Size Propor-tion	*4-Pdr*	*6-Pdr*	*9-Pdr*	*12-Pdr*	*18-Pdr*	*24-Pdr*	*32-Pdr*	*42-Pdr*
Cap Square (continued)									
Thickness	0.125	0.38	0.44	0.50	0.55	0.63	0.69	0.76	0.84
Bend	1.082	3.30	3.78	4.33	4.76	5.45	6.00	6.61	7.23
Fore Flat	1.171	3.57	4.09	4.69	5.16	5.90	6.50	7.15	7.83
Hind Flat	0.721	2.20	2.52	2.90	3.17	3.63	4.00	4.40	4.82
Head of Joint Bolt,									
Length	0.631	1.93	2.20	2.52	2.78	3.18	3.50	3.85	4.22
Breadth	0.216	0.66	0.75	0.86	0.95	1.09	1.20	1.32	1.44
Head of Eyebolt,									
Length	0.415	1.27	1.45	1.66	1.83	2.09	2.30	2.53	2.77
Breadth	0.216	0.66	0.75	0.86	0.95	1.09	1.20	1.32	1.44
Rounding at Ends of Cap Square	0.216	0.66	0.75	0.86	0.95	1.09	1.20	1.32	1.44
Joint Bolt Projects Out of Cap Square	0.207	0.63	0.72	0.83	0.91	1.04	1.15	1.26	1.38
Thickness of Key	0.054	0.17	0.19	0.22	0.24	0.27	0.30	0.33	0.36
Bolts									
Diameter	0.270	0.82	0.94	1.08	1.19	1.36	1.50	1.65	1.80
Diameter of Burrs and Heads	0.360	1.10	1.26	1.44	1.58	1.81	2.00	2.20	2.41
Diameter of Burring (Washer)	0.486	1.48	1.70	1.95	2.14	2.45	2.70	2.97	3.25
Loops									
Inner Diameter	0.300	0.92	1.05	1.20	1.32	1.51	1.66	1.83	2.01
Outer Diameter	0.721	2.20	2.52	2.88	3.17	3.63	4.00	4.40	4.82
Breeching Ring									
Inner Diameter	0.800	2.44	2.80	3.20	3.52	4.03	4.44	4.88	5.35
Outer Diameter	1.300	3.97	4.54	5.20	5.72	6.55	7.21	7.94	8.69
Stool Bed									
Whole Length	5.822	17.77	20.34	23.29	25.63	29.34	32.29	35.54	38.92
Thickness	0.721	2.20	2.52	2.88	3.17	3.63	4.00	4.40	4.82
Breadth Before	1.082	3.30	3.78	4.32	4.76	5.45	6.00	6.61	7.23
Behind	1.803	5.50	6.30	7.21	7.94	9.09	10.00	11.01	12.05
Bolster Length	2.974	9.08	10.39	11.90	13.09	14.99	16.50	18.16	19.88
Breadth	1.000	3.05	3.50	4.00	4.40	5.04	5.55	6.11	6.68
Depth	1.250	3.82	4.37	5.00	5.50	6.30	6.93	7.63	8.36
Let In	0.090	0.28	0.31	0.36	0.40	0.45	0.50	0.55	0.60
Fore Notch Breadth	0.342	1.04	1.20	1.37	1.51	1.72	1.90	2.09	2.29
Depth	0.234	0.71	0.82	0.94	1.03	1.18	1.30	1.43	1.56
Distance	0.613	1.87	2.14	2.46	2.70	3.09	3.41	3.74	4.10
Transom Length	3.000	9.16	10.48	12.00	13.21	15.12	16.64	18.32	20.05
Thickness	1.000	3.05	3.50	4.00	4.40	5.04	5.55	6.11	6.68

Source: *Nautical Research Journal* 20, no. 1 (October 1973): 113–16.

* All dimensions except gun-size proportions are given in inches. Gun-size proportion is shot diameter. All carriage dimensions were proportional to the gun and based on its shot diameter.

TABLE 35

SHOT, U.S. NAVY SERVICE*

	Diameter of Shot, 1798	Diameter of Shot, 1816–40	Windage, 1816–40	Diameter of Bore	
				1816–40	*1845*
Long guns					
4-pdr	3.053	—	—	—	—
6-pdr	3.495	3.521	0.147	3.668	—
9-pdr	4.000	4.032	0.168	4.200	4.29
12-pdr	—	4.438	0.185	4.623	4.62
18-pdr	—	5.080	0.212	5.292	5.30
24-pdr	—	5.591	0.223	5.824	5.82
32-pdr	6.105	6.154	0.256	6.410	6.40
42-pdr	—	6.737	0.281	7.018	7.00
8-in	—	—	—	—	8.00
10-in	—	—	—	—	10.00
Carronades					
12-pdr	—	4.438	0.093	4.531	—
18-pdr	—	5.080	0.106	5.186	—
24-pdr	—	5.591	0.117	5.708	—
32-pdr	—	6.154	0.128	6.282	—
42-pdr	—	6.737	0.141	6.878	—

Sources: National Archives, Record Group 45, letter book, pp. 259 and 411; RG 74, no. 1544; RG 217, Regulations for the proof and inspection of cannon, shot, and shells, 1845; and John D. Brandt, *Gunnery Catechism* (New York: D. Van Nostrand, 1864), 195.

* All dimensions given in inches unless otherwise noted.

APPENDIX B

Glossary

APRON. A thin piece of lead tied with marline over the touchhole to keep it dry and prevent chance ignition.

AT RANDOM. Long range. Extreme range was *at utmost random.*

AXLETREE. The part of the carriage holding the wheels, known as trucks.

BALLOTING. The bounding of the ball down the bore, which resulted from too much windage and caused the ball to exit the muzzle in an uncertain direction.

BASE OF THE BREECH. The portion of the gun at the rear of the base ring.

BASE RING. The band encircling the gun at the junction of the reinforce and the base of the breech. It served as a point of support for the breech sight and rested on the head of the elevating screw (when that was used). Later omitted.

BASTARD. The lightest or smallest ordnance.

BATTERY. All the main armament of a vessel. Guns run out and ready to fire are said to be in battery.

BOMBARD. Short early cannon with bell mouths.

BOMB KETCH (BOMB). A two-masted vessel with no foremast, only a main mast and mizzenmast. There was a stout chain for the mainstay, and the forward part of the vessel was equipped with mortars.

BORE. The interior cavity, which received the charge and projectile and directed the flight of the latter. The bottom of the bore was slightly rounded to increase strength and facilitate cleaning.

BORING BIT. A tool that removed obstructions from the vent when the priming wire did not work. By the time of the Civil War boring bits were made of steel.

BRACKETS. The side pieces of a gun carriage.

BREAST PIECE. A rounded wooden projection added to the transom to position the carriage for oblique fire. First it was stationary; later it was a hinged shelf.

BREECH. A mass of metal behind the bottom of the bore and extending to the rear of the base ring.

BREECHING. Stout rope secured to the neck of the cascabel, run through ringbolts (later shackles) on the sides of the carriage, and clinched to large ringbolts on either side of the gun port. Breeching was used to limit the gun recoil.

BREECHLOADER. Ordnance that loaded from the rear or breech, as opposed to the muzzleloader.

BRIG. A two-masted square-rigged ship; comparable in armament to a medium sloop. Mainsail extended by a gaff above and a boom below. Also *brig sloop.*

BRIGANTINE. A two-masted vessel, square rigged to top-gallants on the fore, but fore-and-aft rigged on the main mast with a top mast.

BROADSIDE. The number of guns that could be brought to bear on a single side of a vessel. Also, the firing of all such guns at once.

BRONZE. Metal from which cannon were made, consisting of ninety parts' copper and ten parts' tin.

BULWARK. The solid wooden work, waist-high or higher, running around the weather deck.

CALIBER. Ordinarily, the weight of solid shot thrown by a gun. For shell guns, however, caliber was expressed by the diameter of the bore in inches (in Britain, by the diameter of the shot).

CANNON. One of the three families of ordnance, the others being culverins and perriers. A medium-range weapon, usually 15 to 20 calibers in length and weighing 100 to 129 times its projectile.

CAP SQUARES. The metal pieces securing the trunnions of a gun to the brackets of a carriage. Cap squares were hinged to permit easy removal of the piece.

CARRIAGE. The mount for a gun. Ship carriages of the muzzle-loading period were generally made of wood. Broadside guns were usually mounted on truck carriages; there were also pivot and slide carriages.

CARTRIDGE. Cylinders containing the gunpowder charge for the gun. They were first made of canvas, later of paper or parchment, then flannel, and finally wool.

CASCABEL. That part of the gun to the rear of the base ring, consisting of the base of the breech, ring, fillet, neck, and knob.

CASCABEL NECK. The concave surface connecting the base of the breech and the knob.

CASCABEL RING. The ring through which breeching was passed. The cascabel ring connected the base of the breech and the knob.

CHAMBER. A cavity at the bottom of the bore that allowed greater thickness of metal in the area of the charge. With light charges, it also improved the proportion of length and diameter to cylinder. Thus the action of the charge would concentrate on the center of the shot, which was supposed to produce higher velocity.

Chambers had disadvantages as well. They were made to take a full charge, and when reduced charges were used the shot, lying against the mouth of the chamber, might not reach the powder. Chambers were also difficult to service with the sponge during fire. In long guns firing full service charges, chambers were not used because they would be too long and would decrease velocity by lengthening the time that powder had to burn. Heavy guns were always cast without chambers, but many light guns including carronades had them. In light guns firing heavy projectiles, recoil could be reduced only by employing small charges of powder.

In American service, the chamber of an 8-inch gun equaled the bore of a 32-pounder; the chamber of a 32-pounder had the same diameter as the bore of a 24-pounder.

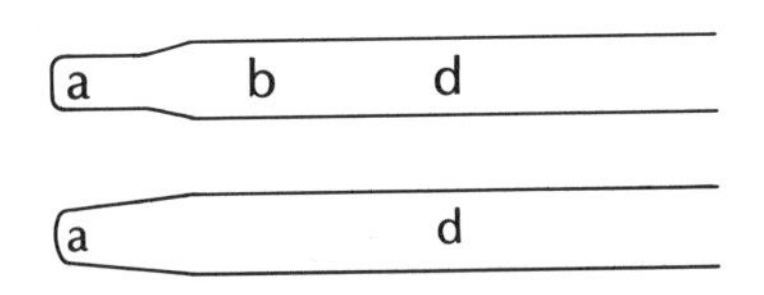

Fig. 130. Chambers.

There were two types of chambers in U.S. Navy muzzle-loading guns. Figure 130 top represents the "new" French chamber, which in the U.S. Navy was used in old-pattern shell guns and the 32-pounder of 27 cwt introduced in the mid-1840s. The chamber is *a*; *b* is the slope; *d* is the cylinder of the bore. Figure 130 bottom is the "old" conical French Gomer chamber, or English General Millar chamber, used by Great Britain. In the U.S. Navy, boat howitzers and new-pattern shell guns had conical chambers.

CHASE. The length of a gun between the chase ring and the second reinforce.

CHASE RING. The band encircling the gun at the point where the neck and chase join. Also muzzle ring.

CHOCKING QUOINS. Small wedges inserted against the trucks of a carriage to keep them, and the carriage, stationary.

CORVETTE. Any man-of-war smaller than a frigate (that is, brigs and sloops).

CROWBAR. Part of the equipment for servicing guns aboard ship. It was made of iron. Generally one end had a claw, the other end was squared off and ended in a point.

CULVERINS. One of the three families of ordnance, the others being cannon and perriers. Culverins had relatively thicker walls to sustain heavier charges for long range. Culverins, referring to most pieces 30 bore-diameters long, weighed 250 to 280 times their shot. Naval guns developed from culverins, which were longer and had thicker metal than cannon.

CUTTER. A single-masted, gaff-rigged vessel with more than one head sail.

CWT. A hundred-weight or 112 pounds. See *weight.*

DISPART. The difference between the diameter of a gun at the base ring and the diameter of its muzzle swell.

DISPART SIGHT. A sight mounted on the second reinforce, about in line with the trunnions, which corrected the difference in thickness of the muzzle and breech and ensured that the sight line would parallel the axis of the bore. It came into general use at the beginning of the nineteenth century.

DOUBLE FORTIFIED. Term used to identify the longest and heaviest guns. It referred to a length of up to 42 calibers and to a weight of 200 or more pounds per pound of shot.

DUMB TRUCKS. Stationary trucks added underneath a carriage to help limit recoil.

ÉPROUVETTE. A short mortar, set at an angle of 45 degrees and throwing a 24-pound solid ball, used to prove cannon powder.

FLASK. Wood or metal box that contained the sand mold for casting guns.

FLINTLOCK. A device that ignited powder in the vent, replacing quick match. The adoption of flintlock by the Royal Navy is credited to Sir Charles Douglas, who demonstrated its effectiveness in the Battle of the Saints in 1782. In conjunction with the goose-quill tube, the flintlock was a much more reliable ignition system and allowed a faster rate of fire.

FRIGATE. A two-decked, square-rigged ship (each mast had crossyards). Heavier guns were below, lighter ones above. Large frigates carried forty to fifty guns and small ones, twenty-six to thirty-eight. These vessels performed scouting for fleet or detached service and were not part of the line of battle in a fleet action.

Galley. In American naval usage, a large oared vessel.

Gunboat. Small warship, usually with a small number of large guns, used on rivers and shoal waters.

Gun port. A square hole cut in the ship's sides through which a gun could be fired.

Gunwale. The stringer running around the inside of the top strake of the ship; broadly, the upper edge of the boat's side.

Handspike. The tool used to train the carriage and to help elevate the gun. It was made of well-seasoned hickory, squared off at the end, and tapered. By 1860 all handspikes were metal shod, stained black, and oiled. Also *handspec.*

Harquebus. Early individual firearm, hand-held, primarily for antipersonnel use.

Hog. Fore and aft stress on the hull, in extreme cases causing the back to break.

Knob. The spherical mass of metal at the end of the gun. Also *nob.*

Ladle. A cylindrical copper spoon used to load loose powder or extract it from the gun. In length it was 3 calibers, in breadth, unfolded, 2. The staff had the same length and diameter as the wormer.

Length. The distance measured from the rear of a gun's base ring along the axis of the bore to the face of the muzzle. Extreme length referred to the distance from the rear of the cascabel along the axis of the bore to the face of the muzzle. The length of the bore was measured from the bottom of the bore to the face of the muzzle.

Linstock. The wooden staff about 2.5 feet tall that held the match. It had a pointed metal end and was stuck upright in the wooden deck or in the match tub.

Match. A rope that ignited the priming powder in the vent. Slow match was made of hemp or cotton and measured about .06 inch in diameter. Three strands were twisted together to form the match, which was woven around the linstock.

Match tub. Used to hold the staff with its burning match. Match tubs were made of oak staves held together by three iron hoops. The top (head) and bottom were made from pine. The head was sunk 1 inch and had three holes in it.

Molding. The raised portion of the reinforce rings on older guns. These were made up of astragals, ogees, and fillets.

Muzzle. The mouth or entrance of the bore. The face of the muzzle, perpendicular to the axis of the bore, was the plane terminating the gun. The muzzle molding consisted of the lip and fillet.

Muzzleloader. Ordnance loaded from the muzzle end.

Neck. The smallest part of the piece in front of the astragal or chase ring.

Ordinary. Term used to denote average metal thickness in ordnance. Originally, the word referred to a length of 30 to 33 calibers. Also *fortified.*

Orlop. Deck below lower deck.

Percussion cap. A cap or wafer of fulminates of mercury fitted over the touchhole which, when struck with a hammer, ignited and set the priming powder on fire. The cap worked almost instantaneously and was reliable in all weather conditions.

Perriers. Literally, "stone-throwers." One of the three families of ordnance, the others being culverins and cannon. Perriers were the shortest, usually 8 to 16 calibers long or less, and weighed only 60 to 80 times their shot. Originally they were large-bore weapons that fired stone shot at low velocity. The perrier was the forerunner of the howitzer.

POINT BLANK. The point at which the trajectory of the shot crossed the line of aim by the sights or along the barrel. The term implied very short range, as opposed to "at random."

POOP. A short raised deck that developed from the after castle. It was the steering and command point in sailing ships.

PORTFIRE. Quick match. Replaced slow match as a means of igniting the powder train to the vent. Portfire consisted of sixty parts' saltpeter or nitre, 40 parts' sulphur, and 20 parts' mealed powder. It was held in a stock and nipped off after firing.

PREPONDERANCE. The additional weight of the breech when it exceeded the weight of the muzzle. Generally the breech was heavier than the muzzle, preponderance being a twentieth the weight of the gun. The position of the trunnions influenced the amount of preponderance.

PRIMING WIRE. An iron wire used to clear the inside of a touchhole so that it might be properly primed. Also *priming iron.*

QUADRANT. The instrument used to determine a gun's angle of elevation. It was bronze or wood and divided into degrees, with each degree in turn divided into ten parts.

QUARTERDECK. The aft part of the spar deck between the mainmast and the poop.

RAMMER. The implement used to seat both the cartridge and the shot in a gun. The rammer head, made of seasoned hardwood, was the size of the shot in diameter and 1.5 times the diameter of the bore in length (for carronades, it was the size of the diameter of the bore in length). An ashwood staff was secured in a hole in the rammer head by means of a hardwood pin. In 1860, the staff was 1.75 inches in diameter and the head was 0.25 inch less than the bore of the gun.

RAZEE. A ship whose hull was altered by the removal of the upper deck(s).

REINFORCE. The thickest part of a gun in front of the base ring. If there was more than one reinforce, the one next to the base ring was the first reinforce, the other the second reinforce.

RIMBASE. A cylindrical mass of metal that increased trunnion strength and prevented lateral movement of a gun on its carriage.

SABOT. The wooden bottom attached to a shell to keep it in the proper position, with the fuse facing the muzzle of the gun. The sabot was made of light, coarse-grained wood turned in a lathe to a diameter slightly less than that of the shell and tapered to fit the slope of a chambered gun. It was attached to the shell with two tin straps.

SCALING. The process of protecting a gun's bore from rust by firing it. A scaling charge was generally a twelfth the weight of the shot.

SCHOONER. A small watercraft employed on lakes, rivers, and coastal waters for dispatch and supply. It was fore-and-aft rigged on two masts. Some schooners were large, with eight to fourteen guns.

SHIP OF THE LINE. A two- to four-decked three-masted, square-rigged ship that carried 64 to 120 guns. It was rated according to number of guns in its main battery (first-rates carried 100 guns or more). Ships of the line formed the main battle line. The three-decked first- and second-rates were dull sailors. The main ship of the fleet at the end of the American Revolution was the 74-gun ship. (By that time, almost half of the Royal Navy's 174 ships of the line were seventy-fours; second most numerous were the 64-gun two-deckers, cheaper to build and maintain but with only two-thirds the firepower of a seventy-four and not strong enough to stand heavy fire in the line of battle.) Lighter guns were carried on the upper deck, heavier ones on lower decks.

SLOOP OF WAR. A term applied to any vessel with its guns on a single deck, usually the upper, uncovered one. It was a single-deck, two-masted, square-rigged vessel like the brig, or a fore-and-aft-rigged ship like the schooner. Small sloops carried ten to sixteen guns; large sloops had eighteen to twenty-four.

SPAR DECK. The open, topmost (lightly built) deck above the main deck.

SPIKING. Rendering a gun useless. Spiking usually meant obstructing the vent by driving a metal spike into it. A gun could also be disabled if its trunnions were knocked off or if it were blown apart.

SPONGE. A tool made of poplar or some other light wood, used to clean a bore between firings. In diameter the sponge head was the size of the shot of the next smallest caliber (That is, 6.2 inches, or the size of a 32-pound shot, for a 42-pounder gun). Staves for sponges in 1860 were made of ash, 1.75 inches in diameter and 18 inches longer than the bore. In the early nineteenth century, some sponges sat at the end of a piece of rope stiffened by spun yarn, with the rammer on the opposite end.

SPRUE. An additional length given to the gun in casting, its purpose being to receive the slag of molten metal as it surfaced and to furnish extra metal when the cast shrank in cooling. Its weight was thought to compress the metal in the cannon proper, increasing the density of the lower portions of the gun where the strain was greatest when the gun was fired. Also *head.*

STAFF. An ash rod used to hold the match. It had a spike in the lower end. The head was large enough to admit two parts of the match rope where the notch was cut.

SWIVEL. A small gun mounted in the rail of a ship.

TACKLE. A rope used to move a carriage forward into battery to fire and out of battery to load. Tackles were also used to train a gun laterally.

TAMPION. A plug of wood or cork used to stop the muzzle of a gun and keep the bore dry.

TANGENT SIGHT. A graduated scale moving in a vertical plane at the base of a gun and employed for distant firing.

TENSILE STRENGTH. The ability of iron to resist rupture when pulled apart by weight.

THICKNESS (OF METAL). Usually about 1 caliber at the breech and first reinforce. In the heaviest pieces it was 1.1 to 1.2 calibers, in lighter guns it was less than 1 caliber, and in carronades it was about 0.8 caliber.

TRANSOM. The front piece of a carriage, connected to the two sides or brackets.

TRUCK. The wheels on which a carriage moved.

TRUNNIONS. Cylinders projecting from a gun in a plane perpendicular to the axis of the bore and supporting the gun on its carriage. Trunnions were located in the second reinforce. They were, in diameter and length, usually equal to 1 caliber. In early guns they were set below the center of the bore. This improved vision to the side and reduced recoil, but it also put a greater strain on the carriage. As early as the 1750s, the English artillerist John Muller asserted that trunnions should be located on the axis of the bore. In the U.S. Navy all guns were eventually to be cast center-hung, with the axis of their trunnions at right angles to that of the bore. The French and the British continued to position their trunnions about half a diameter below the axis of the bore, where it was felt they formed a better bond and did not impede sighting.

TUBE. Priming device that replaced loose powder, which tended to erode the vent. The first tubes were made of tin, later of goose quills. *Tube* is also the term for an individual gun.

TULIP. The increase in the diameter of the metal toward the muzzle. (In mortars, a muzzle band took the place of the swell of the muzzle.) It appeared on older guns and was designed to provide additional reinforcing where the shot left the gun in its last bound down the bore. Also *muzzle swell.*

VENT. The conical channel through which fire met a charge. With the introduction of the lock, a vent patch was cast on the gun; it took the lock and reinforced metal to compensate for that removed in boring the vent. The vent field was a zone about the gun whose width equaled the length of the vent patch. The vent was drilled on the centerline at a 70- or 90-degree angle to the axis of the bore. The juncture of the vent and the bore was near, but not at, the vent's bottom. Experiment showed that higher velocity was obtained when the vent hole was positioned to enter one-sixth of a caliber from the bottom of the charge.

A considerable amount of gas escaped through the vent during fire and gradually enlarged it. This was more of a problem with bronze than iron guns. Bronze guns were bouched, that is, a 1-inch diameter bolt of pure copper containing the touchhole was screwed into the gun. Pure copper stood the discharge through the vent better than bronze, and the bouching was easily replaced. An armorer could rebore the vent back to its original size. When quill tubes and matches were used for the priming and firing, the only problem with enlarged vents was the reduction they brought in the velocity of shot. But with the introduction of friction primers or percussion wafers, there was the additional problem that they might not explode or would do so unevenly. When the gun was not in use the vent was protected by an apron.

WAD. This separated the powder and the shot and was also on occasion laid over the shot to keep it in place. Wads were hard or junk (made from loose pieces of cordage), and grommet or selvagee (a piece of rope shaped like a ring with two crosspieces of rope to keep it from collapsing).

WEIGHT. The weight of a gun was based on the long ton of 2,240 pounds and was expressed in hundredweights or cwt (112 pounds), quarter-hundredweights (28 pounds), and individual pounds. Thus a gun marked 10-3-4 would weigh $10 \times 112 + 3 \times 28 + 4$, or 1,208 pounds. Long guns known as double-fortified were about 200 times heavier than their shot weight. Broadside firing guns could be about 100 times their weight of shot. Some heavier long guns were necessary in a ship's battery, however, since they could take heavier powder charges and had more velocity and range. By the time of the Civil War, a long gun that weighed about 140 to 150 times its shot was considered average.

WINDAGE. The difference in diameter between the projectile and the bore.

WORM. A device used to extract the wad and cartridge from the bore if necessary. It was a metal corkscrew mounted at the end of a ramrod. The worm was 1.75 the size of the bore of the gun in length and the size of a shot in diameter (for carronades, it was smaller: 0.67 of a bore-diameter in length and 0.8 the diameter of the bore in diameter). Also *wad hook*.

APPENDIX C

U.S. Navy Cannon Contracts, June 1794 to April 1861*

18 June 1794

Samuel Hughes, Cecil Furnace, Cecil County, Maryland: ninety 24-pounders for frigates at $106.67/ton, plus allowance for boring from the solid. (By 1798 thirty-six had been delivered, but no settlement had been reached with Hughes owing to a dispute over the amount of allowance for boring from the solid.)

8 August 1794

Brown and Francis, Hope Furnace, Rhode Island: sixty 24-pounders for frigates at $106.67/ton. (By 1798 fifty-nine had been delivered. An additional $5,953.68 was paid for boring from the solid.)

25 October 1796

Samuel Hughes: Forty 12-pounders at $133.15/ton with no extra allowance for boring from the solid. (By 1798 only three cannon had been delivered. By November 1801 Hughes had delivered at least fourteen 6-pounders that were charged to this contract.)

12 July 1798

William Neilson, New York, and David Waterman, Salisbury Furnace, Salisbury, Connecticut: guns for a ship of war designed to carry not more than twenty-two on her main gun deck at £55 Pennsylvania/ton. (One entry noted that the guns were thirty 24-pounders of the same dimensions as those last cast at the same place for the State of New York.)

* The information in this appendix is taken from National Archives, Record Group 45, entries 235 and 464, Record Group 74, entries 157 and 162, and Record Group 217. All tons in the contracts of 1794–1860 are 2,240 pounds.

13 December 1798
William Lane, Philadelphia, and William Salter, New Jersey: $23,000 worth of cannon, the largest 24-pounders, at 200 pounds/pound of ball.

4 January 1799
Henry Foxall and Company, Eagle Foundry, Philadelphia: $23,000 worth of cannon at $146.67/ton.

3 March 1799
Samuel Hughes, Havre de Grace, Maryland: fifty-six 32-pounders, fifty-six 18-pounders, and thirty-six 9-pounders at $130/ton.

11 October 1800
William Lane, Philadelphia: 148 cannon, not less than 9-pounders or larger than 42-pounders and 200 times the weight of ball unless requested lighter, at $130/ton.

17 October 1800
Henry Foxall, Philadelphia: 148 cannon. (Same size, price, and weight as in preceding contract.)

1 July 1807
Henry Foxall, Columbia Foundry: fifty 24- and fifty 32-pounder cannon at a price of £50 Pennsylvania/ton. (Not a contract but a letter from Foxall to the Navy Department indicating he was "ready to commence" casting these.) Secretary of the Navy Robert Smith wrote to Foxall on 31 July authorizing fifty 32-pounders and fifty 42-pounder cannon.

6 August 1807
Samuel Hughes: fifty 32- and fifty 24-pounder cannon. (Not a contract but a letter from the Navy Department agreeing to have Hughes produce these. No money was to be paid until a congressional appropriation was made.)

20 August 1807
Samuel Richards, Philadelphia: fifty 32- and fifty 24-pounders at $133.33/ton. (Not a contract but a letter from the Navy Department agreeing to take delivery of these.)

February–March 1813
Henry Foxall, Columbia Foundry: thirty-seven 32-pounder carronades to arm two brigs. (Not a contract but a series of letters. The guns were among supplies shipped to Lake Erie for Perry.)

6 May 1813
William H. Walter and John Dorsey, Baltimore: 100 32-pounder carronades at $139.05 each. (All were to conform in form, size, weight, and workmanship to those made by Foxall.)

19 February 1814
Joseph McClurg, Pittsburgh: twenty 42-, forty 32-, twenty 24-, and twenty 18-pounder carronades priced, respectively, at $200, $175, $133, and $100 each.

14 January 1815
Peter Townsend, Orange County, New York: 400 tons of cannon and carronades, cannon at $133.33/ton and carronades on a sliding scale from $58.75 to $200. (Beds for carronades were to cost $6.75/cwt.)

15 March 1815

John Clarke and William Wirt, Richmond, Virginia: 175 tons of cannon and carronades. (Same payment scale as preceding contract.)

20 March 1815

John E. Dorsey, Etna Furnace, Baltimore: 300 tons of 32-pounder cannon. (In July Dorsey had completed thirty-five cannon and said he would have the whole ready by 1 September.)

1 June 1816

John Mason, Georgetown: thirty-two 42-pounder and thirty-six 32-pounder cannon at $125/ton, and twenty-four 32-pounder carronades at $135 each. (There was an $8/ton allowance for turning and chiseling the guns. The moldings were to be turned and the rest of the exterior was to be chiseled to a smooth surface. On 14 January 1818, the caliber of the guns was changed to sixty-eight 32-pounder long guns and twenty-four 42-pounder carronades.)

14 December 1816

John Swartout, Robert Swartout, Joseph G. Swift, Gouverneur Kemble, and James Rees, West Point: thirty-two 42- and thirty-six 32-pounder cannon and twenty-four 32-pounder carronades. (Same prices as in preceding contract. The guns were modified, as were those in the preceding contract, to sixty-eight 32-pounder long guns and twenty-four 42-pounder carronades.)

1817

Swartout and others: cannon and carronades for a 74-gun ship, cannon at $125/ton and carronades at $185 each. (The prices reveal that the latter are 42-pounders.)

1817

John Mason: cannon and carronades for a 74-gun ship, the latter at $135 each, assumed to be 32-pounders.

4 April 1819

John Mason: twenty 42-pounder carronades and thirty-four 32-pounder long guns. (Same prices.)

14 July 1819

John Clarke and Company: twenty-four 42-pounder carronades and thirty-two 42- and thirty-six 32-pounder cannon. (Same prices as in preceding three contracts, plus $8/ton for turning and chiseling the guns. An account of 1822 lists thirty-one 32- and twenty-eight 42-pounder cannon and twenty-seven 42-pounder carronades produced under this contract.)

4 December 1819

West Point Foundry Association: twenty 42-pounder carronades and thirty-four 32-pounder cannon. (Same prices as in preceding four contracts.)

10 April 1820

John Mason: twenty 42-pounder carronades and thirty-four 32-pounder cannon. (Same prices as in preceding five contracts.)

11 July 1820

West Point Foundry Association: 42-pounder cannon.

20 July 1820
West Point Foundry Association: thirty-two 42-pounder cannon. (Same price as in preceding contract.)

11 November 1820
John Mason: twenty-four 42-pounder carronades and thirty-two 42- and thirty-six 32-pounder cannon. (Same prices as in preceding two contracts.)

1 December 1820
West Point Foundry Association: twenty-four 42-pounder carronades and thirty-two 42- and thirty-six 32-pounder cannon. (Same prices as in preceding three contracts.)

4 December 1820
West Point Foundry Association: twenty 42-pounder carronades and thirty-four 32-pounder cannon. (Same prices as in preceding four contracts and continued allowance of $8/ton for chiseling.)

6 January 1821
John Clarke and Company: twenty-four 42-pounder carronades and thirty-two 42- and thirty-six 32-pounder cannon. (Same prices as in preceding five contracts.)

5 April 1822
John Mason: twenty 42-pounder carronades and thirty-four 32-pounder cannon. (Same prices as in preceding six contracts.)

12 September 1822
Gouverneur Kemble: Kemble to receive the 32-pounder carronades from the *Erie* and replace them with an equal number of 32- or 42-pounder carronades and beds. (Price to be the difference in value.)

11 January 1823
John Mason: twenty-four 42-pounder carronades at $185 each and thirty-two 42- and thirty-six 32-pounder cannon at $125/ton. (There was an additional allowance of $8/ton for turning and chiseling the guns. Deducted from the amount paid would be $7,736.45 for old cannon and shot sold to Mason.)

12 August 1823
West Point Foundry Association: twenty 42-pounder carronades and thirty-four 32-pounder cannon for a 44-gun ship. (Same prices as in preceding contract.)

8 October 1823
John Mason: twenty 42-pounder carronades and thirty-four 32-pounder cannon, the ordnance for a frigate. (Same prices as in preceding two contracts.)

10 March 1824
John Mason: twenty-five 42-, twenty 32-, and twenty 24-pounder cannon. (Same prices as in preceding three contracts.)

19 May 1824
West Point Foundry Association: twenty-five 42-pounder, eighteen 32-pounder, and twenty 24-pounder cannon. (Same prices as in preceding contracts.)

20 July 1824
John Mason: twenty-six 42-pounder carronades at $185 each.

1 September 1824

West Point Foundry Association: twenty-six 42-pounder carronades. (Same price as in preceding contract.)

20 May 1825

John Clarke and Company: twenty-eight 32-pounder cannon and forty-two 42-pounder carronades. (Same prices as in preceding two contracts.)

29 April 1826

West Point Foundry Association: eighty 24-pounder medium cannon at $138.14 per ton. (No allowance for chiseling or turning the guns smooth.)

21 June 1826

John Mason: eighty 24-pounder medium cannon. (Same price as in preceding contract.)

16 September 1826

John Clarke: eighty 24-pounder medium guns. (Same price as in preceding two contracts.)

21 November 1837

West Point Foundry Association: forty 32-pounder guns, twenty at $133/ton and twenty at $136/ton.

1 July 1841

Cyrus Alger, Boston: Forty-four 8-inch guns with 32-pounder chambers of 60 cwt at $130/ton. (From the Charleston Navy Yard Alger was also to receive sixteen 42-pounders and bore them out to 8 inches, leaving a chamber. He was to be paid $40/gun.)

1841

West Point Foundry Association: thirty-six 8-inch guns with 32-pounder chambers of 60 cwt at $130/ton. (Mason was also to bore up four 42-pounders to 8-inch bore. The one reference to this contract is not signed, so it may not have been let.)

1841

John Mason: thirty-six 8-inch guns with 32-pounder chambers at $133/ton (Mason was also to bore up eight 42-pounder guns to 8-inch size. The one reference to this contract is not signed, so it may not have been let.)

20 January 1842

John Mason: 100 8-inch cannon with 32-pounder chambers of 63 cwt at $140/ton, and 25 10-inch cannon with 42-pounder chambers of 86 cwt at $156/ton.

22 January 1842

West Point Foundry Association: 100 8-inch and 25 10-inch cannon. (Type and price the same as in preceding contract.)

28 January 1842

Cyrus Alger of Boston: sixty 32-pounder cannon with 24-pounder chambers of 4,650 pounds at $133.33/ton. (For the frigate *Congress.*)

18 February 1842

Freeman and Knap, Pittsburgh: 100 32-pounder cannon at $133.33/ton. (By December 1842, 125 guns of 56 cwt had been delivered on this contract marked completed.)

1 March 1842
Bellona Foundry: 100 32-pounder cannon of 56 cwt. (Same price as in preceding contract. The contract indicates completion as of 4 May 1847. More than 80 32-pounders cast by Bellona in 1843–46 and believed to come under this contract were 9 feet 4 inches long and 62 to 63 cwt.)

20 July 1842
Tredegar Iron Company, Richmond: 100 32-pounder cannon of 56 cwt. (Same price as in preceding two contracts.)

5 November 1842
George Page, Baltimore: thirty 8-inch "Paixhan" [*sic*] of 63 cwt at $95/ton and seventy 32-pounder guns of 41 cwt at $95/ton. (Contract canceled on 30 June 1843.)

13 August 1843
E. T. Sterling, Cuyahoga Steam Foundry Company, Cleveland: thirty 8-inch Paixhans of 63 cwt at $110/ton and seventy 32-pounder guns of 41 cwt at $100/ton.

3 October 1843
Daniel Treadwell, Cambridge, Massachusetts: four iron and steel cannon at $1,000 each. (Delivered at Boston on 6 January 1845.)

28 August 1844
R. Anderson, Richmond: twenty-four 32-pounder chambered guns of 42 cwt and fifty 32-pounder chambered guns of 27 cwt at $133/ton.

28 August 1844
West Point Foundry Association: twenty-six 32-pounder chambered guns of 42 cwt and fifty 32-pounder chambered guns of 27 cwt. (Same prices as in preceding contract.)

3 September 1844
Freeman, Knap and Totten, Pittsburgh: four 8-inch chambered guns of 10,000 pounds at $168/ton. (The guns were delivered by 16 June 1845.)

5 November 1844
Freeman, Knap and Totten: thirty 8-inch chambered guns of 63 cwt and seventy 32-pounder chambered guns of 42 cwt, both at $128/ton. (Guns delivered by 24 October 1845. These were the guns for the Great Lakes, which were not produced under two previous contracts with other firms. Ten 8-inch and twenty-five 32-pounder guns were delivered to Sacketts Harbor, New York, and to Erie, Pennsylvania; ten 8-inch guns and twenty 32-pounders went to Buffalo.)

17 September 1845
Cyrus Alger: sixty 32-pounders of 46 cwt and forty 32-pounder chambered cannon of 27 cwt at $.065/pound or $145.60/ton. (All but three cannon were completed by 11 December 1846.)

18 September 1845
West Point Foundry Association: forty 8-inch cannon of 53 cwt and sixty 32-pounder cannon of 27 cwt. (Same price as in preceding contract.)

1 October 1845
Knap and Totten: seventy-two 8-inch guns of 53 cwt. (Same price as in preceding two contracts. By 20 November 1846 seventy-three had been delivered.)

1 October 1845

Joseph Anderson: 112 32-pounder chambered cannon of 32 cwt. (Same price as in preceding three contracts.)

14 October 1845

John Mason: sixty 32-pounder cannon of 32 cwt each. (Same price as in preceding four contracts. Completed November 1846.)

18 October 1845

Junius L. Archer: sixty 32-pounder cannon of 32 cwt each. (Same price as in preceding five contracts. Completed by 29 April 1847. Archer was Clarke's successor at the Bellona Foundry. At the end of the contract there is a notation from Archer signing over any proceeds from this contract to Knap and Totten.)

14 August 1846

Joseph R. Anderson: seventy 32-pounders of 51 cwt and ten 32-pounders of 46 cwt each at $.065/pound. (There is a note on the contract indicating that the ten of 46 cwt were changed to eighteen of 42 cwt. Completed on 30 July 1847.)

17 August 1846

West Point Foundry Association: ninety 32-pounder cannon of 57 cwt. (Same price as in preceding contract. Completed on 27 April 1847.)

19 August 1846

Knap and Totten: sixty-eight 32-pounders of 32 cwt and fifty 32-pounders of 57 cwt. (Same price as in preceding two contracts. Completed 29 April 1847.)

7 September 1846

Cyrus Alger and Company: ninety 32-pounders of 57 cwt. (Completed.)

11 June 1847

Knap and Totten: thirty-nine 8-inch cannon of 53 cwt and forty 32-pounders of 57 cwt at $.065/pound. (Completed 29 September 1847.)

16 June 1847

West Point Foundry Association: ninety 32-pounders of 57 cwt each. (Same price as in preceding contract. Completed on 22 June 1849, with eighty-nine guns delivered on 8 May 1848.)

18 June 1847

Joseph R. Anderson: sixty 32-pounder cannon of 57 cwt and thirty-two 32-pounders of 51 cwt. (Same price as in preceding two contracts. Through February 1848 Anderson had delivered only fifty-five 32-pounders of 57 cwt and ten of 51 cwt. There is an entry indicating an additional order with Anderson on 5 June 1848 for thirty 32-pounders of 57 cwt, which was filled on 15 October 1848.)

14 July 1847

Junius L. Archer: 114 32-pounder cannon of 42 cwt. (Same price as in preceding three contracts. Completed in May 1849.)

17 September 1847

Cyrus Alger and Company: ninety 32-pounder cannon of 57 cwt. (Same price as in preceding four contracts. By 23 March 1849 eighty-eight guns had been delivered.)

24 July 1848
West Point Foundry Association: twelve 64-pounder cannon of 8-inch bore and 12,000 pounds each. (Same price as in preceding five contracts. Eleven were delivered on 22 June 1849, one on 9 May 1850.)

4 August 1849
West Point Foundry Association: thirty 32-pounder cannon of 57 cwt. (Same price as in preceding six contracts. Completed on 4 June 1852.)

6 August 1848
Knap and Totten: thirty 32-pounder cannon of 57 cwt. (Same price as in preceding seven contracts. Completed on 29 July 1852.)

6 August 1849
Joseph R. Anderson: thirty 32-pounder cannon of 57 cwt. (Same price as in preceding eight contracts. Completed on 1 November 1849.)

17 August 1849
Cyrus Alger and Company: thirty 32-pounder cannon of 57 cwt. (Same price as in preceding nine contracts. Completed on 25 October 1850.)

11 September 1849
Junius Archer: thirty 32-pounder cannon of 57 cwt. (Same price as in preceding ten contracts. Completed on 1 April 1850.)

21 July 1851
Robert P. Parrott: thirty-eight 8-inch cannon of 63 cwt. (Same price as in preceding eleven contracts. Completed on 4 June 1852.)

22 July 1851
Tredegar: twenty 32-pounder cannon of 57 cwt. (Same price as in preceding twelve contracts. Only fourteen delivered.)

30 July 1851
Cyrus Alger and Company: thirty 8-inch cannon of 55 cwt. (Only twenty-eight were delivered by 10 April 1852.)

2 August 1851
Junius L. Archer: thirty 32-pounder cannon of 57 cwt at $.065/pound. (Completed by 24 January 1853.)

20 December 1854
Robert P. Parrott: seven XI-inch cannon of 16,000 pounds each at $.08/pound, seven X-inch cannon of 12,000 pounds each at $.075/pound, twenty-eight IX-inch cannon of 9,000 pounds each at $.0725/pound, and eight 8-inch cannon of 63 cwt each at $.065/pound. (The seven XI-inch guns were not delivered, being replaced by subsequent orders. Additions were made to the contract so that by 8 June 1857 sixteen XI-inchers, sixteen X-inchers, thirty-four IX-inch guns, twelve 8-inch guns, and two 64-pounders of 11,900 pounds each at $.0675/pound had been delivered.)

27 December 1854
Knap and Wade: fifty IX-inch cannon of 9,000 pounds each at $.075/pound. (These were manufactured by others, twenty-five each by Parrott and Anderson.)

3 January 1855

Cyrus Alger and Company: seven XI-inch cannon of 16,000 pounds each at $.08/pound, seven X-inch cannon of 12,000 pounds each at $.075/pound, and twenty-five IX-inch cannon of 9,000 pounds each at $.0725/pound. (No note of deliveries; contract closed on 14 February 1857.)

6 February 1855

Joseph R. Anderson, Mathew Delany, Francis T. Glasgow, and William Steptoe, Richmond, Virginia: fifty IX-inch guns of 9,000 pounds at $.0725/pound.

6 August 1856

J. R. Anderson: twenty-seven IX-inch shell guns of 9,000 pounds at $.075/pound. (Twenty-seven guns were delivered on 25 August 1857, twenty-four on behalf of Knap and Wade.)

10 March 1857

Junius L. Archer: twenty-four IX-inch shell guns at $.075/pound. (Completed.)

2 May 1857

Cyrus Alger and Company: thirty IX-inch shell guns of 9,000 pounds. (Same price as in preceding contract. Thirty-one guns were delivered.)

26 April 1858

Robert P. Parrott: two X-inch shell guns of 12,000 pounds each and sixteen IX-inch shell guns of 9,000 pounds each at $.075/pound. (Ten guns were delivered in August and eight in December 1858.)

28 May 1858

Robert P. Parrott: three XI-inch guns of 15,000 pounds each. (Same price as in preceding contract. Subsequent orders with Parrott were placed on 28 June 1858 for two additional XI-inch guns and on 10 August 1858 for two X-inch guns and twelve IX-inchers at the same weights and prices.)

3 July 1858

Joseph R. Anderson: twenty IX-inch shell guns. (Same price and size as in preceding two contracts. Ten were delivered on 26 October and ten on 21 December 1858.)

19 July 1858

Cyrus Alger: thirty IX-inch shell guns. (Same size and price as in preceding three contracts. Contract completed in May 1859.)

24 November 1858

Joseph R. Anderson: twenty IX-inch guns. (Same size and price as in preceding four contracts. Ten were delivered on 12 May and ten on 13 August 1859.)

22 December 1858

Cyrus Alger: six IX-inch shell guns. (Same size and price as in preceding five contracts. Contract completed on 6 June 1859.)

12 April 1860

Joseph R. Anderson: nine IX-inch guns. (Same size and price as in preceding six contracts. Nine guns were delivered on 12 January 1861.)

16 April 1860

Robert P. Parrott: nine IX-inch guns. (Same size and price as in preceding seven contracts. Completed on 29 August 1860.)

6 September 1860*

Robert P. Parrott: eight IX-inch guns. (Same size and price as in preceding eight contracts. Seven were delivered on 16 January and one on 6 March 1861.)

* This is the last contract before the Civil War. After April 1861, the records largely refer to deliveries from founders.

Notes

Chapter I

1. Nicholas, *Royal Navy* 1: 107. For a discussion of Greek fire see Brooks, "Naval Armament in the Thirteenth Century," 116–19, and Hall, "A Note on Military Pyrotechnics," 374–78. For a discussion of shipboard castles see Howarth, *Sovereign of the Seas*, 37.

2. Brooks, "Naval Armament in the Thirteenth Century," 127–28.

3. Nicolas, *Royal Navy* 1: 186. Clowes repeated Nicolas's error in *The Royal Navy: A History,* published in 1897, as did Brackenbury in "Ancient Cannon in Europe," 291. T. F. Tout asserted that the document on which Nicolas relied dated from the early fifteenth century (*Firearms in England,* 18–19). See also Alan Moore, "Accounts and Inventories of John Starlying, Clerk of the King's Ships to Henry IV," 20–26.

4. *The Cannon Hall: Guide to the Royal Danish Arsenal Museum,* 6. See also Anderson, *The Sailing-Ship,* 117, and Nicolas, *Royal Navy* 1: 185.

5. Anderson, *The Sailing-Ship,* 117. One of these, the *Christopher (Xprofer),* carried three iron guns and five chambers for them. She also had one hand gun, ten bows, and six sheaves of arrows (Howarth, *Sovereign of the Seas,* 60).

6. Cipolla, *Guns and Sails,* 39–46, and Lewis, "Armada Guns: Section VII," 116.

7. Oppenheim, *The Administration of the Royal Navy,* 115.

8. Cipolla, *Guns and Sails,* 65.

9. William Eldred, *The Gunners Glasse,* 1646, quoted in Hogg, *English Artillery,* 13.

10. Corbett, *Drake and the Tudor Navy,* 362. For further discussion of early gun types, see pp. 362–78. Also see Laughton, "Early Tudor Ship-Guns," 242–85, and Lewis, "Armada Guns: Section VI," 100–107.

11. Gulieimotti, *Storia della Marina Pontifica,* 166.

12. William Monson, *Naval Tracts: In Six Books: The Whole from the Original Manuscript,* in Churchill, *A Collection of Voyages,* 313–14. Weights and sizes vary considerably for each of these types (see Perrin, "Early Naval Ordnance," 51–52). Contemporary tables seem close to Monson's. See also a table of ordnance of 1574, James Sheriffe's table (1592), one of Thomas Smith's (1628), Robert Norton's (1643), and William Eldred's (1646), all in Hogg, *English Artillery,* 21 and 26–29.

13. Robert Norton, *The Gunner, Showing the Whole Practyse of Artillerie* (1628), quoted in Garbett, *Naval Gunnery,* 7.

14. Cipolla, *Guns and Sails,* 81.

CHAPTER II

1. These, and all subsequent dimensions, are for 1821. They are drawn from a document of that year in National Archives, Record Group 45, BG subject file, "Proportional Dimensions of Gun Furniture by the Caliber and Length of the Gun." Other comments are drawn from Ward, *Elementary Instruction,* 97–98, and Bureau of Ordnance, *Ordnance Instructions for the United States Navy,* 1860, 34, 44–52, and 155–57.

2. For a detailed description of the manufacture of gunpowder in the mid-nineteenth century see Simpson, *A Treatise on Ordnance and Naval Gunnery,* 148–90.

3. Muller, *A Treatise of Artillery,* 201.

4. Sir William Congreve, *An Elementary Treatise,* 15.

5. Jeffers, *A Concise Treatise,* 141.

6. National Archives, Record Group 45, entry 464.

7. Beauchant, *The Naval Gunner,* 10.

8. Ward, *Elementary Instruction,* 120.

9. This is a cursory treatment of the sequence of firing. Much more detailed, and differing, descriptions for the period around 1815 are to be found in Falconer and Burney, *A New Universal Dictionary,* 141–42; Simmons, *The Sea-Gunner's Vade-Mecum,* 146–49; and Tousard, *American Artillerist's Companion,* 395–405. For the period around 1850 see Garbett, *Naval Gunnery,* 27–30; Jeffers, *A Concise Treatise,* 166–67 and 227–35; Douglas, *A Treatise on Naval Gunnery,* 454–57; and Bureau of Ordnance, *Ordnance Instructions,* 1860, 454–57.

10. Beauchant, *The Naval Gunner,* 31.

11. For a discussion of this engagement see Robison, *A History of Naval Tactics,* 494–505; Robertson, *The Evolution of Naval Armament,* 154–56; Douglas, *A Treatise on Naval Gunnery,* 370 and 544–52; and Padfield, *Broke and the Shannon.*

12. Robison, *A History of Naval Tactics,* 503.

13. Jeffers, *A Concise Treatise,* 258. See also Bureau of Ordnance, *Ordnance Instructions,* 1860, 52–54.

14. National Archives, Record Group 74, entry 159.

CHAPTER III

1. This is a rather simplistic explanation of the process. See the fifty drawings by Jan Verbruggen illustrating founding and machining techniques in Jackson and de Beer, *Eighteenth Century Gunfounding.* See also Monge, *Description de l'art de fabriquer les canons,* and Tousard, *American Artillerist's Companion,* 2: 516–51.

2. Tousard, *American Artillerist's Companion,* 2: 550.

3. Ward, *Elementary Instruction,* 54–58.

4. Barck and Lefler, *Colonial America,* 341–42.

5. Bishop, *A History of American Manufacturers,* 486.

6. Navy Department, *Naval Documents of the American Revolution* 3: 1285.

7. Brewington, "American Naval Guns," 11–13.

8. Letter of 19 November 1808, in National Archives, Record Group 45, M-124-1808-VI, 85–86.

9. *Ibid.*

10. *Calender of Virginia State Papers* 8: 456, quoted in Bruce, *Virginia Iron Manufacture,* 114.

11. Letter from Secretary of State Timothy Pickering to James and Ebenezer Watson, navy agents in New York, 14 November 1798, in Navy Department, *Naval Documents Related to the Quasi-War,* November 1798–March 1799, 22.

12. Navy Department, *Naval Documents Related to the Quasi-War,* January 1800–May 1800, 291–92. For a discussion of this see Smelser, *The Congress Founds the Navy,* 139–40.

13. National Archives, Record Group 45, letter book 1: 407.

14. Navy Department, *Naval Documents Related to the Quasi-War,* November 1798–March 1799, 207.

15. *Ibid.,* April 1798 to July 1799, 68.

16. National Archives, Record Group 45, general letters book 2: 402.

17. Navy Department, *Naval Documents Related to the Quasi-War between the United States and France,* January 1800–May 1800, 77.

18. Davis felt this was the case; he suggested that it may well have been at the behest of President Thomas Jefferson that Foxall made the move ("The Old Cannon Foundry above Georgetown," 24 and 31).

19. *American State Papers,* Class III, Finance 2: 429.

20. From 1809 to 1813, 235 iron cannon were produced: 13 4-pounders, 172 6-pounders, and 50 12-pounders. In the period from 1809 to 1819, it cost approximately $51.75 to produce a 6-pounder at the Virginia Manufactory—$24.00 for half a ton of pig iron, $3.75 for twenty-five bushels of coal, $1.25 for sand and other materials, $16.00 for labor, $4.67 for seven pounds of powder for proof, $0.75 for three shot, also used in proving the piece, and $1.33 for japanning the barrel (Cromwell, *The Virginia Manufactory,* 133 and 136).

21. *American State Papers,* Class V, Military Affairs 1: 215–17, and 6: 82–91.

22. National Archives, Record Group 45, M-124-1806, III, 123. In July 1806, Hughes responded favorably to a Navy Department request that he cast fifty 32-pounders but required a higher price to offset an increase in the cost of pig iron. He added that the last 32-pounders he had cast for the navy had been praised by naval officers and could not be improved on except by a reduction in weight. They weighed 60 cwt and were 18 bore-diameters long. He thought they might be reduced to 55 to 56 cwt on the same proportions and made even lighter if their length was reduced. But, he noted, "less than 18 diameters has been condemned by the officers I have heard speak on the subject." If a reduction in length to 14 or 15 diameters was desired, the guns could be made to weigh 48 to 50 cwt. They would stand the highest proof, but as Hughes observed, " . . . They would not be thought as handsome or serviceable."

On 7 August 1807, the navy authorized Hughes to produce fifty 24-pounders and fifty 32-pounders and inquired about terms for delivery of a considerable quantity of round shot, double round shot, and stands of grape and cannister. Hughes noted that the latest 24-pounders he had cast, on a draft approved by Commodore Rodgers, were 9 feet in length, but if those just contracted for were made 18 diameters in length as proposed, they would be only 8 feet 3 inches, only 3 inches longer than the first short 24-pounders he had cast and which had been condemned for being too short (National Archives, Record Group 45, M-124, 1807-III, 104).

23. National Archives, Record Group 45, letter of 28 June 1808, M-124-1808-IV, 119.

24. *Ibid.,* letter of 29 August 1808, V, 88.

25. *Ibid.,* E235, II, 210–11.

26. *Ibid.,* entry 464. Bellona continued to have difficulties with its guns. In August 1842, the army subjected to proof sixteen 32-pounders and four 42-pounders (pattern of 1840). Four 32-pounders and three 42-pounders burst during the proving. As the percentage was so high, the remaining guns were also rejected. It was found on inspection, however, that a number had been cast of "bad iron." Those found to be of good metal were reproved with a powder charge "equal to one half of the weight of the shot, one shot and two wads." The eleven 32-pounders of good iron passed proof and were accepted by the army. Apparently all the 42-pounders were of bad iron (Record Group 74, communication from the Ordnance Office to the Bureau of Ordnance and Hydrography, 14 May 1844, entry 159).

27. In July 1826, a number of "medium" 24-pounders were proved at WPFA, presumably those of the April contract. The inspector, A. Wadsworth, wrote to the Navy Board expressing doubt as to whether the 24-pounders he was then proving were part of the Gradual Increase Act and whether they should be marked GI, as his other guns had been. There is a pencil notation at the bottom of the letter, presumably the board's, that they were "for sloops to be marked S" (Record Group 45, letter of Wadsworth to Bainbridge, 1 October 1826, entry 464).

28. Dew, *Ironmaker to the Confederacy,* 12. Bruce gives a figure of 1,200 cannon cast for the government (Bruce, *Virginia Iron Manufacture,* 198).

29. National Archives, Record Group 45, entry 464.

30. The *Quarterly Trade Circular* (Pittsburgh), quoted in *Scientific American* 11, no. 11 (10 Sept. 1864), 165.

31. Dew, *Ironmaker to the Confederacy,* 50. See pp. 40–45 for details of Anderson's opposition.

32. Dahlgren, *Memoir of John A. Dahlgren,* 172.

33. *Ibid.,* 173–74.

34. Testimony of Charles Knap in U.S. Congress, *Report of the Joint Committee,* 86. The date given by Knap for the meeting with Morris is too early, however; the first regular contracts for the new Dahlgren IX- and XI-inch guns were not let until 1854 (National Archives, Record Group 74, entry 157, 136).

35. The major points were as follows: Sufficient metal for all the guns was to be collected before any guns were made. The guns were to endure one thousand service rounds. To determine the strength of all the guns, the bureau had to be satisfied that all had been produced under the same conditions (quantity of fuel, temperature of pits and molds, time of cooling, etc.). The bureau would not determine tensile strength and metal density for the founder, but "undue departures and variations from the standard" would have a negative influence on the bureau. The iron was to be of approved quality, smelted with charcoal, and could not be used for any other purpose (this included gun heads as well as parts of all other castings). The form of the casting was to "conform directly to that assigned by the red lines on the draft of the IX-inch gun, being at the plane of the muzzle sixteen inches in diameter and connected by rightlines with the diameter of the gun." After casting, metal should be cooled as slowly as possible. After inspection, one of the twenty-four IX-inch guns would be selected for ordinary, and then for extreme, proof; the extreme proof would consist of one thousand service rounds (10 pounds of powder and one sabotted shell of 72 pounds with no wads, with the gun fired from a pendulum). If the gun endured a thousand rounds it would be paid for. It not, the bureau would not accept the other guns in the lot and they would be broken up. Particular care was to be taken to avoid previous defects, such as brittle metal for the sights, and "to make [the] dimensions quite full." If the inspecting officer had any doubts about the guns, he was to refer to the chief of the bureau, whose decision would be final.

36. The Trenton Locomotive and Machine Manufacturing Company may have made three XI-inch guns for the navy. In addition, both Charles T. Ames of Chicopee, Massachusetts, and Cyrus Alger produced boat howitzers. Dew puts Northern ordnance production during the Civil War at some eight thousand pieces (*Ironmaker to the Confederacy,* 290).

37. Mallet, "Work of the Ordnance Bureau," 145.

38. Daniel and Gunter, *Confederate Cannon Foundries,* 93.

Chapter IV

1. Miller, *Sea of Glory,* 110–11.

2. Knox, *A History of the United States Navy,* 5–6; Maclay, *A History of American Privateers,* viii; and Allen, *A Naval History* 2: 614.

3. Stephenson, "The Supply of Gunpowder," 277.

4. James Breck Perkins, *France in the American Revolution,* 107.

5. Miller, *Sea of Glory,* 193.

6. By September 1777, Beaumarchais had already shipped to America five million livres worth of cargo.

7. Clark, *George Washington's Navy,* 35.

8. *Ibid.,* 39.

9. Harold L. Peterson, preface to the reprint of Muller, *A Treatise of Artillery.*

10. Tousard, *American Artillerist's Companion,* 1: 193.

11. Simpson, *A Treatise on Ordnance and Naval Gunnery,* 127.

12. Muller, *A Treatise of Artillery,* 97–98.

13. Bolander, "The Introduction of Shells and Shell-Guns in the United States Navy," 108.

14. John Rodgers of the Board of Navy Commissioners, in National Archives, Record Group 45, entry 464.

15. Chapelle, *The History of the American Sailing Navy,* 92.

16. Report of Secretary of War Henry Knox, 2 December 1794, quoted in Clark et al., *The Navy* 1: 34.

17. Mackenzie, *Life of Stephen Decatur,* 157.

18. Chapelle, *The History of the American Sailing Navy,* 172–73.
19. Tousard, *American Artillerist's Companion* 1: 193.
20. Falconer and Burney, *A New Universal Dictionary,* 174 and 184.
21. *Ibid.,* 29.
22. Tousard, *American Artillerist's Companion* 1: introduction, XX.
23. National Archives, Record Group 45, entry 4, p. 5, and entry 464.
24. *Ibid.,* entry 4, p. 25; and Navy Department, *Naval Documents Related to the Quasi-War,* January 1800 to May 1800, 202.
25. Letter from British minister to the United States Roberton Liston to Foreign Secretary William Grenville, 8 June 1798, Public Record Office R05, 25A.
26. Secretary of the Navy Stoddert, who wanted carronades for the quarterdeck of the sloop *General Greene,* noted, "It is impossible I believe, to get the right kind from the fall importations" (letter to Gibbs and Channing, 24 November 1798, in National Archives, Record Group 45, I, 407. The first record of actual imports refers to a shipment of guns to Philadelphia in the *Connecticut.*
27. National Archives, Record Group 74, entry 174. The *Congress* was broken up in 1836.
28. Letter of 9 November 1798 in National Archives, Record Group 45, general letters book, I, 384–87.
29. Ward, *Elementary Instruction in Naval Ordnance and Gunnery,* 34, 39.
30. Robert Simmons, *The Sea-Gunner's Vade-Mecum* 2: 131.
31. James, *A Full and Correct Account of the . . . Late War,* appendix, no. 51.
32. Dahlgren, *Shells and Shell Guns,* 8–10.
33. Dahlgren, *Report on the Thirty-two Pounder,* 99–107.

CHAPTER V

1. Douglas, *A Treatise on Naval Gunnery,* 361.
2. *American Ships of the Line,* 22. Charles Stewart, commanding the frigate *Constitution,* gave slightly different figures for the same period: ships of the line of seventy-four guns had twenty-eight 42-pounders on the lower gun deck, thirty 24-pounders on the upper gun deck, sixteen 42-pounder carronades on the quarter deck, eight 42-pounder carronades on the forecastle, two 24-pounders on the forecastle, and four 68-pounder carronades on the poop. This meant a total of eighty-eight guns, or forty-four in broadside with 1,612 pounds of shot. Frigates of fifty guns had thirty 24-pounder long guns on the gun deck, fourteen 32-pounder carronades on the quarterdeck and six 32-pounder carronades on the forecastle. Stewart proposed keeping the same armament for ships of the line and frigates of fifty. Frigates rated as thirty-twos, however, would be armed with twenty-six 18-pounders on the gun deck and sixteen 24-pounder carronades on the quarterdeck and forecastle, for a total of forty-two guns. Corvettes rated at sixteen guns would have eighteen 32-pounder carronades and two long 12-pounders for a total of twenty guns.
3. The Rush-Bagot agreement of April 1817 provided for disarmament on the lakes, limiting the naval forces of Britain and the United States to four single-gun vessels of 100 tons each (one each on Lakes Ontario and Champlain and two on the upper lakes). It also prohibited new construction. As a result of this agreement, cannon and shot were to be removed from the lakes. From 10 June through 15 September 1825, the following amounts were removed in two shipments (*American State Papers,* Class VI, 4: 163):

Cannon	12-pdr	6	15
	18-pdr	25	35
	24-pdr	41	72
	32-pdr	68	68
Carronades	18-pdr	2	10
	24-pdr	14	16
	32-pdr	44	69
	42-pdr	111	114
	68-pdr	1	1

Shot	12-pdr	—	2,466
	18-pdr	3,937	6,925
	24-pdr	18,005	18,707
	32-pdr	6,639	6,639
	42-pdr	2,676	2,676
	68-pdr	5	5

4. Roosevelt, *The Naval War,* 65.

5. Straith, *Treatise on Fortification and Artillery* 2: 111.

6. Letter to Secretary of War John Armstrong of 20 March 1814, in National Archives, Record Group 74, Letters from Navy Department of Secretary of War, etc., June 20, 1798 to June 15, 1824, pp. 96–97.

7. In 1834 her armament was ninety guns: on the lower deck, thirty-two 42-pounders; on the main deck, thirty-two 32-pounders; and on the spar deck, twenty-four 42-pounders and two 32-pounders. In 1846 she was armed as follows: on the lower deck, four 8-inch chambered cannon; on the main deck, four 8-inch chambered cannon and twenty-eight 32-pounders; and on the spar deck, two 32-pounder guns, one 9-pounder, and twenty-two 42-pounder carronades (National Archives, Record Group 74, entry 174, and *American Ships of the Line,* 22–40).

8. *Ibid.* In 1845 the *Ohio* was armed as follows: on the spar deck, two 32-pounder long guns and twenty-four 42-pounder carronades; on the main deck, thirty-two 32-pounder long guns; and on the lower deck, thirty-two 42-pounder long guns. In January 1847 the armament was again changed, as follows: on the spar deck, four 8-inch shell guns, four 32-pounders, and twelve 32-pounders; on the main deck, four 8-inch shell guns and twenty-eight 32-pounders; and on the lower deck, four 8-inch shell guns and twenty-eight 42-pounders.

9. *Ibid.* In 1845 the *North Carolina* was armed as follows: on the spar deck, two 32-pounders, twenty-four 42-pounder carronades, and two 9-pounders (temporarily on board as signal guns), one 6-pounder carronade, and one boat gun; on the main deck, four 8-inch chambered cannon reamed up from 42-pounders and twenty-four 32-pounders; and on the lower deck, thirty-two 42-pounder guns.

10. *Ibid.* In 1846 a Bureau of Ordnance register listed the *Pennsylvania*'s ordnance as follows: on the spar deck, two 9-pounder cannon and one small bronze swivel; on the main deck, four 8-inch, 63–64 cwt, chambered cannon and thirty-two 32-pounders; on the middle deck, four 8-inch chambered cannon and thirty GI 32-pounders; and on the lower deck, four 8-inch chambered cannon and twenty-eight 32-pounders.

11. *American State Papers*, Class VI, 1: 788–97.

12. Dahlgren, *Shells and Shell Guns,* 286–87 and 369.

13. Extract from journal of Commodore Charles Morris, in National Archives, Record Group 45, BG file.

14. *Ibid.*

15. U.S. Congress, "Heavy Ordnance," 30.

16. *Niles' Weekly Register,* 2 March 1844.

17. National Archives, Record Group 74, entry 159.

CHAPTER VI

1. Millis, *Arms and Men,* 77; Bennett, *The Monitor and the Navy*, 21–22; Emmons, *The Navy of the United States,* 31; and Morison, *Old Bruin,* 127–29.

2. Morison, *Old Bruin,* 128.

3. Bennett, *The Monitor and the Navy,* 27.

4. Simmons, *Ideas as to the Effect of Heavy Ordnance,* 2.

5. Dahlgren, *Memoir of John A. Dahlgren,* 87.

6. W. H. Parker, *Recollections of a Naval Officer,* quoted in Paullin, *Paullin's History,* 181.

7. James, *A Full and Correct Account of the Chief Naval Occurrences of the Late War,* 5.

8. Lewis, "The Ambiguous Columbiads," 111.

9. *Ibid.*

10. Mackenzie, *Life of Stephen Decatur,* 338–39.

11. They had raised vent fields, no breeching rings, and their trunnions were located on the centerline of the bore. Bore diameter was 7.35 inches with an 8-inch chamber; bore length was

54 inches. The extreme length was 75.5 inches, and from the end of the knob to the fore part of the trunnions it was 41.7 inches. The diameter immediately before the trunnions was 18 inches, the extreme diameter at the breech, 21 inches, and the extreme diameter at the muzzle, 16.2 inches. The diameter of the trunnions was 6.9 inches and their length was 6.2 inches. The two guns weighed 35-2-9 and 35-1-1 cwt.

12. Maclay, *A History of the United States Navy* 3:18.

13. Letter of 27 August 1841, in National Archives, Record Group 45, entry 464.

14. Sixteen of these guns weighed between 65-1-26 and 68-2-7 cwt and had a length of 9 feet 1 inch.

15. Douglas, *A Treatise on Naval Gunnery,* 302.

16. Navy Department, Bureau of Ordnance, *Ordnance Instructions,* 1860, 4.

17. Letter from John A. Dahlgren in National Archives, Record Group 74, entry 142.

18. Dahlgren, *Memoir of John A. Dahlgren,* 174.

19. *Ibid.,* 179–80.

20. In drawing up a list of ordnance supplies for the *Plymouth,* Dahlgren requested rifled muskets of his design. These were struck out of the initial appropriation but later authorized and tested aboard the *Plymouth.* An 1864 report from the chief of ordnance noted there were then in service 10,000 of these muzzle-loading, 0.69-caliber "Plymouth" muskets.

21. Dahlgren, *Memoir of John A. Dahlgren,* 200.

22. Muller, *A Treatise of Artillery,* 98.

23. Dahlgren, *Memoir of John A. Dahlgren,* 228.

24. Testimony of Captain James Alden, in Congress, *Report of the Joint Committee,* 170.

CHAPTER VII

1. Brandt, *Gunnery Catechism,* 112.

2. Dahlgren, *Memoir of John A. Dahlgren,* 258–59.

3. Edwin Olmstead, letter to author, 18 November 1978; James Hazlett and Edwin Olmstead, Dahlgren weapons inventory; and Dahlgren, *Memoir of John A. Dahlgren,* 295 and 311. Ripley gives the new X-inch gun's weight at 16,500 pounds (*Artillery and Ammunition of the Civil War,* 101).

4. Ward, *Elementary Instruction,* 149.

5. Simpson, *A Treatise on Ordnance and Naval Gunnery,* 418.

6. Dahlgren, *Memoir of John A. Dahlgren,* 301.

7. By the Civil War, breeching for broadside guns was not to be less than 7.5 inches or more than 8 inches in circumference, except for the IX-inch gun, where it was to be 9 inches. In 1863, breeching size for the IX-inch gun was increased to 9.5 inches and to 10.5 inches for the XI-incher. Breeching was not to be covered or blackened. By 1860, the Bureau of Ordnance specified that tackle for U.S. Navy guns was to be made of manila or other pliable rope, and that it could not be blackened. Tackle was 2.25 to 2.5 inches for smaller guns and 3 inches for larger.

Gun tackle blocks were to have pins of hardened copper, turned smooth, and sheaves of lignum vitae. Blocks for 3-inch falls were to be 10 inches long, those for 2.5-inch falls, 9 inches, and those for 2.25-inch falls, 8 inches. Metal blocks with nibs designed by Dahlgren had been found successful and would replace the old wooden blocks. Hooks for the gun tackle blocks were not less than 1.5 inches in diameter at the bend for heavy, 1.25 inches for light, broadside guns (Navy Department, Bureau of Ordnance, *Ordnance Instructions for the United States Navy,* 1860, 150). Dahlgren noted in 1848 while test-firing the 32-pounder of 32 cwt that its breeching was the "usual kind" and 7.75 inches in diameter (National Archives, Record Group 74, Records of the Bureau of Ordnance, section I, "Report on firing of 32-pounder gun," 22). It is believed that the reference here and in Atkinson and Clarke is really to circumference. Edwin Rich reached the same conclusion in "The Sizes of Gun Tackles and Breechings."

8. Quoted in Garbett, *Naval Gunnery,* 32–33. See also Lloyd and Hadcock, *Artillery,* 23.

9. Congress, *Report of the Joint Committee on the Conduct of the War,* 89.

10. Simpson, *A Treatise on Ordnance and Naval Gunnery,* 423–26, and Lossing, *History of American Industries and Arts,* 236. Edwin Olmstead documents large Parrotts as being cast by Rodman, with "water/core" muzzle stamping on 6.4-inch navy Parrotts received at the New York Navy Yard as early as June 1864 (letter from Olmstead to the author, 18 November 1984).

11. Simpson, *A Treatise on Ordnance and Naval Gunnery,* 423–24.
12. Holley, *A Treatise on Ordnance and Armor,* 54.
13. Report of 30 June 1865, in National Archives, Record Group 74, entry 191.
14. Congress, *Report of the Joint Committee on the Conduct of War,* 168–69.
15. Testimony of Admiral John A. Dahlgren, in *ibid.,* 122.
16. Dahlgren, *Memoir of John A. Dahlgren,* 226.
17. *Ibid.,* 245–46.
18. *Ibid.,* 249.
19. Ward, *Elementary Instruction in Naval Ordnance and Gunnery,* 154.
20. Simpson, *A Treatise on Ordnance and Naval Gunnery,* 414–15.
21. Brooke, *John M. Brooke,* 270.
22. *Ibid.,* 262–64. George Brooke gives three patterns for the 7-inch Brooke, but Edwin Olmstead noted that the Brooke report drawings show four for the 7-inch gun (letter from Olmstead to the author, 25 August 1985).
23. Dew, *Ironmaker to the Confederacy,* 111. Navy smoothbores cast during the war by Tredegar included 12- and 24-pounder howitzers in bronze, 32-pounders, IX-inch Dahlgrens, and 10- and 11-inch banded guns. Rifles were 6-pounders (made of iron?), 12-pounders made of bronze, rifled 32-pounders, and 6.4-, 7-, and 8-inch Brookes (Dew, 324).
24. Dahlgren, *Memoir of John A. Dahlgren,* 301–2.

Bibliography

Books

Allen, Gardner, W. *A Naval History of the American Revolution.* 2 vols. Boston: Houghton Mifflin, 1913.

American Secretaries of the Navy. Vol. 1, *1775–1913.* Edited by Paolo E. Coletta. Annapolis, Maryland: Naval Institute Press, 1980.

American Ships of the Line. Washington, D.C.: Naval History Division, Navy Department, 1969.

Anderson, R. C. *Oared Fighting Ships.* London: Percival Marshall, 1962.

Anderson, Robert. *Cut the Rigging, and Proposals for the Improvement of Great Artillery.* London: Robert Morden, 1691.

———. *To Hit a Mark as Well Upon an Ascent and Descent as Upon the Plain of the Horizon . . .* London: Robert Morden, 1691.

Anderson, Romola and R. C. *The Sailing-Ship: Six Thousand Years of History.* London: George G. Harrap, 1926.

Archibald, E. H. H. *The Wooden Fighting Ship in the Royal Navy,* A.D. *897–1860.* London: Blandford Press, 1968.

Atkinson and Clarke, *The Naval Pocket Gunner; or, Compendium of Information Relating to Sea Service Gunnery, Including Proportions of Guns and Ordnance Storés for Every Class of Ships and Vessels in the British Navy.* London: Robert Scholey, 1814.

Barck, Oscar T. and Hugh Talmage Lefler. *Colonial America.* New York: Macmillan, 1958.

Barrett, Lieutenant Edward. *Gunnery Instructions, Simplified for the Volunteer Officers of the U.S. Navy; with Hints to Executive and Other Officers.* New York: D. Van Nostrand, 1862.

Bathe, Greville. *Ship of Destiny: A Record of the U.S. Steam Frigate* Merrimack, *1855–1862.* St. Augustine, Florida, 1951.

Battles and Leaders of the Civil War. Edited by Robert U. Johnson and C. C. Buell. 4 vols. New York: Century, 1867–88.

Baxter, James Phonney. *The Introduction of the Ironclad Warship.* Cambridge, Massachusetts: Harvard University Press, 1933.

Beauchant, Theophilus S. *The Naval Gunner.* London: Hurst, Chance, 1829.

Belidor, Bernard Forest de. *Le Bombardier français, ou, nouvelle methode de jetter les bombes avec précision.* Paris: Impr. royale, 1731.

Bennett, F. M. *The Monitor and the Navy Under Steam.* New York: Houghton Mifflin, 1900.
Benton, Colonel J. G. Brevet. *A Course of Instruction in Ordnance and Gunnery: Prepared for the Use of the Cadets of the United States Military Academy.* 3rd ed. New York: D. Van Nostrand, 1867.
Bining, Arthur C. *Pennsylvania Iron Manufacture in the Eighteenth Century.* Vol. 4, in *Publications of the Pennsylvania Historical Commission.* Harrisburg, Pennsylvania, 1938.
Biringucci, Vannuccio. *The Pirotechnia of Vannoccio Biringuccio.* Translated with an introduction and notes by Cyril Stanley Smith and Martha Teach Gnudi. New York: The American Institute of Mining and Metallurgical Engineers, 1942.
Birnie, Rogers, Jr. *Gun Making in the United States.* Washington: GPO, 1907.
Bishop, J. Leander. *A History of American Manufactures from 1608 to 1860.* Vol. 1. 3rd ed. Philadelphia: Edward Young, 1868.
Boismele, Jean Baptiste Torchet de. *Histoire General de Marine.* 3 vols. Amsterdam, 1754–58.
Boudriot, Jean. *Le Vaisseau de 74 canons.* 4 vols. Grenoble: Editions des quatre seigneurs, 1973–77.
Bourne, William. *The Arte of Shooting in Great Ordnaunce; Contayning Very Necessary Matters of all Sorts of Seruitoures Eyther by Sea or by Lande.* London: Imprinted for Thomas Woodcocke, 1587.
Brady, William N. *The Kedge-Anchor; or, Young Sailors' Assistant.* 3rd ed. New York, 1848.
Brandt, John D. *Gunnery Catechism as Applied to the Service of Naval Ordnance Adapted to the Latest Official Regulations, and Approved by the Bureau of Ordnance, Navy Department.* New York: D. Van Nostrand, 1864.
Brodie, Bernard. *Sea Power in the Machine Age.* Princeton: Princeton University Press, 1943.
Brooke, George M., Jr. *John M. Brooke, Naval Scientist and Educator.* Charlottesville, Virginia: University Press of Virginia, 1980.
Bruce, Kathleen. *Virginia Iron Manufacture in The Slave Era.* New York: The Century Company, 1930.
Buchnern, J. S. *Theoria et praxis artilleriae.* Nuremberg, 1682.
Buckner, Lieutenant William P. *Calculated Tables of Ranges for Navy and Army Guns, with a method of Finding the Distance of an Object at Sea.* New York: D. Van Nostrand, 1865.
Campbell, R. H. *Carron Company.* Edinburgh: Oliver and Boyd, 1961.
Canfield, Eugene B. *Civil War Naval Ordnance.* Naval History Division, Navy Department. Washington: GPO, 1969.
The Cannon Hall: Guide to the Royal Danish Arsenal Museum. Copenhagen: Royal Artillery Museum, 1948.
Catalogue of the Museum of Artillery in the Rotunda at Woolwich. Part 1, *Ordnance.* London: Her Majesty's Stationery Office, 1963.
Channing, Edward. *A History of the United States.* Vol. 3, *The American Revolution, 1761–1780.* New York: Macmillan, n.d.
Chapelle, Howard I. *The History of the American Sailing Navy: The Ships and Their Development.* New York: Bonanza Books, n.d.
Chapman, Fredrik Henrik af. *Architectura navalis mercatoria.* Magdeburg: Robert Loef, 1769.
Charpentier, Francois E. A. *Essai sur le materiel de l'artillerie de nos navires de guerre.* Paris: Bachelier, 1845.
Chatterton, Edward Kebie. *Ships and Ways of Other Days.* Philadelphia: J. B. Lippincott, 1913.
Church, William Conant. *The Life of John Ericson.* 2 vols. New York: Scribner's, 1897.
Churchill, Awnsham, comp. *A Collection of Voyages and Travels.* 3rd ed. London: Henry Lintot and John Osborn, 1732.
Cipolla, Carlo M. *Guns and Sails in the Early Phase of European Expansion, 1400–1700.* London: Collins, 1965.
Clark, George R., William O. Stevens, Carroll S. Alden, and Herman F. Kraft. *The Navy, 1775–1909.* Baltimore: The Lord Baltimore Press, 1910.
Clark, William Bell. *George Washington's Navy, Being an Account of His Excellency's Fleet in New England Waters.* Baton Rouge: Louisiana State University Press, 1980.
Clowes, William Laird. *The Royal Navy: A History From the Earliest Times to the Present.* Vols. 2 and 3. London: Sampson Low, Marston, 1898.

Coggins, Jack. *Ships and Seamen of the American Revolution.* Harrisburg: Stackpole Books, 1969.

Collado, Luis. *Pratica manual de artilleria.* Milan: Pablo Gotardo Poncio, 1592.

Confederate Military History. Edited by General Clement A. Evans. Vol. 12. Atlanta, Georgia: Confederate Publishing, 1899.

Congreve, Sir William. *An Elementary Treatise on the Mounting of Naval Ordnance: Shewing the True Principles of Construction for the Carriages of Every Species of Ordnance, so as to Obtain the Power of Working the Heaviest Metal with the Fewest Hands; with the Least Possible Strain to the Ship; and with Reference to Every Other Desideratum which can Possibly Enter into the Combination: Demonstrated by a Variety of Diagrams and Copper Plates.* London: J. Egerton, 1811.

Corbett, Julian S. *Drake and the Tudor Navy, with a History of the Rise of England as a Maritime Power.* New York: Franklin, 1965.

———. *The Campaign of Trafalgar.* London: Longmans, Green, 1919.

Cromwell, Giles. *The Virginia Manufactory of Arms.* Charlottesville: University Press of Virginia, 1975.

Dahlgren, John A. *A Few Hints to Captains of the New IX. Inch Shell Guns.* Boston: Printed for the Bureau of Ordnance and Hydrography by Ticknor and Fields, 1856.

———. *Form of Exercise and Manuvre for the Boat-Howitzers of the U.S. Navy.* Philadelphia: A. Hart, 1852.

———. *Ordnance Memoranda: Naval Percussion Locks and Primers, Particularly Those of the United States.* Philadelphia: A. Hart, 1853.

———. *Shells and Shell Guns.* Philadelphia: King and Baird, 1856.

———. *System of Boat Armament in the United States Navy: Reported to Commodore Charles Morris, Chief of Bureau of Ordnance and Hydrography.* Philadelphia: A. Hart, 1852.

Dahlgren, Madeleine Vinton. *Memoir of John A. Dahlgren.* New York: Charles L. Webster, 1891.

Dalafield, Richard. *The Art of War in Europe in 1854, 1855, and 1856.* Washington: G. W. Bowman, 1860.

Daniel, Larry J. and Biley W. Gunter. *Confederate Cannon Foundries.* Union, Tennessee: Pioneer Press, 1977.

Davis, William C. *Duel Between the First Ironclads.* New York: Doubleday, 1975.

Dew, Charles B. *Ironmaker to the Confederacy: Joseph R. Anderson and the Tredegar Iron Works.* New Haven, Connecticut: Yale University Press, 1966.

Dickinson, Henry W. *Robert Fulton, Engineer and Artist: His Life and Works.* Reprint of 1913 edition. Freeport, New York: Books for Libraries Press, 1971.

Douglas, General Sir Howard. *A Treatise on Naval Gunnery.* Original edition published in 1819. 3rd ed., revised. London: John Murray, 1851.

———. *On Naval Warfare with Steam.* 2nd ed. London: J. Murray, 1860.

Duane, William. *A Military Dictionary; or, Explanation of the Several Systems of Discipline of Different Kinds of Troops, Infantry, Artillery, and Cavalry; the Principles of Fortification, and all the Modern Improvements in Science of Tactics: Comprising the Pocket Gunner, or Little Bombardier; the Military Regulations of the United States; . . . the Technical Terms and Phrases of the Art of War in the French Language, Particularly Adapted to the Use of the Military Instructions of the United States.* Philadelphia: William Duane, 1810.

Dupin, Charles. *Voyages dans la Grande-Bretagne, entrepris relativement aux services publics de la guerre, de la marine, et des ponts et chausées, en 1816, 1817, 1818 et 1819.* 6 vols. and atlas (3 vols.). Paris: Bachelier, 1826–29.

Emmons, George F. *The Navy of the United States: From the Commencement, 1775 to 1853; with a Brief History of Each Vessel's Service and Fate as Appears upon Record.* Washington: Gideon, 1853.

Entick, John. *A New Naval History: or, Compleat View of the British Marine.* London: R. Manby, 1757.

Essenwein, August Ottomar von. *Quellen zur Geschichte der Feuerwaffen: Facsimiliette Nachbildungen alter Originalzeichnungen, Miniaturen, Hoizschnitte und Kupferstiche, nebst auf Nahmen alter original Waffen und Modelle.* F. A. Brockhaus, 1872.

Falconer, William. *An Universal Dictionary of the Marine: or, A Copious Explanation of the Technical Terms and Phrases Employed in the Construction, Equipment, Furniture,*

Machinery, and Military Operations of a Ship. First edition published in 1769. London: T. Cadell, 1789.

Falconer, William, and William Burney. *A New Universal Dictionary of the Marine; Being a Copious Explanation of the Technical Terms and Phrases Usually Employed in the Construction, Equipment, Machinery, as Well as Naval Operations of Ships...* Originally compiled by Falconer; added to and updated by Burney. London: T. Cadell and W. Davis, 1815.

Das Feuerwerkbuch von 1420: 600 Jahre Deutsche Pulverwaffen und Büchsenmeisterei. Edited and translated by W. Hassenstein. Munich: Deutsche Technik, 1943.

Floukes, Charles J. *The Gun-Founders of England, with a List of English and Continental Gun-Founders from the XIV to the XIX Centuries.* Cambridge: The University Press, 1937.

Fincham, John. *A History of Naval Architecture.* London: Whittaker, 1851.

Forester, C. S. *The Age of Fighting Sail: The Story of the Naval War of 1812.* Garden City: Doubleday, 1956.

Freeman, Fred. *Duel of the Ironclads.* New York: Time-Life Books, 1969.

Garbett, H. *Naval Gunnery: A Description and History of the Fighting Equipment of a Man of War.* London: G. Bell, 1897.

Gardner, Robert E. *Arms Fabricators, Ancient and Modern.* Columbus, Ohio: F. J. Heer, 1949.

———. *Five Centuries of Gunsmiths, Swordsmiths and Armourers, 1400–1900.* Columbus, Ohio: F. J. Heer, 1949.

Gaya, Louis de. *Gaya's* Traite des armes, *1679.* Edited by Charles Ffoulkes with a preface by Viscount Dillon. Reprinted in facsimile of 1678 Paris edition. London: Clarendon Press, 1911.

Gibbon, John. *The Artillerist's Manual, Compiled from Various Sources, and Adapted to the Service of the United States.* New York: D. Van Nostrand, 1860.

Gibson, Charles E. *The Story of the Ship.* New York: Henry Schuman, 1948.

Glascock, William N. *The Naval Officer's Manual, for Every Grade in Her Majesty's Ships.* 3rd ed. London: Parker, Furnivall and Parker, 1854.

Goldenberg, Joseph A. *Shipbuilding in Colonial America.* Charlottesville: The University Press of Virginia for the Mariner's Museum, Newport News, 1976.

Greeley, Horace, et al. *The Great Industries of the United States: Being an Historical Summary of the Origin, Growth and Perfection of the Chief Industrial Arts of This Country.* Hartford, Connecticut: J. B. Burr and Hyde, 1872.

Greener, William. *Gunnery in 1858: Being a Treatise on Rifles, Cannon and Sporting Arms; Explaining the Principles of the Science of Gunnery, and Describing the Newest Improvements in Firearms.* London: Smith, Elder, 1858.

———. *The Gun and Its Development.* 9th ed. New York: Bonanza Books, 1910.

———. *The Science of Gunnery, as Applied to the Use and Construction of Firearms.* London: Longman, 1841.

———. *The Gun; a Treatise on the Various Descriptions of Small Fire-Arms.* London: Longman, Reese, Orme, Brown, Green, and Longman, 1835.

Gulieimotti. *Storia della marina pontifica.* Vol. 4. Rome: Tipografia Vaticanna, 1886–93.

Halsted, Edward P. *England's Navy Unarmed.* London, 1864.

Hartley, E. N. *Iron-Works on the Sangus.* Norman: University of Oklahoma Press, 1957.

Hazlett, James C., Edwin Olmstead, and M. Hume Parks. *Field Artillery Weapons of the Civil War.* Newark, Delaware: University of Delaware Press, 1983.

Hewitt, John. *Ancient Armor and Weapons in Europe from the Iron Period of the Northern Nations to the End of the Seventeenth Century.* 3 vols. London: J. Henry and J. Parker, 1855–60.

Hime, Lieutenant Colonel Henry W. L. *The Origin of Artillery.* London: Longman, Green, 1915.

Hogg, Ian, and John Batchelor. *Naval Gun.* Poole, Dorset: Blandford Press, 1978.

Hogg, Oliver F. G. *English Artillery, 1326–1716.* London: Royal Artillery Institution, 1963.

Holley, Alexander L. *A Treatise on Ordnance and Armor.* New York: D. Van Nostrand, 1865.

Hough, Richard. *Fighting Ships.* New York: Putnam, 1969.

Howarth, David. *Sovereign of the Seas: The Story of Britain and the Sea.* New York: Atheneum, 1974.

Howell, Kenneth T., and Einar W. Carlson. *Men of Iron: Forbes and Adam.* Lakeville, Connecticut: Pocketknife Press, 1980.

Hughes, Major General B. P. *British Smooth-Bore Artillery.* Harrisburg: Stackpole Books, 1969.

Inman, James. *An Introduction to Naval Gunnery.* Portsea: W. Woodward, 1928.

Instructions for the Exercise and Service of Great Guns on Board Her Majesty's Ships. Portsea: W. Woodward, 1849.

Instructions Upon the Art of Pointing Cannon, for the Use of Young Sea Officers. Translated from the French by an officer of the U.S. Navy. Washington: Gideon, 1848.

Jackson, Melvin H., and Charles de Beer. *Eighteenth Century Gunfounding.* Washington: Smithsonian Institution Press, 1974.

James, William. *A Full and Correct Account of the Chief Naval Occurrences of the Late War Between Britain and the United States of America.* London: T. Egerton, Whitehall, 1817.

Jane's Dictionary of Naval Terms. Compiled by Joseph Palmer. London: MacDonald and James, 1975.

Jeffers, William N. *A Concise Treatise on the Theory and Practice of Naval Gunnery.* New York: D. Appleton, 1850.

Jerningham, Arthur W. *Remarks on the Means of Directing the Fire of Ships' Broadsides, with a Proposed Method of Controlling and Delivering a Simultaneous Converging Fire.* London: Parker, Furnivall, and Parker, 1851.

Jervis, Captain Jervis-White, *Our Engines of War, and How We Got to Make Them.* London: Chapman and Hall, 1859.

Jurien de la Graviere, Jean Pierre Edmond. *Sketches of the Last Naval War.* 2 vols. Translated by Captain Plunkett. London: Longman, Brown, Green and Longman, 1848.

Kennish, William. *A Method for Concentrating the Fire of a Broadside of a Ship of War, with an Appendix Containing Several Important Subjects, Connected with the Naval Service.* London: J. Bradley, 1837.

Knox, Dudley W. *A History of the United States Navy.* New York: Putnam, 1936.

Lafay, Jules Joseph. *Aide-Memoire d'artillerie navale, imprimé avec authorisation de Ministre de la Marine et des Colonies (dépêche du 11 Septembre, 1848).* Paris: J. Correard, 1850.

Lallemand, Henri Domonique. *Service of a Ten-Inch Mortar; Fabrication of a Cannon.* Abridged from the French. West Point, 1833.

Lescallier, Daniel. *Traité pratique de gréement des vaisseaux et autres batiments de mer.* 2 vols. in one. Paris: Clousier, imprimeur du roi, 1791.

Lewal, Lieutenant M. L. *Traité pratique d'artillerie navale et tactique des combats de mer.* 3 vols. Paris: Librairie maritime et scientifique, 1863.

Lloyd, E. W., and A. G. Hadcock. *Artillery: Its Progress and Present Position.* Portsmouth: J. Griffin, 1893.

Lossing, Benson J. *History of American Industries and Arts.* Philadelphia: Porter and Coates, 1878.

Macartney, Clorence E. *Mr. Lincoln's Admirals.* New York: Funk and Wagnalls, 1956.

Mackenzie, Alexander Slidell. *Life of Stephen Decatur, A Commodore in the Navy of the United States.* Boston: Little and Brown, 1848.

Maclay, Edgar Stanton. *A History of American Privateers.* New York: D. Appleton, 1924.

———. *A History of the United States Navy from 1775 to 1901.* New and enlarged ed., 3 vols. New York: D. Appleton, 1901.

Magoun, F. Alexander. *The Frigate* Constitution *and Other Historic Ships.* New York: Bonanza Books, 1928.

Mahan, Alfred Thayer. *Sea Power in Its Relations to the War of 1812.* 2 vols. London: Sampson Low, Marston, 1905.

———. *The Major Operations of the Navies in the War of American Independence.* London: Sampson Low, Marston, n.d.

Mallet, Alain Manesson. *Les Traveaux de Mars, ou l'art de la guerre: Divisé en trois parties.* 3 vols. Paris: D. Thierry, 1691.

Marcus, G. J. *A Naval History of England: The Formative Centuries.* Boston: Little, Brown, 1961.

Marshall, Warrant Gunner George. *Marshall's Practical Marine Gunnery; Containing a View of the Magnitude, Weight, Description and Use, of Every Article Used in the Sea Gunner's Dept, in the Navy of the United States.* Norfolk: T. G. Broughton and Dubby C. Hall, 1822.

Martin de Brettes, Jean Baptiste. *Les Bouches à feu les plus remarkables.* Paris, 1852.
Masefield, John. *Sea Life in Nelson's Time.* New York: Macmillan, 1925.
Mauncy, Albert. *Artillery through the Ages: A Short Illustrated History of Cannon, Emphasizing Types Used in America.* National Park Service Interpretive Series: History No. 3. Washington: GPO, 1949.
Michel, Jules. *Memorial de l'artilleur marin: Redige suivant l'ordre alphabetique des matieres.* Paris: Dehansy, 1828.
Middlebrook, Louis Frank. *Salisbury Connecticut Cannon, Revolutionary War.* Salem: Newcomb and Gauss, 1935.
Miller, Nathan. *Sea of Glory: The Continental Navy Fights for Independence, 1775–1783.* New York: David McKay, 1974.
Millis, Walter. *Arms and Men: A Study in American Military History.* New Brunswick: Rutgers University Press, 1981.
Monge, Gaspard. *Description de l'art de fabriquer les canons.* Paris: L'Imprimerie de Comité de Salut Public, 1794.
Moore, William. *A Treatise on the Motion of Rockets, to Which Is Added an Essay on Naval Gunnery in Theory and Practice; Designed for the Use of the Army and Navy, and All Places of Military, Naval, and Scientific Instruction.* London: G. and S. Robinson, 1813.
Moretti, Tomaso. *Trattato dell' artiglieria.* Brescia: Gio. Battista Gromi, 1672.
Morison, Samuel Eliot. *John Paul Jones: A Sailor's Biography.* Boston: Little, Brown, 1959.
———. *Old Bruin: Commodore Matthew Galbraith Perry.* Boston: Little, Brown, 1967.
———. *The Oxford History of the American People.* New York: Oxford University Press, 1965.
Morla, Tomas de. *Laminas pertenecientes al tratado de artilleria que se ensena en el Real Collegio Militar de Segovia.* Madrid: En la imprinta real, 1803.
Mountaine, William. *Practical Sea-Gunner's Companion: An Introduction to the Art of Gunnery.* London, 1747.
Muller, John. *A Treatise of Artillery.* London: Printed for John Milan, Whitehall, 1780. Reprint by Museum Restoration Service, Ottawa, Canada, 1965.
Mushet, David. *Papers on Iron and Steel, Practical and Experimental.* London: John Weale, 1840.
A Naval Encyclopaedia: A Dictionary of Nautical Words and Phrases; Biographical Notices, and Records of Naval Officers; Special Articles of Naval Art and Science. . . . Philadelphia: L. R. Hamersly, 1884.
Nicolas, Nicholas Harris. *A History of the Royal Navy, from the Earliest Times to the Wars of the French Revolution.* 2 vols. London: Bentley, 1847.
Oppenheim, Michael. *The Administration of the Royal Navy, and of Merchant Shipping in Relation to the Navy, from 1509 to 1660.* London: J. Lane, 1896.
Padfield, Peter. *Broke and the Shannon.* London: Hodder and Stoughton, 1968.
———. *Guns at Sea.* New York: St. Martin's Press, 1974.
Paixhans, Henri Joseph. *An Account of the Experiments Made in the French Navy for the Trial of Bomb Cannon.* Translated by John A. Dahlgren. Philadelphia: E. G. Dorsey, 1838.
———. *Experiences faites par la marine française, sur une arme nouvelle.* Paris: Bachelier, 1825.
———. *Nouvelle force maritime, et application de cette force à quelques parties de service de l'armée de terre . . .* Paris: Bachelier, 1822.
Parker, William Harwar. *Instruction for Naval Light Artillery, Afloat and Ashore, Prepared and Arranged for the U.S. Naval Academy.* Newport: J. Atkinson, 1862.
Paullin, Charles Oscar. *Paullin's History of Naval Administration, 1775–1911.* Annapolis: Naval Institute Press, 1968.
———. *The Navy of the American Revolution: Its Administration, Its Policy and Its Achievements.* Chicago: The University of Chicago, 1906.
Peck, Taylor. *Round Shot to Rockets: A History of the Washington Navy Yard and U.S. Naval Gun Factory.* Annapolis: Naval Institute Press, 1939.
Perkins, James Breck. *France in the American Revolution.* Williamstown, Massachusetts: Corner House Publishers, 1970.
Perlmutter, Tom. *War Machines Sea.* London: Octopus Books, 1974.
Persy, N. *Elementary Treatise on the Forms of Cannon and Various Systems of Artillery.*

Translated for the cadets of the U.S. Military Academy by Professor N. Persy. West Point: U.S. Military Academy, 1832–33.

Peterson, C. Stewart. *Admiral John A. Dahlgren, Father of U.S. Naval Ordnance.* New York: The Hobson Book Press, 1945.

Petrejus, E. W. *Modeling the Brig-of-War* Irene. Hengelo, Holland: N. V. Uitgeversmaatschappij "De Esch," 1970.

Rees, Abraham. *The Cyclopedia; or, Universal Dictionary of Arts, Sciences, and Literature ...* Vol. 4 of 41 vols. Philadelphia: Samuel Bradford, 1810.

Regulations for the Proof and Inspection of Cannon, Shot and Shells, Adopted by a Board of Officers, Consisting of Commodore C. Morris, Commodore L. Warrington, Commodore W. M. Crane, Commodore A. B. Wadsworth, Commodore W. B. Shubrick, and Approved by the Secretary of the Navy, June 1845. Washington: C. Alexander, 1845.

Ripley, Warren. *Artillery and Ammunition of the Civil War.* New York: Van Nostrand Reinhold, 1970.

Robertson, Frederick L. *The Evolution of Naval Armament.* London: Harold T. Storey, 1968.

Robertson, John. *A Treatise of Such Mathematical Instruments as Are Usually Put Into a Portable Case ...* London: Printed for J. Hourse, 1775.

Robins, Benjamin. *New Principles of Gunnery; Containing the Determination of the Force of Gun-Powder, and an Investigation in the Resisting Power of the Air to Swift and Slow Motions.* London: J. Hourse, 1742.

Robison, Admiral Samuel S. and Mary L. *A History of Naval Tactics from 1530 to 1930.* Annapolis: Naval Institute Press, 1942.

Rodgers, William L. *Naval Warfare under Oars, 4th to 16th Centuries: A Study of Strategy, Tactics and Ship Design.* Annapolis: Naval Institute Press, 1939.

Roosevelt, Theodore. *The Naval War of 1812; or the History of the United States Navy during the Last War with Great Britain.* New York: Putnam, 1882.

Rovira, D. Francisco Xavier. *Tratado de artilleria para el uso de los cavalleros guardias-marinas en su academia.* La Academia de los Guardias-Marinas, 1773.

Rudyerd, C. W. *A Course of Artillery at the Royal Military Academy.* Notebook of 1793. Ontario: Museum Restoration Service, 1970.

Sadler, J. *Account of Various Improvements in Artillery, Fire-Arms, Etc.* 1798.

St. Julien. *La Forge de Vulcain ou l'appareil des machines de guerre.* La Haye: Guill. de Boys, 1606.

Saint-Remy, Pierre Surirey de. *Mémoires d'artillerie.* 2 vols. Paris: J. Anisson, 1697.

Sanders, Clyde A., and Dudley C. Gould. *History Cast in Metal: The Founders of North America.* Cast Metals Institute, American Foundrymen's Society, 1976.

Saverien, Alexandre. *L'Art de mesurer sue mer le sillage du vaisseau. Avec une idée de l'état d'armament des vaisseau de France. Dédie aux marins.* Paris: C. A. Jombert, 1750.

Scheel, Heinrich Otto von. *A Treatise of Artillery Containing a New System, or the Alterations Made in the French Artillery Since 1765.* Translated by Jonathan Williams. Philadelphia, 1800.

Scoffern, John. *Projectile Weapons of War and Explosive Compounds.* London: Longman, Brown, Green, and Longman, 1858.

Siemenovicz, Casimir. *Ars magna artilleria.* Amsterdam, 1650.

———. *The Great Art of Artillery ...* Translated by George Shelvocke. London: J. Tonson, 1729.

Simmons, Robert. *The Sea-Gunner's Vade-Mecum; Being a New Introduction to Practical Gunnery ...* London: Steel, 1812.

Simmons, Thomas F. *A Discussion on the Present Armament of the Navy; Being a Supplement to Ideas as to the Effect of Heavy Ordnance Directed Against and Applied by Ships of War.* London: P. Pinkney, 1839.

———. *Ideas as to the Effect of Heavy Ordnance Directed Against and Applied by Ships of War, Particularly with Reference to the Use of Hollow Shot and Loaded Shells.* London: P. Pickney, 1837.

Simpson, Edward. *A Treatise on Ordnance and Naval Gunnery.* Compiled and Arranged as a Text Book for the U.S. Naval Academy. 2nd ed., revised and enlarged. New York: D. Van Nostrand, 1862.

Singh, R. John. *French Diplomacy in the Caribbean and the American Revolution.* Hicksville, New York: Exposition Press, 1977.

Smelser, Marshall. *The Congress Founds the Navy, 1787–1798.* South Bend: University of Notre Dame Press, 1959.

Spearman, J. Morton. *The British Gunner.* 4th ed., revised and enlarged. London: Parker, Furnivall and Parker, 1850.

Sprout, Harold and Margaret. *The Rise of American Naval Power, 1776–1918.* Princeton: Princeton University Press, 1939.

Stevens, Edwin Augustus. *The Stevens Iron Clad Battery.* New York: D. Van Nostrand, 1874.

Stewart, Duncan. *Notes on Steam Evolutions and Their Bearing on Naval Gunnery.* Edinburgh, 1862.

Straith, Major Hector. *Treatise on Fortification and Artillery.* 2 vols. 6th edition. London: W. H. Allen, 1852.

Swank, James M. *History of the Manufacture of Iron in All Ages, and Particularly in the United States from Colonial Times to 1891.* Philadelphia: The American Iron and Steel Association, 1892.

Tennent, James Emerson. *The Story of the Guns.* London: Longman, Green, Longman, Roberts and Green, 1864.

Texier De Norbec. *Recherches sur l'artillerie en générale, et particulièrement sur celle de la marine.* Paris, 1792.

Thiroux, M. *Instruction theorique et practique d'artillerie à l'usage des élèves de l'école militaire de Saint-Cyr.* 3rd ed. Paris: Librarie militaire de J. Dumaine, 1849.

Tousard, Louis de. *American Artillerist's Companion, or Elements of Artillery.* 2 vols. Philadelphia: C. and A. Conrad, 1809.

Tout, Thomas F. *Firearms in England in the Fourteenth Century.* York, Pennsylvania: George Shumway, 1968.

Turnbull, Archibald D. *John Stevens, An American Record.* New York: The Century Company, 1928.

Ward, Commander James H. *Elementary Instruction in Naval Ordnance and Gunnery.* Revised ed. New York: D. Van Nostrand, 1861.

Wescott, Allan, ed. *American Sea Power Since 1775.* Philadelphia: J. B. Lippincott, 1947.

Wilson, Lieutenant A. W. *The Story of the Gun.* Woolich, England: Royal Artillery Institution, 1944.

Wood, William, and Ralph Henry Gabriel. *The Pageant of America.* Vol. 6, *The Winning of Freedom.* New Haven: Yale University Press, 1927.

Zeni and Deshays. *Renseignements sur le materiel de l'artillerie de la Grande Bretagne.* Paris, 1840.

ARTICLES

Bolander, Louis H. "The Introduction of Shells and Shell-Guns in the United States Navy." *The Mariner's Mirror* 17, no. 2 (April 1931): 105–12.

Boudriot, Jean. "L'Artillerie de mer de la Marine Française, 1674–1856." *Neptunia* 89 (first trimester, 1968): 1–16.

Brackenbury, Lieutenant Henry. "Ancient Cannon in Europe." *Minutes of Proceedings of the Royal Artillery Institution* 4 (1865): 291.

Brewington, M. V. "American Naval Guns, 1775–1785." *The American Neptune* 3, no. 1 (January 1943): 11–18, and 3, no. 2 (April 1943): 148–58.

Brooks, F. W. "Naval Armament in the Thirteenth Century." *The Mariner's Mirror* 14, no. 2 (April 1928): 114–31.

Cairo, Robert F. "Samuel Bentham: Forgotten Shipbuilder and Engineer." Part 4. *Nautical Research Journal* 24, no. 2 (September 1978): 125–31.

Davis, Madison. "The Old Cannon Foundry above Georgetown, D.C., and Its First Owner, Henry Foxall." *Records of the Columbia Historical Society.* Vol. 2 (1908): 16–70.

Denoix, L., and J. N. Muracciole, "Historique de l'artillerie de la marine de ses origines a 1870." *Mémorial de l'artillerie française* 38, no. 4 (1963): 893–958, no. 1 (1964): 7–80, no. 2 (1964): 271–358, and no. 3 (1964): 516–602.

Gillingham, Harrold E. "Some Colonial Ships Built in Philadelphia." *The Pennsylvania Magazine of History and Biography* 56 (1932): 156–78.

Hall, A. R. "A Note on Military Pyrotechnics," *A History of Technology* (edited by Charles Singer, *et al*). Vol. II, 374–382. Oxford: Clarendon Press, 1955.

———. "Military Technology," *A History of Technology* (edited by Charles Singer, *et al*). Vol. 2, 695–730, and vol. 3, 347–75. Oxford: Clarendon Press, 1955.

Hamilton, Edward P. "Colonial and Revolutionary Artillery." *The Bulletin of the Fort Ticonderoga Museum* 12, no. 5 (December 1969): 313–27.

Hornsby, Thomas. "Oregon and Peacemaker, 12-inch Wrought Iron Guns." *The American Neptune* 6, no. 3 (July 1946): 212–25.

Laughton, L. C. Carr. "Early Tudor Ship-Guns." *The Mariner's Mirror* 46, no. 4 (November 1960): 242–85.

Lewis, Emanuel Raymond. "The Ambiguous Columbiads." *Military Affairs* 28, no. 3 (Fall 1964): 111–22.

Lewis, Michael A. "Armada Guns." *The Mariner's Mirror* 29, no. 2 (April 1943): 100–121, and no. 3 (July 1943): 163–78.

Mallett, Lieutenant Colonel J. W. "Work Of the Ordnance Bureau of the War Department of the Confederate States, 1861–1865." *Southern Historical Papers* 37 (January–December 1909). Reprinted in William A. Albaugh III and Edward N. Simmons, *Confederate Arms* (Harrisburg: The Stackpole Company).

Martin, Commander Tyrone G., and William Gilkerson. "Top Guns in the Early Sailing Navy," *Man at Arms* 9, no. 4 (July–August 1987): 12–20.

McKee, Christopher. "Constitution in the Quasi-War with France: The Letters of John Roche, Jr., 1798–1801." *The American Neptune* (April 1967): 135–49.

M'Crea, Major. "A Synopsis of the American Experiments on the Strength and Other Properties of Metal for Cannon, Selected and Abridged from the Official Reports Made at the Different Foundries in the United States." *Minutes of Proceedings of the Royal Artillery Institution* 2 (1861): 81–102.

Miles, Commander A. H. "The Princeton Explosion." *United States Naval Institute Proceedings* 52, no. 11 (November 1926): 2225–45.

Moody, J. D. "Old Naval Gun-Carriages." *The Mariner's Mirror* 38, no. 4 (November 1952): 301–11.

Moore, Alan. "Accounts and Inventories of John Starling, Clerk of the King's Ships to Henry IV." *The Mariner's Mirror* 4, no. 1 (January 1914): 20–26.

Pearson, Lee M. "The *Princeton* and the Peacemaker." *Technology and Culture* 7, no. 2 (Spring 1966): 163–83.

"Report on the Explosion of the Gun on Board the Steam Frigate *Princeton*." *Journal of the Franklin Institute* 7 (1844): 206–16.

"Revolutionary Letters Concerning the Hibernia Iron Furnace." *Proceedings of the New Jersey Historical Society* 8, no. 1 (January 1923): 22–30, and 8, no. 2 (April 1923): 144–49.

Rich, Edwin. "The Sizes of Gun Tackles and Breechings." *Nautical Research Journal* 12 (no. 1): 14–17.

Simons, Commander Bentham. "Some Notes on Old Guns." *United States Naval Institute Proceedings* 53, no. 5 (May 1937): 653–66.

Simpson, Rear Admiral Edward. "United States Naval Artillery." *Harper's New Monthly Magazine* 73 (no. 437): 779–94.

Snow, Captain Elliot. "The Battery of Old Ironsides." *Army Ordnance* 6, no. 33 (November–December 1925): 153–61.

Stephen, Walter W. "The Brooke Guns from Selma," *Alabama Historical Quarterly* 20, no. 3 (Fall 1958): 462–75.

Stephenson, O. W. "The Supply of Gunpowder." *American Historical Review* 30 (January 1925): 271–81.

Tucker, Colonel Cary S. "The Early Columbiads." *Military Collector and Historian* 10, no. 2 (Summer 1958): 40–42.

Tucker, Spencer C. "American Naval Ordnance of the Revolution." *Nautical Research Journal* 32, no. 1 (March 1976): 21–28.

———. "Cannon Founders of the American Revolution." *National Defense* 60 no. 331 (July–August 1975): 33–37.
———. "Introduction of Cannon at Sea." *Nautical Research Journal* 22, no. 2 (June 1976): 55–66.
———. "Mr. Jefferson's Gunboat Navy." *The American Neptune* 43, no. 2 (April 1983): 135–41.
———. "The Carronade." *The United States Naval Institute Proceedings* 99, no. 8 (August 1973): 65–70.
———. "U.S. Navy Gun Carriages from the Revolution Through the Civil War." *The American Neptune* 47, no. 2 (Spring 1987): 108–18.
Winton-Clare, C. "A Shipbuilder's War." *The Mariner's Mirror* 28, no. 3 (July 1943): 139–48.

PUBLIC DOCUMENTS AND UNPUBLISHED WORKS

American Archives. 4th series, vol. 6. Washington, 1846. 5th series, vol. 1. Washington, 1848. Vol. 2. Washington, 1851.
American State Papers: Documents, Legislative and Executive of the Congress of the United States. Class VI, *Naval Affairs.* Vols. 1–4. Class V, *Military Affairs.* Vols. 1–4. Washington: Gales and Seaton, 1832–61.
Archives of Maryland. *Journal and Correspondence of the Maryland Council of Safety, August 29, 1775–July 6, 1776.* Edited by William H. Browne. Baltimore: Maryland Historical Society, 1892.
Danish gunnery notebook. Mariner's Museum, Newport News, Virginia.
de Pardo y Tovar, Diego. "Encyclopaedia de function de artilleria Valloadolid, 30 May 1603." Manuscript. University Library, Cambridge, England.
National Archives. Record Group 45, Naval Records Collection of the Office of Naval Records and Library. Record Group 74, Records of the Bureau of Ordnance. Record Group 217, General Accounting Office.
Naval Records of the American Revolution, 1775–1788. Compiled by Charles Henry Lincoln. Washington: GPO, 1906.
O'Reilly, Montagu F. Manuscript on naval artillery and gunnery of HMS *Excellent*, August 1843. Mariner's Museum, Newport News, Virginia.
U.S. Census Office. Eighth Census, 1860. *Manufactures of the United States in 1860.* Washington: GPO, 1865.
U.S. Congress. Joint Committee on the Conduct of the War. "Heavy Ordnance." In *Report of the Joint Committee on the Conduct of the War at the Second Session, Thirty-Eighth Congress.* Washington: GPO, 1865.
U.S. Navy Department. Bureau of Construction and Repair. *United States Frigate* Constitution. Washington: GPO, 1932.
U.S. Navy Department. Bureau of Ordnance. *Instructions in Relation to the Preparation of Vessels of War for Battle, to the Duties of Officers and Others When at Quarters, and to Ordnance and Ordnance Stores.* Washington: C. Alexander, 1852.
U.S. Navy Department. Bureau of Ordnance. *Ordnance Instructions for the United States Navy.* Washington: GPO, 1866.
U.S. Navy Department. Bureau of Ordnance. *Ordnance Instructions for the United States Navy, Relating to the Preparation of Vessels of War for Battle, to the Duties of Officers and Others When at Quarters, to Ordnance and Ordnance Stores, and to Gunnery.* 2nd ed. Washington: G. W. Bowman, 1860.
U.S. Navy Department. *Naval Documents Related to the Quasi-War between the United States and France. Naval Operations from February 1797 to October 1798.* GPO, 1935. *April 1799 to July 1799.* 1936. *August 1799 to December 1799.* 1937. *January 1800 to May 1800.* 1936. *June 1800 to November 1800.* 1936. *December 1800 to December 1801.* 1938.
U.S. Navy Department. *Naval Documents Related to the United States Wars with Barbary Powers.* Vol. 1, *Naval Operations Including Diplomatic Background from 1785 through 1801.* GPO, 1939. Vol. 2, *January 1802 through August 1803.* 1940. Vol. 3, *September 1803 through March 1804.* 1941. Vol. 4, *April to September 6, 1804.* 1942. Vol. 5, *September 7, 1804 through April 1805.* 1944. Vol. 6, *May 1805 through 1807.* 1944.

U.S. Navy Department. Office of Naval Records and Library. *Naval Documents of the American Revolution.* Vol. 1, *American Theatre, Dec. 1, 1775–Sep. 2, 1775, European Theatre, Dec. 6, 1775–Aug. 9, 1775.* GPO, 1964. Vol. 2, *American Theatre, Sept. 3, 1775–Oct. 31, 1775, European Theatre, Aug. 11, 1775–Oct. 31, 1775, American Theatre, Nov. 1, 1775–Dec. 7, 1775.* 1966. Vol. 3, *American Theatre, Feb. 19, 1776–Apr. 17, 1776, European Theatre, Nov. 1, 1775–Jan. 31, 1776, American Theatre, Jan. 1, 1776–Feb. 18, 1776.* 1968. Vol. 4, *American Theatre, Feb. 19, 1776–Apr. 17, 1776, European Theatre, Feb. 1, 1776–May 25, 1776, American Theatre, Apr. 18, 1776–May 8, 1776.* 1969.

U.S. Navy Department. Office of Naval Records and Library. *Register of Officer Personnel, United States Navy and Marine Corps and Ships' Data, 1801–1807.* Washington: GPO, 1945.

U.S. Navy Department. *Regulations for the Proof and Inspection of Cannon, Shot, and Shells Adopted by a Board of Officers . . . and Approved by Secretary of the Navy, June 1845.* Washington: J. and G. S. Gideon, 1848.

Index

G

H

I

J

U

V

W

The Naval Institute Press is the book-publishing arm of the U.S. Naval Institute, a private, nonprofit professional society for members of the sea services and civilians who share an interest in naval and maritime affairs. Established in 1873 at the U.S. Naval Academy in Annapolis, Maryland, where its offices remain today, the Naval Institute has more than 100,000 members worldwide.

Members of the Naval Institute receive the influential monthly naval magazine *Proceedings* and substantial discounts on fine nautical prints, ship and aircraft photos, and subscriptions to the Institute's recently inaugurated quarterly, *Naval History*. They also have access to the transcripts of the Institute's Oral History Program and may attend any of the Institute-sponsored seminars regularly offered around the country.

The book-publishing program, begun in 1898 with basic guides to naval practices, has broadened its scope in recent years to include books of more general interest. Now the Naval Institute Press publishes more than forty new titles each year, ranging from how-to books on boating and navigation to battle histories, biographies, ship guides, and novels. Institute members receive discounts on the Press's more than 300 books.

For a free catalog describing books currently available and for further information about U.S. Naval Institute membership, please write to:

Membership Department
U.S. Naval Institute
Annapolis, Maryland 21402

or call, toll-free, 800-233-USNI.